Devon Leather

An outline history of a lost industry:
nineteenth century tanners and tanneries

Martin Bodman

Leat Press

First published 2008

Published in the United Kingdom by
Leat Press
27 Water Lane
Tiverton
Exeter EX16 6RA

British Library Cataloguing in Publication Data
A catalogue record for this book is available from the British
Library

ISBN 978-0-9548758-1-7

Origination by Leat Press
Final formatting, platemaking, printing and binding by
Short Run Press Limited, Exeter, Devon

Cover images
Top left
Baker's Tannery, Colyton. The last surviving oak-bark tannery
in the United Kingdom
Top right
Working the beam. A hide being prepared for tanning. From
W H Pyne's Microcosm, 1808
Centre left
Barking in the early twentieth century. The bark has been
removed from a six foot section of a trunk of an oak tree.
Photograph courtesy Museum of Rural Life, Reading
Centre right
Section of the Rew family tree, Exeter tanners
Bottom left
Adapted from the Ordnance Survey 25" to the mile map of
1866, showing the tannery site at Plympton
Bottom right
Waterwheels were used extensively in Devon tanneries to crush
the oak bark for tannic acid, to work the tanpit pumps and also
to agitate hides in the pits. Horse power and steam power were
alternatives. This wheel is at the Rhaeadr Tannery, re-erected at
the National History Museum, St Fagans, Cardiff

Contents

Acknowledgements 4

Preface 5

Introduction 7

Map of tanneries in Devon 10

The operation of a Devon tannery 11

The Sharlands – a family of tanners 14

Rounding a hide – a diagram 18

Gazetteer 19

Other nineteenth century sites 148

Earlier sites 149

Glossary 150

Appendix
Devon-born leather workers
living in Bermondsey, London
in 1871 152

Index 159

Acknowledgements

I am indebted to Barbara Keene who, seeing my research develop, encouraged me to look beyond the valleys of the Culm and Exe, and tackle the whole county of Devon. Together we have travelled many miles to view the sites of vanished tanyards, and occasionally discover surviving buildings.

My thanks also go to my half-sister June Webb, who has undertaken research into a number of the tannery owners, through the census returns and the Mormon Church's International Genealogical Index. This study could not have been written without her help. The following individuals, some from local history societies and museums, have assisted in compiling this survey by providing additional information. I'm also indebted to them:

Bampton – Sheila Howells and Tom McManamon. *Barnstaple* – Mike Bone, Steve Knight, Alison Mills, Avril Stone, Philip Tonkin, Julian Vayne and Keith Vingoe. *Bideford* – Mr Littlejohn. *Bow* – Peter Green. *Broadhembury* – Sir Michael Stear. *Cheriton Fitzpaine* – Professor J M Anderson. *Chudleigh* – John Moore. *Chulmleigh* – Catherine Sherlock. *Colyton* – Andrew Parr, John Cochrane and Alan Stoyel. *Crediton* – Albert Labbett, John Madin and Penny Sexton of the Royal Albert Museum, Exeter. *Cullompton* – Muriel Coxhead, Jane Evans, Judy Morris and Syd Staddon. *Dalwood* – Derrick Warren. *Exeter* – Peter Thomas. *Hartland* – Stephen Hobbs. *Holcombe Rogus* – Leslie and Ruby Tristram. *Holsworthy* – Liz Curtis. *Kingsbridge* – Sharon Wellington. *Kingston* – Jill Trumble. *Loxbeare* – Mr Burnett. *Milton Abbot* – Helen and Chris Snow. *Modbury* – Nancy Savery and David Mitchell. *Petrockstowe* – Alan and Audrey Anthony. *Plymouth and Devonport* – Cynthia Gaskell Brown. *Sampford Peverell* – Peter Bowers and David King. *Sandford* – Mr Hipkiss. *South Molton* – Dick and Sue Pearce, Shirley Bray /The South Molton Archive. Also Katherine Dunhill, of Devon Library and Information Services. *Swimbridge* – Mary Balment and Mervyn Dalling. *Tavistock* – Mary Freeman, Sue Davies, Roderick Martin and the Tavistock and District Local History Society. *Tiverton* – Barbara Keene and Jane Evans. *Totnes* – David Holman. *Withleigh, Tiverton* – Stanley Britton. *Uffculme* – Mr Pattinson. *Winkleigh* – Mr Cowl. *Woodbury* – Jill Selley.

In addition the librarians, archivists and staff of Devon Record Office, North Devon Record Office, West Country Studies Library, Exeter and the Devon & Exeter Institution have greatly aided my research over a period of years and I'm grateful to them all.

Out of the county my thanks go to Gerallt Nash and Gareth Beech at the National History Museum, St Fagans, Cardiff and to Mike Glasson, Curator, Leather Museum, Walsall, all of whom have provided advice and help as have Jeff Hawksley of Romsey and Caroline Benson of the Museum of English Rural Life, Reading. Fellow members of the Somerset Industrial Archaeological Society have read drafts of the text and offered advice and I'm grateful to Geoff Fitton, Brian Murless and Derrick Warren. My thanks also go to Mary Freeman, Cynthia Gaskell Brown, Andrew Parr, Dick and Sue Pearce, and Martin Watts for reading and commenting on sections of the publication.

Private property

Please note that all the surviving sites referred to in this book are on private property and there is no right of entry or access to any site – with the exception, of course, of the out-of-county Rhaeadr Tannery, re-erected at the National History Museum, St Fagans, near Cardiff.

Those genuinely seeking to further the history of the Devon tanneries and needing to visit remaining structures should first seek permission, by contacting the respective owners in advance. Some old tannery sites, however, may be viewed from a nearby road, lane or footpath.

Abbreviations

b	born
bp	baptism
bu	buried
d	died
D&CRS	Devon and Cornwall Record Society
DCC	Devon County Council
DCNQ	Devon and Cornwall Notes and Queries
dia.	diameter
FIP	Fire insurance policy
DRO	Devon Record Office
OS	Ordnance Survey
HM	Head of family, married
HW	Head of family, widower/widow
IGI	Mormon Church's International Genealogical Index
jun	junior
KEO	Knightshayes Estate Office
m	married
PROB	The National Archives Prerogative Court of Canterbury wills [PROB series]
SFIP	Sun Fire Insurance Policy
se'nnight	obsolete term for a week – as 'fortnight' used for two weeks, or fourteen nights
snr	senior
TA	tithe apportionment
TM	tithe map

D&CRS transcriptions:
A H Shorter, The Tanning Industry in Devon and Cornwall, 1550-1850. Devon and Cornwall Notes and Queries, Volume XXV, 1952, 10-16: the information comes from parish registers transcribed by the Devon and Cornwall Record Society

Preface

In researching this book I've asked librarians and information officers in Devon towns about their tanneries. The standard response is 'I've never been asked that question before'. Tanning in Devon is a forgotten industry. In the nation at large it was, eventually, centralised and industrialised and now few realise that the country tanner was once almost as universal as the village miller in Devon. The county has 422 civil parishes; 180 tannery sites have been identified here. Not all operated concurrently, but places such as Bow and Cullompton relied on tanning as their leading industry in the nineteenth century. Crediton's industrialised shoemakers worked cheek by jowl with the town's tanners.

The tannery was not an object of appeal like a sailing vessel or a windmill. And while the journeyman tanner was reputedly the highest paid working man in the county, his work was not exactly pleasant. These factors may also explain why the history of tanning in Devon has largely gone unrecorded.

Tanners contributed significantly to the local economy and at a time of population growth their product was much in demand, especially when transport relied on horse-power rather than the internal combustion engine. Devon leather provided work, in addition to the tanner's labour force, for slaughtermen, curriers, boot and shoemakers, saddlers and harness makers.

Because this research covers new ground I cannot claim that it is definitive, although I have attempted to record all the significant sites. Inevitably with such a volume of new material there will be errors and I can only apologise where these occur.

Why did I research tanneries? For some years I've been trawling local west country newspapers for information on watermills in Devon and Cornwall – usually found in auction notices. A number of these sale notices related to tanneries. This is how the hunt started. Once I realised the extent of the industry and then found its history had never been published, I thought it a project I ought to attempt to put on record.

Towards the end of my research, a team from Exeter Archaeology discovered an Anglo-Saxon shoe – which was originally thought to be more than 2,000 years old – preserved, waterlogged, in a hollowed out tree trunk in a quarry at Whiteball on the Devon-Somerset border. Stitch and lace holes were still extant in the leather.

While this shoe wasn't necessarily fashioned from Devon leather, there is a reasonable chance that it was. And it serves as a reminder that the records of nineteenth century tanneries that follow only scratch the surface of the history of leather working which has functioned in the county for at least a thousand years and probably more.

Martin Bodman
Cullompton
January 2008

Tanners were respected members of the community and George Barne was a leading light amongst their number, appointed a partner of the Tiverton and Devonshire Bank in 1808, and elected mayor of Tiverton in 1818. He rallied the tanners of Devon into defending their trade against a leather tax imposed by the government of the time. This memorial can be found in St Peter's Church, Tiverton. Photograph courtesy Jane Evans

Barking in the early twentieth century. The bark has been removed from a six foot section of a trunk of an oak tree. The tree will now be felled before the remainder of the bark is removed. Photograph courtesy Museum of Rural Life, Reading

Remains of an edge runner stone at East Street, South Molton. Used to crush oak bark in a bark mill to produce tannin, the essential element in oak-bark tanning. Edge runners were supplanted by more sophisticated machinery during the course of the 19th century

Barking: Stan Britton of Withleigh, Tiverton, using a barking iron to strip bark from a log. He last used this tool 'in anger' in 1942

Introduction

Leather-working is possibly man's oldest industry. Neanderthal man was working with hides one hundred thousand years ago. The tanning process was certainly in use by 3000 BC. An 18th century tannery would have differed little from the yard found at Pompeii – which had fifteen tan pits – except in size. [1] In the medieval period there had been a tendency for tanners to use portable vats – there were 15 at Meaux Abbey in 1396; [2] in 1568 Robert Hussey, a tanner of Uffculme, left vats to his brother and to his servant. [3] By the seventeenth century the 'tan-yard' with established stone-lined pits was more typical and in line with Roman practice. [4] Oak-bark tanning was a significant activity in Devon from early times; it appears that Totnes was exporting leather to Ireland, Normandy and Brittany in the 12th century. [5] Expansion came in the period 1780-1850, and peaked during the Napoleonic Wars.[6] Oak bark provided tannin – and, ground to a powder, diluted in water – tannic acid, the essential solution in producing leather from hides.

Devon was among the leading counties making leather in 1840: the census in the following year indicated Surrey first with 507 tanners, Lancashire with 420 and Devon with 397. Yorkshire's West Riding had 355, followed by Somerset and Northumberland, both with 245. These numbers included journeyman tanners and operatives as well as tannery owners. [7] The county was well placed – hides were readily available, both locally and from overseas. This sale notice from 1834 indicates the significant industry in imported hides:
'Auction .. Falmouth .. for disposing of about 2,400 Damaged Ox Hides, just landed from the schooner, City of Exeter, William Long, master, from Rio Grande, forced into this port in distress, on her voyage up Channel .. At the same time will be offered for sale, the sound portion of the said vessel's cargo, consisting of about 2250 Ox-Hides .. The superior quality of the Rio Grande Hides is well known to the trade.' [8]

Oak woods were part of the county's landscape and streams and rivers provided the abundant water power necessary for grinding bark and working the tanyard pumps. [9]

Tanning was undoubtedly a messy, noxious, unglamourous business as some older Devonians still recall today. Devon tanneries were often, but not always, sited at the edge of town or village, ideally to the east, to avoid the prevailing winds – Bow, Crediton, South Molton and the Tiverton yard near Townsend are examples.[10] However Cullompton, Uffculme and Swimbridge, for instance, had less well-placed yards. Other tanneries in the county were constructed in quite remote spots – Winkleigh's tannery was some miles away from the village, as was Cheriton Fitzpaine's and Loxbeare's tannery was also a rural site.

In the right hands and given some capital the trade could be rewarding. There were restraints. Oak bark became exceptionally expensive before and during the Napoleonic Wars – in 1790 an Exeter meeting of tanners from Devon, Cornwall and Dorset resolved 'That the free exportation of Oak Bark is highly injurious to the revenue, and to the Tanning Bufinefs in this Kingdom ..' and recommended imposing a duty on such exports. [11] One of the Cornishman Humphry Davy's first tasks at London's Royal Institution as director of chemistry in 1801 was to analyse and make recommendations for improved tanning operations. In the summer of 1801 he visited tanneries and recorded the processes. His published work was later used in the industry as a tanner's guide and he noted that the compound catechu – found in Eastern India, was a useful alternative to the expensive oak extracts. [12]

Tanners were again in conflict with the government when it introduced a tax on leather manufacture in 1812. [13] Leather was much in demand in the wars with France – boots for the infantry, saddles and harness for the cavalry and tanned hides were part of the equipment of gunners on the Royal Navy's many men-of-war. [14]

After 1815 there was a slump in demand for leather and a number of tanners faced bankruptcy, but oak bark was still expensive:
'.. The extreme scarcity, and consequent high price, of Oak Bark, and the great disadvantages under which the very important trade of tanning has long and still labours on this account, is presumed are all too well known .. many fruitless attempts have been made at different times to find some substance or auxiliary, whereby this discouragement may be removed or alleviated.
William Good, shipbuilder of Bridport Harbour has the satisfaction to acquaint the trade, that, after considerable pains and expense, he has discovered certain vegetable substances ..' [15]

Trading conditions were difficult at Plymouth in 1832:
'The bark sale .. on Thursday last, was fully attended, but, from the great depression in the leather trade, prices were from five to six shillings per coppice load less than last year.' [16]

At Bristol leather market in 1834 new oak bark was selling at £6 to £8 a ton and valonia – acorn cups from the Mediterranean, used for sole leather tanning – at £14 to £18 a ton. The equivalent 2004 prices would be: oak bark at £492 to £656 a ton and valonia at £1148 to £1476. [17]

Oak bark was still being exported in the nineteenth

A horse-powered bark mill, from W H Pyne's 'Microcosm' of 1808. Edge runner stones were supplanted by more sophisicated grinding machines in the 19th century

century as evidenced by the stranding of a vessel at Teignmouth in 1843:

'..The schooner Catharine and Ellen, Hughes [the vessel's master], of Aberystwyth, drove on shore here in the terrific gale of Friday last .. She was laden with oak bark, from Plymouth to Belfast .. The vessel is not damaged as she was bedded in the sand ..' [18]

Chrome tanning was introduced in the late 19th century and greatly speeded up the process which, until then, had taken from a year to 18 months. [19] The new process – the one really radical change in the industry in thousands of years – hastened the closure of many rural sites and by 1918 only ten tanneries were listed in the county. [20] Railways promoted centralised production, so that boots and shoes came to be made in factories in towns such as Kendal, Northampton and Street, established following Singer's invention of the sewing machine. Local boot and shoe makers shut up shop. Tanners lost much of their market.

In the boom from 1780-1850 as many as 115 tan yards were in operation; a further 60 possible sites may have existed in the eighteenth century. [21] Devon leather clearly had a good reputation – in 1843 Mr Turner of Barnstaple manufactured a saddle for Queen Victoria. [22] Devon leather may have been used in Brunel's ill-fated atmospheric railway in south Devon, abandoned in 1852. Water acting in combination on the iron pipes and leather flaps conspired to leach the tannin from the leather, and with rats feeding on the grease used to keep the flaps airtight the system was doomed. [23] Local tanneries were probably involved in making one new product – belt drives for the many watermills in the county, not to mention steam-powered factories in the towns and their hinterland. Carriage builders – Torquay alone had fourteen in 1907 – were also users of leather. [24]

Plymouth possessed several tanyards, one of which was in Mill Street, powered by the water from Drake's Leat, brought to the city along a 17-mile watercourse from Dartmoor. Exeter's tanneries were all outside the city walls – at Heavitree, Lions Holt, Westgate and St Thomas's, with a further yard nearby at Alphington. Several Devon towns had more than one establishment; these included Ashburton, Barnstaple, Crediton, Cullompton, Kingsbridge/Dodbrooke, Moretonhampstead, Newton Abbot, Tiverton, Torrington and Totnes. Woodbury also claimed two yards. [25]

Leather working was Crediton's salvation. After the collapse of its woollen industry in the eighteenth century, partly as a result of the disastrous fire of 1743 and latterly due to Yorkshire competition, a number of townspeople found work in two tanneries and three boot and shoe factories, but these didn't become permanently established to the extent of those in Kendal, in Cumbria, and Street in Somerset. [26]

Torrington's tanyards were small scale and its reputation rested on gloving, rather like Yeovil, in Somerset. [27] This was a separate industry undertaken by fellmongers and glovers rather than the tanners, curriers and cordwainers, the trades necessary for making boots and shoes. The archaic word 'cordwainer' relates to the maker of shoes from Spanish leather, and derives from the town of Cordoba which had the reputation for making the best shoe leather in the medieval era.

One traditional oak-bark tannery survives in Devon today: J & J F Baker of Colyton. Few structures remain elsewhere. Barnstaple, Bickleigh – near Tiverton – Petrockstowe, Swimbridge and South Molton provide examples, the latter surveyed and recorded by the local history group and adapted to other activities. Other tanneries have been flattened. The Broadclyst site at Beare lay in the path of the M5 Motorway and one of Barnstaple's yards lies under the town's ring road. Council offices were built on one Crediton tannery site, and these were later converted to serve as the town's library.

And yet evidence of this almost vanished trade remains in many places – most notably in the tanner's residence. At Bow the rank of workers' cottages has gone, and a large residence stands on the tannery site, but the owner's house, Colliton, lives on; likewise Beare House at Broadclyst, Tannery House at Swimbridge and Gilbrook at Woodbury. Sanctuary at Raddon Hills, Shobrooke, set in its own parkland, is possibly the grandest example. Elsewhere prominent marble memorial tablets in parish churches point to the social standing and income of the nineteenth century tanner – those to the Sharland family at Cheriton Fitzpaine, the Dunning family of Winkleigh and Sellwood of Cullompton are examples. Millhayes, at Bickleigh near Tiverton, somewhat against the odds, retains the tanner's house and the tanyard outbuildings shown on the tithe map in 1842.

A west countryman who confirms the status of the trade in the boom period, and whose name survives today through his literary circle, is the Somerset tanner Thomas Poole (1765-1837). His home was the seven-bay residence at 21 Castle Street, Nether Stowey. Poole was Samuel Taylor Coleridge's patron and entertained a group which included William and Dorothy Wordsworth, Robert Southey, Charles Lamb and Sir Humphrey Davy. He no doubt gave the latter advice on the operation of a tannery. [28]

A number of tanners died in middle age – the industry was not without its risks and longevity was not a common feature of 19th century life. Several widows ran tanyards, most notably Mrs Courtice at Milton Abbot, Elizabeth Gillett at Musbury and Laura Landick at Okehampton. In Mrs Landick's case, she ran the firm for well over a quarter of a century, from 1873 to circa 1906. [29]

With the industry in decline in the late 19th century, what became of the families involved? Many tanners had come from farming families and some appear to have returned to agriculture when the going became difficult. The Vicary family of Newton Abbot and North Tawton provided at least two of the county's magistrates and members of the Tanner family of Plymouth and White family of Moretonhampstead became barristers or solicitors. The Ware family of Woodbury became tanners on a large scale in Bristol and some of the Sharlands and their relatives uprooted to yards near Fareham and Chichester.

Devon labourers sought work in London rather than in Devon tanneries, despite journeymen tanners being the highest paid workmen in the county. Railways not only encouraged centralised production of footwear but also provided greatly improved transport to the metropolis. In the period 1850-1870 at least 100 workers born in Devon, resettled – many with their families – in Bermondsey, south London, the centre of the leather trade in nineteenth century England. The parish of Bow, near Crediton, saw no less than thirty individuals or families leave in these decades. Its population declined by 33 per cent in the 50 years to 1901. [30]

An oak bark tannery can be seen at the National History Museum, St Fagans, outside Cardiff, where buildings and pits from Rhaeadr have been re-erected, complete with water-powered bark mill. But Colyton retains the last working oak bark tannery in the country.

Introduction – sources

1   R S Thompson, Tanning. Man's First Manufacturing Process? Transactions of the Newcomen Society 53, 1981-2, 139-156 and citing
    J Gimpel, The Medieval Machine, Gollanz, 1977, 5-14
2   Arthur Raistrick, Industrial Archaeology. An Historical Survey. Eyre Methuen, 1972, 99-102
3   Peter Wyatt and Robin Stanes, editors. Uffculme: a Peculiar Parish. A Devon Town from Tudor Times. Uffculme Archive Group, 1997, 231
4   Raistrick, op cit, 99
5   Percy Russell, The Good Town of Totnes, The Devonshire Association, 1984, 10
6   Oliver Rackham, The History of the Countryside, Phoenix Press, 2000, 92
7   Herbert Mayhew, The Morning Chronicle Survey of Labour and the Poor: The Metropolitan Districts. Volume 6. Caliban Books, 1980, 167-168, using a summary from the 1841 census.
8   Woolmer's Gazette 1 February 1834 p 1 col 4
9   E A G Clark, The Ports of the Exe Estuary, 1660-1860. A Study in Historical Geography. The University of Exeter, 1960, 81
10 Frances and Joseph Gies, Cathedral, Forge and Waterwheel. Technology and Invention in the Middle Ages. Harper Collins, 1994, 190: '..Tanners and Dyers were usually restricted to the city's outer limits'
11 Rackham, op cit, 92; L A Clarkson, The English Bark Trade, The Agricultural History Review, 22, 1974, Part II, 136-152 citing Parliamentary Papers 1812-13, IV, p 602; Meeting of tanners, Exeter, 2 August 1790 – Bristol Mercury 30 August 1790
12 Dr J A Paris, The Life of Sir Humphry Davy, 1831
13 Meetings of tanners were held in Exeter under the chairmanship of George Barne Esq, tanner and banker of Tiverton and Butterleigh. Exeter Flying Post 20 August 1812 p 4 col 5
14 Brian Lavery, Building the Wooden Walls. The Design and Construction of the 74-gun Ship Valiant. Conway Maritime Press 1991, 178. 'On 16 October [1760] the Valiant was sent 353 barrels of gunpowder, 1412 copper hoops for the barrels and 11 *tanned hides* for the gunners stores – PRO Adm 160/2
15 Sherborne Mercury 22 November 1819
16 The Western Times 26 May 1832 p 2 col 6
17 Woolmer's Gazette 23 Jan 1834 p 4 col 6
18 Woolmer's Gazette 4 November 1843 p 3 col 5
19 Encyclopaedia Britannica, 15th edition, 1976, 810
20 Kelly's Directory of Devonshire and Cornwall, 1919, 1116
21 Research by the author based on evidence in contemporary newspapers, trade directories, ordnance and tithe maps; A H Shorter, The Tanning Industry in Devon and Cornwall, 1550-1850. Devon and Cornwall Notes and Queries, XXV, 1952, 10-16
22 Woolmer's Gazette 29 April 1843 p 3 col 4 'Mr Turner, Sadler of Barnstaple, has manufactured a splendid saddle for her Majesty, on Mr Bencraft's patent ..'
23 Keith Beck and John Copsey, The Great Western in South Devon, Wild Swan Publications Ltd, 1990, 3
24 Kelly's Directory of the Leather Trades, 1907, 66
25 Contemporary newspapers and trade directories; Ordnance Survey maps, 25"=1 mile first edition
26 Crediton map of 1743 comes home. Devon Archaeological Society Newsletter, 95, Autumn 2006, 11-12
27 H W Strong, The Industries of North Devon, Barnstaple, 1889, 29-34
28 Robin Bush, Somerset. The Complete Guide. The Dovecote Press, 1994, 153
29 Laura Landick's husband, the tanner Samuel Landick the younger of Okehampton, died 14 January 1873. Will proved by Laura Landick, widow, estate worth £600.
30 For details, see the appendix, based on research undertaken by Frank Clements of Catford, circa 1980.

Location of nineteenth century tanneries in Devon

Devon towns and villages with tanneries. Most of these sites are referred to in the gazetteer. Places such as Plymouth, Exeter, Barnstaple and Crediton operated with three or more tanyards. The majority of the tanyards recorded here lasted into the nineteenth century and a few survived into the twentieth century. Colyton, in east Devon, has the only remaining active oak bark tannery in the country. The last such tannery in Wales, at Rhaeadr, closed in the 1950s and the last Cornish oak bark tannery, at Grampound, closed in 2002

The operation of a Devon tannery

A typical tanyard

Tanyards would sometimes be let or sold and the following notice in the local press provides details of the business at Whimple in 1838:

'To Tanners. To be Let, for a term of 18 years, with possession at Lady-Day next, a most desirable TAN-YARD, capable of carrying from 70 to 80 hides per week, situate in the parish of Whimple ...
The yard consists of 60 Handlers, 29 Layers, 15 Spenders, 6 Lime Pits, and 2 Grainers, and has a stream of water running through it. Also two Drying Lofts, Store Rooms, Bark Barns .. The Yard is now in full work and the business has been carried on by the owner for the last forty years .. There are two bark mills in the Yard, one of which is driven by water, which mills must be taken by the Lessee at a valuation.
The taker may be accommodated with any quantity not exceeding thirty three Acres of good Orchard, Arable and Grazing Land .. For a view apply to the Owner, Mr Edward Richards, Whimple ..' [1]

Tanning hides

Making leather was a slow process, and even when the tanner had completed his tasks the currier had further work to do before the product was saleable. The sequence of operations ran as follows:

• Hides were cleaned then washed in water pits to remove preservatives and traces of blood; then soaked until supple. Salt had to be removed from imported hides. Dry hides were made supple.
• Through immersion in a series of lime pits fats and epidermis were removed from the hides – a process that took up to six weeks, employing increasing strengths of slaked lime.
• Hides were then worked on over a sloping beam. All remaining traces of flesh were removed from the inner surface and hair roots from the outer. Workmen used two-handled semicircular shaped scrapers. Tanners would advertise for men to work 'at the beam': it was probably one of the most unpleasant tasks in the yard, but fleshing was highly skilled.
• Mastering pits were dung pits – often a mixture of pidgeon and dog dung in warm water – and used to eradicate the lime introduced in earlier operations and soften the hides. This operation took mere hours: if left too long the bacteria in the pit would destroy the hide.
• Rounding. Hides were divided into cheeks, shoulders, bellies and butts prior to tanning. These had different skin qualities and thus required separate processing.
• Leaching pits. Where ground oak bark and water were mixed and left to stand for several weeks before being used in the tanning process, as tannic acid or 'liquor', which would then be pumped to the tan pits.

• Spenders. The first set of a series of tan pits through which the hides progressed. Also known as suspender pits, where hides were hung vertically. These pits contained weak tannic acid or 'liquor', preparing the hides for more concentrated treatment later. Weak liquor was used to penetrate through the hide. Too strong a liquor would 'case harden' the outside of a new hide, leaving the middle un-tanned: a process to be avoided at all costs.
• Handlers. Hides were moved regularly through the handlers, containing stronger concentrations of liquor. In these pits the hides acquired their colour.
• Layers. These pits contained the strongest liquor. Hides were laid between layers of ground oak bark, and the pits filled with water. Immersion could take a number of months. Sole leather and saddles tended to require longer and thus heavier tanning. Such pits would typically process 80 hides at a time.
• On completion of the tanning process the hides were left to dry in a ventilated loft, in the dark, to prevent discolouration.
• Rolling. The hide – now leather – would be levelled and flattened under a brass roller, if to be used as sole leather. For harness and boot and shoe uppers and saddles, leather would go to a currier for further work, before being received by a harness-maker, shoemaker or saddler. [2]

Oak bark

The demands of tanneries were such that the provision of oak bark became a separate industry. A typical tanner would require the bark of 40 or more mature oak trees a year. Coppice oak woods produced the finest bark: it was more expensive but, with smaller girths, more than forty trees would need to be stripped to gain an equivalent quantity of tannin. [3] Twice the weight of a hide in bark was thought necessary to effect a good tan.

Stripping oak trees, either standing or felled, was done in May and into June. This was sometimes known as the 'bark harvest' or 'barking season': spring is the time when the sap in the oak rises and tannin is at its most concentrated.

Stanley Britton of Withleigh noted that stripping was best done in the second week of May. The oak would be sawn down to 4ft or 3ft sections and then he would run down the bark with a special stripping tool, or spud – Stanley has one preserved – and if you did it right the bark would *'come off like an old overcoat'*. He'd attempt to keep the bark in one piece and handle carefully and *'like haymaking – let it dry for a fortnight'*. When he collected the bark, he'd roll it up and tie it with hazel binds. Stanley took bark into Crediton where he'd *'get quite a bit of money for it .. the better the weather the better the result.'* Rain was most undesirable as the tannin would leach out. [4] At the tannery, bark barns were used to store this expensive material in the dry until required. A barn might hold from 100 to 200 tons of bark.

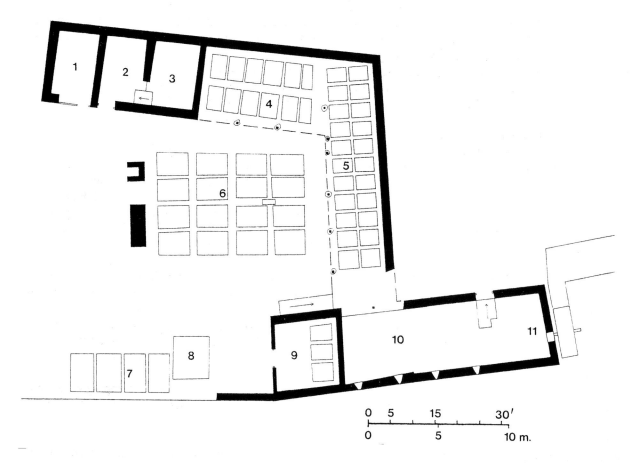

Plan of Rhaeadr Tannery, courtesy of the National History Museum, St Fagans, Cardiff. Some Devon tanneries were also built round a courtyard.

1   Office, formerly fellmongering room
2   Weighing room
3   Cellar, for storage of horn hides
4   12 Layer pits
5   22 Handler or floater pits under cover with drying lofts over
6   8 Leaching pits and 8 suspender pits
7   3 Lime pits and 1 offal pit
8   Water pit
9   Beam house with three mastering pits
10 Bark store
11 Bark mill with external overshot waterwheel

Overshot waterwheel used to work the bark mill

Three views of the Rhaeadr Tannery rebuilt at the National History Museum, St Fagans, Cardiff, and open to the public. Handler pits in the immediate foreground, under cover, beneath the drying lofts. In the open – leaching pits and suspender pits

May witnessed the arrival at Bow tannery of *'carts from miles around .. laden with oak bark'*. Their numbers were sometimes so great that they lined the village street and Bow's five inns stayed open all night to serve the carters as they queued to unload their valuable goods at the tannery at Halse. [5]

As early as 1691, Matthew Frost, a Shobrooke tanner paid the Chamber of the City of Exeter £900 for oaks felled from Duryard on the edge of the city: capital was necessary to run a tanyard. [6]

Bark was sometimes obtained at auction, sometimes through agents. Many auction notices appeared in the press, for example in 1799:
'Devonshire. To be sold, together, or in Lots, 136 Oak and 15 Ash Trees, with their Tops and Bark, to be cut the next Barking Seafon; now ftanding on this Barton of Paddaford, in the parifh of Crediton – the timber is near the Turnpike Road ..' [7]
In 1812 bark at £10 a ton was being sought in Exeter. [8] Later in the century it could be had at £4.50 a ton. Wippell and Rew of the Alphington tannery obtained some of their supplies from estates and woods belonging to the Fulfords of Dunsford. Ripping and delivering the bark was undertaken in May and June and the firm was typically charged 50s [£2-50] per ton in addition to the cost of the bark. Wippell and Rew paid £20-11s-8d for 4 tons 14 cwt 2qrs 7lbs of bark in June 1881. £11-16s-3d was deducted for ripping and delivery, leaving £5-0s-07d owed. The overall cost of bark at that time was typically £4-10s per ton [£4-50] or £4-12s per ton if some small coppice bark was included. Bark came from oak woods near Dunsford, from Tedburn, and from Duryard, near Cowley Bridge. Mr Searle of St Thomas's Tannery, Exeter, also obtained bark from the same source. [9]

Bark mills
To produce tannin, bark, with its dead outer layer discarded, had to be ground. In some tan yards this was done by hand but by the 18th century most tanneries used some form of bark mill. The simplest mill consisted of an upright runner stone with a serrated edge, driven round a circular paving or trough with an axle by a horse or an ox. The earliest known reference to a tan or bark mill in England is to *'I molend tanerez'* in Cumberland, now Cumbria, from the Pipe Roll, 11 Henry II (1164-5). In France, water-powered bark crushing mills had been extant in the Paris hinterland from about 1138. By the end of the 18th century they were a common feature of west country tanneries. [10]
The milling process became more sophisticated and in 1801 George Bodley, an Exeter ironfounder, together with James Whitby, a Cullompton tanner and John Davis, patented an improved bark mill made from iron castings which could be driven by horse power, wind power or water power. [11] Bodley stood to gain by manufacturing the machinery and several

Devon tanners bought the equipment. The following is from a notice to lease the Ottery St Mary tan yard in 1823:
'.. The situation is considered equal to any in the county for procuring Raw Hides, Skins and Bark.— There is on it an excellent Bark-Mill, by Bodley .. .. Mr Richard Salter, the owner ..' [12]

By the 1860s the foundry was supplying tanners with iron goods as far away as Bristol, Fareham, Havant and Chichester; the Hampshire and Sussex towns probably by sea. [13] Bodley's rival, Huxhams & Brown, also of Exeter, exhibited a *'mill to grind bark for tanners making but little dust'* at the Great Exhibition, in London, in 1851. [14]

Valonia, which was used in the production of sole leather, was shipped from the Mediterranean through ports such as Exmouth and Teignmouth. It was a soluble powder made from crushed acorn cups which was added to the tannic acid or liquor, intensifying the action. It is still used today at Colyton.

Water power was also useful for pumping water and the liquor or ooze around the tanyard.

Leather mills
Several leather mills were operating in Devon in the 18th and 19th centuries – these have been noted at Bradninch, Cullompton, Exeter, Pilton, South Brent, Torrington and Upton Pyne. They were not, however the domain of the tanner or the currier, but rather, of the fellmonger, and were used to make chamois or shammy leather. Chamois is the inner half of the skin. The mills were similar to fulling mills, but instead of cloth, wet sheepskins, previously limed, were fulled with sawdust until semi dry and then tanned with cod liver oil. Modern processing utilises hydraulic presses. [15]

Steam power
As the 19th century wore on so tanners invested in steam power. One of the first recorded as doing so was Richard Reynolds of Shobrooke. His engine had been installed by 1821 and came with steam apparatus *'to heat the oozes'*.[16] Alphington, near Exeter, also had a tanyard equipped with steam power before 1821. [17] Another early application of steam power was at Frankfort Street, Plymouth, in 1826, where a large-scale fellmongering operation was carried on in addition to tanning. [18]
In 1863 Bodley's Old Quay Foundry undertook work for John Smyth, tanner of Swimbridge. It appears that the foundry supplied a new 10" cylinder horizontal steam engine for £85-5s-5d. An additional £35-14s-4d was paid for the driving gear to the bark mill and the liquor and water pumps were powered at a cost of £19-8s-1d. [19]
Other tanneries employing steam power included Halse at Bow; East Street, South Molton; Beare at Broadclyst and St Thomas's Tannery, Exeter. [20]

Andrew Parr, managing director of Baker's Tannery, Colyton – the last oak-bark tannery in the country – raising a hide from a suspender pit

Drives to the bark mill at Colyton. Photograph courtesy Alan Stoyel

Capacity and output

Devon tanyards varied in size but would typically have had between 30 and 100 tanpits. The yard at Sampford Peverell was advertised with a throughput of 50 hides per week in 1819 [21] and in 1831 comprised:

'.. *a dwelling-house, bark shed, bark mill by water, 40 handlers under sheds, 6 latches, 24 troughs, 4 stone pits, 3 lime pits, 2 masonry pits covered and necessary lofts, stables, outhouses and walled garden ..*' [22]

Because oak-bark tanning was such a slow process several sets of pits would be needed to work through each week's input of hides. Pits in Cheriton Fitzpaine's two yards, worked together, could contain 8000 to 9000 hides in 1864. While the number of pits here is known for 1824, it is thought the tannery expanded in the intervening period, and so a match between numbers of pits and numbers of hides is not possible.

Larger tanyards such as Frankfort Street, Plymouth, and Beare, Broadclyst, worked 200 hides per week. The Plymouth yard also handled up to 2000 sheep skins a week. [23]

The operation of a Devon tannery – sources

1 Exeter Flying Post 21 June 1838 p 2 col 2
2 Herbert Mayhew, The Morning Chronicle Survey of Labour and the Poor: The Metropolitan Districts. Volume 6. Caliban Books, 1980, 172-173; Arthur Raistrick. Industrial Archaeology. An Historical Survey. Eyre Methuen, 1972, 99-102; J Geraint Jenkins, The Rhaeadr Tannery, National Museum of Wales 1973, 9-15; Trevor Bowen, Nailsea Tannery, Nailsea and District LHS, 1997, 2-3, based on an 1883 report of a visit to Avonside Tannery, Bristol
3 L A Clarkson, The English Bark Trade, The Agricultural History Review, 22, 1974, Part II, 136-152
4 From a conversation with Stanley Britton at Quirkhill, Tiverton, 1 August 2003
5 Barbara Carbonell and Mary Wauton, Thirteen Centuries in Bow alias Nymet Tracy with Broadnymet, Devon, 1949, 23-24
6 Michael Havinden, The Woollen, Lime, Tanning and Leather Working and Paper-Making Industries c. 1500 – c.

1800, in Kain and Ravenhill, Historical Atlas of South-West England, University of Exeter Press, 1999, 342, citing Robert Newton, Eighteenth Century Exeter, Exeter, 1984, 4
7 Exeter Flying Post 17 January 1799 p 1 col 5
8 Exeter Flying Post 6 August 1812 p 4 col 5
9 Devon Record Office 1926D/FU/F7/22
10 I am grateful to Martin Watts for the following sources: Cumberland – Pipe Roll 11 Henry II (1164-5) from Pipe Roll Society, 1887, 54. Paris reference from Richard Holt, Mills of Medieval England, 1988, 148, citing A-M Bautier 'Les Plus Ancient Mentions de Moulins, 1960. Additionally Frances and Joseph Gies in 'Cathedral, Forge and Waterwheel. Technology and Invention in the Middle Ages', Harper Collins, 1994, 114, suggest the Cistercians were responsible for spreading the technology in the early Middle Ages
11 'Messrs Whitby, Bodley and Co refpectfully inform Tanners in general that they have invented a Bark Mill upon a fuperior conftruction to any .. apply to James Whitby, tanner, Cullompton, Devon, or to George Bodley, ironfounder, Exeter.' Sherborne Mercury 11 January 1802; Patent 2537 of 30 September 1801. Specification by Whitby, Bodley and Davis.
12 Exeter Flying Post 10 April 1823 p 1 col 4 But by 1869 the Ottery tan yard was using an 'improved patent Bark Mill, by Huxham (nearly new) ..' Exeter Flying Post 17 March 1869 p 1 col 2
13 Bodley Foundry ledgers. DRO 67/5/22A and B of 1860-1877
14 Woolmer's Gazette 10 May 1851 p 6 col 5 [stand 446]
15 For processing shammy leather see J H Sharphouse, Leather Technicians Handbook, Leather Producers Association, 1983, 212 et seq, and H R Proctor, The Making of Leather, Cambridge University Press, 1914
16 Exeter Flying Post 26 April 1821 p 1 col 2
17 Woolmer's Gazette 4 August 1821 p 4 col 5
18 Exeter Flying Post 13 April 1826 p 1 col 2
19 Devon Record Office – Bodley journals 67/5/2/1 folios 461-466
20 Devon Record Office – Bodley journals, 67/5/2/1 folios 293-294 [Bow], folio 187-188 [St Thomas's, Exeter]; Exeter Flying Post 29 September 1875 p 1 col 2 [Broadclyst]
21 Sherborne Mercury 23 August 1819
22 Exeter Flying Post 15 September 1831 p 2 col 2
23 Exeter Flying Post 13 April 1826 p 1 col 2 [Plymouth], Exeter Flying Post 29 September 1875 p 1 col 2

The Sharlands – a family of tanners

Devon tanners were notably close knit: tanning families would inter-marry and tanneries would be handed down from father to son. The Sharland family and its connections produced 12 tanners in three generations.

Peter Sharland was baptised in May 1738 and married Jane Mogridge at Witheridge in August 1773. [1] Of their eight known offspring, three sons – William, Peter and Edward – became tanners and their youngest daughter Elizabeth married John Ashford of Woodbury who also entered the trade. Peter was occupying Lower Waterhouse, Cheriton Fitzpaine by 1775 and probably operated a tannery there before 1811, although he was tanning at Loxbeare when Elizabeth married.[2]
In 1812 Peter and his son William were appointed to a committee of Devon tanners lobbying the Board of Trade on the damage that would be caused by a new leather tax the government was intent on imposing.[3] Peter died in 1829. Eight of his grandchildren were to become tanners.

William Sharland, Peter's eldest son, was baptised in May 1776 and married Elizabeth Comins in February 1812. [4] Comins was an old-established Witheridge family of solicitors and surgeons. The couple's only son Thomas Melhuish Comins Sharland was baptised in January 1813 at Cheriton Fitzpaine. Two sisters followed. When his father died William inherited the farm and tannery at Lower Waterhouse. [5] By 1838 he also occupied a farm and second tannery at West Upham, nearby, and a further estate at South Combe. [6] Business was successful and William retired to Exeter: he was living there in 1851, having handed over the running of the yards and farms to his son Thomas M C Sharland. [7] William died in March 1855, aged 79, and is commemorated on a marble tablet in the south aisle of Cheriton Fitzpaine church, together with his wife Elizabeth who died in March 1859.

Peter Sharland, Peter's second son, was baptised in April 1778. [8] He married but appears to have had no descendants. He had no tannery to inherit and so moved to Woodbury. About 1830 a partnership was established between Peter and his nephew Henry Wippell: Peter's sister Catherine had married a Wippell as had his elder sister Jane. Peter and Henry ran the tannery at The Green, Woodbury, but appear to have met stiff competition from the established yard in the village, run by James Sanders and William Walter Ware. [9] In 1831 Sharland and Co – probably this concern – imported a shipload of bark from Antwerp in the brig *Jean de Lochquigehan*. [10]

The Sharland Wippell partnership was dissolved at the end of November 1837. [11] Peter Sharland died in May 1842, aged 64. [12] His estate was worth nearly £7000 and his executors were his brother William Sharland of Cheriton Fitzpaine, tanner; his only son Thomas M C Sharland and Joseph Wippell, Peter's brother in law, a tea dealer and grocer of Fore Street, Exeter. [13] The tannery at The Green later became the works of George Berry and his family, agricultural implement makers. [14]

Edward Sharland, Peter Sharland's third son, was baptised in March 1785. [15] Again, he had no tannery to inherit and took over an existing establishment at Dulford in the parish of Broadhembury. It was located near the Honiton - Cullompton road which had been turnpiked in 1765. [16] His marriage was celebrated in 1810:

'On Saturday last was married, at Sampford Peverell, Mr Edward Sharland, of Broadhembury, tanner, to Miss S Rowe, third daughter of the late Mr T Rowe of Sampford Peverell.' [17]

Thomas Row was variously listed as a mercer and a shopkeeper of Sampford [18] and it is probable that a memorial stone which has been inserted in the south wall of the parish church, by the entrance, commemorates him.

Eight children had been born to Edward and Sarah at Broadhembury by 1824, [19] but the following year the family moved to Hampshire. Edward came to run a tannery at Wallington, near Fareham, where his wife bore him five more offspring. The Wallington concern was no mean establishment: Edward employed 27 men and six boys there in 1851. [20] Two of his sons, Edward and Henry, born in 1816 and 1823 respectively, continued the business and were notably successful; Edward left £49,000 in 1886 and Henry died young in 1875, aged 51, with an estate of £30,000. [21] In 1860 Edward had demonstrated the close-knit nature of the tanning community by marrying Mary Ann, daughter of the tanner James Wippell of Alphington, at St Thomas's, Exeter. [22] Henry had learnt the business working as an assistant to his cousin T M C Sharland, at Cheriton Fitzpaine, [23] of whom more later.

In 1851 their younger sister Elizabeth married a member of the Ashford family from Woodbury – Samuel H J Ashford, who had moved from Devon to run a tannery at Send in Surrey. [24] Two of their six offspring were baptised at Cheriton Fitzpaine, the family home.

What prompted the move away from Devon for Edward Sharland and Samuel Ashford? Devon tanners had attempted to send their product to London, where the market no doubt had more potential than at Exeter. But the costs of road transport before the coming of the railways may have made them uncompetitive. In the year Edward made his move to Fareham – in 1825 – the Plymouth and Portsmouth Steam Packet Company commenced running paddle steamers between the two ports. [25] And by 1844 a rival company's vessel, the Zephyr, was sailing or rather steaming direct between Topsham and Portsmouth and on to London. [26] Edward's sons maintained family connections with Devon and ordered some of their tannery machinery from Bodley's Exeter foundry, which was no doubt delivered by this route. [27] Likewise their leather could be sent to London by paddle steamer, although Portsmouth was linked to London by railway from 1847 and by a 'direct' route from 1859. [28]

Elizabeth Sharland, Peter Sharland's third daughter, was baptised in June 1787. She married **John Ashford** of Woodbury in April 1817. [29] It seems the lease of the Loxbeare tannery at Chopland may have been Elizabeth's dowry as John Ashford became its tanner and was active there in 1841. [30] The Loxbeare estate, including Chopland, was then owned by the Acland family. [31] John was a widower by 1851, but worked the tanyard with eight men. [32] The couple had four known offspring and two sons both became tanners. Peter Sharland Ashford, born at Loxbeare in 1821, was a tanner of 92 Cambridge Street, Plymouth in 1851. His sister Elizabeth kept house. [33] His brother John Henry Ashford was a farmer at Leigh Barton, almost adjoining Chopland tannery, in 1851. By 1871 his father had retired to the Barton and John H Ashford farmed 191 acres with seven men and ran the tanyard with a further nine. [34]

Thomas Melhuish Comins Sharland was the last of the family in Devon to run a tannery. Some time after 1838 his father William retired to Exeter, leaving Thomas in charge of two tanneries at Lower Waterhouse and West Upham, Cheriton Fitzpaine. He also had a farm to run. He kept in touch with his Hampshire cousins – Henry Sharland, from Fareham, worked as Thomas's assistant for a time, no doubt learning the trade. And Henry's sister Ann married Thomas at Fareham, Hants in September 1848. [35] In 1851 aged 38, he was farming 225 acres with 10 labourers and employed 36 staff in the tanneries. [36] The following year witnessed a tragic event – Thomas lost his wife, possibly in childbirth. A marble tablet on the south wall of Cheriton Fitzpaine church provides the record:
'Sacred to the Memory of Ann, the beloved wife of Thomas Melhuish Comins Sharland, of Lower Waterhouse in this parish. September 15, 1852 aged 34.'

Following his wife's death, it appears Thomas pulled in his horns, as his cousin T Melhuish Comins, the Witheridge solicitor, placed the following notice in the press in September 1854:
'.. South Coombe and West Upham to let .. Now in the occupation of Mr Sharland .. for viewing the farms apply to Mr Sharland, Waterhouse, Cheriton Fitzpaine .. ' [37]
A year later his father died, aged 79. Thomas married again in 1859. His bride, Mary Kiln, also came from Fareham, Hampshire, and they wed in December 1859. In 1860 the railway from Salisbury to Exeter

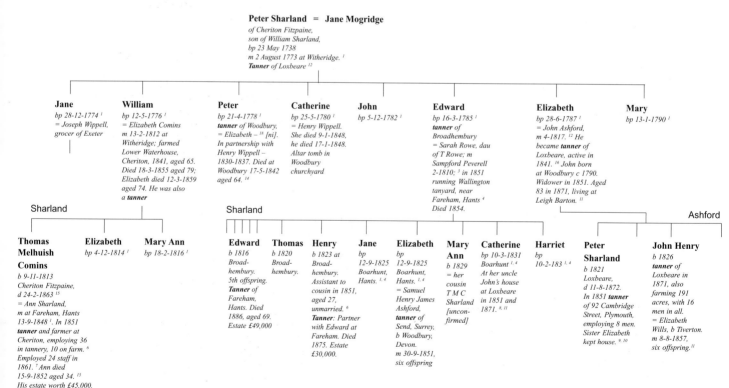

A simplified Sharland family tree, focusing on those who became tanners

opened and the Sharlands would have been able to visit Hampshire by train rather than relying on small paddle steamers in the chops of the Channel.

Work at the tannery continued: Thomas had 24 staff engaged in 1861, two of them boys. [38]

In February 1863, at the early age of 49, Thomas died leaving nearly £45,000. A second tablet in the church at Cheriton records his life:

'Sacred to the memory of a beloved husband Thomas Melhuish Comins Sharland of Lower Waterhouse in this parish. Born 9 November 1813. Died 24 February 1863.'

Two of his three executors were tanners: Thomas Gibbings, who had taken over the tannery at The Green, Woodbury, from Thomas's uncle, but left to become a tanner of Chichester in 1857, [39] and who was related by marriage and Henry Sharland, his cousin, of Fareham, Hants. £45,000 was a fortune in the mid 19th century. [40]

Thomas's estate was put on the market:

'To Tanners and others. Cheriton Fitzpaine .. Sell by Auction .. extensive and substantial Tanyards, Dwelling Houses, Cottages, and several good Farms, now let to respectable tenants .. late the property of Mr T M C Sharland, deceased .. The tanpits will contain from eight to nine thousand hides and the drying and bark sheds are of ample dimensions with good water power, and well supplied with bark of excellent quality ..

The whole of the above property is freehold and in good repair, having been occupied by the late Mr Sharland and his father, where a handsome fortune by the trade was made by them, and it affords a good opportunity for a man of capital and energy to do the same ..' [41]

With Thomas's death it appears that the properties reverted to farms and tanning ceased at Cheriton Fitzpaine. An old farm at Waterhouse was devastated by fire in 1938 [42] – this may possibly have been Thomas's home at one time. The pond that would have supplied water power to the bark mill there has been remodelled but West Upham survives as a farm today, with a large number of outbuildings.

Family tree sources
1. Mormon IGIs
2. Cheriton Fitzpaine 1841 census – HO107 2091 f 3
3. Exeter Flying Post 15 February 1810 p 4 col 3
4. Fareham, Hants, census for 1851– HO107 1661 f 171
5. Loxbear census for 1841 – HO107 255 f 3 p 7
6. Cheriton Fitzpaine, census for 1851– HO107 1887 f 456 p 12
7. Cheriton Fitzpaine, census for 1861 – RG9 1474 f 48 p 7
8. Loxbear census for 1851 – HO107 1889 f 381 p 5
9. Will of Peter Sharland Ashford, late of Plymouth, proved by widow and John Henry Ashford, of Loxbeare, tanner, brother.
10. Plymouth St Andrews census for 1851 – HO107 1879 f 408 p 30
11. Loxbeare census for 1871 – RG10 2174 f 62 p 7; marriage – The Western Times 15 August 1857 p 5 col 2
12. Exeter Flying Post 1 May 1817 p 4 col 2
13. Exeter Flying Post 14 December 1837 p 2 col 4
14. Exeter Flying Post 26 May 1842 p 2 col 5

15. Memorial tablets, south wall, Cheriton Fitzpaine church
16. Loxbeare census for 1841 – HO107 255\3 f 7 p 6
17. Will of Peter Sharland of Exeter, 1829. DRO 1078/IRW/S/491
18. Will of Peter Sharland of Woodbury, 1842. DRO 1078/IRW/S/492

The Sharlands – a family of tanners. Sources
1. Mormon IGI
2. [1775] R R Sellman, Cheriton Fitzpaine. Notes from the parish records and other sources, 1978, 56; [1811] Devon Record Office 1481A/PO 708/78; Exeter Flying Post 1 May 1817 p 4 col 2 [marriage]
3. Exeter Flying Post 20 August 1812 p 4 col 5
4. IGI
5. Devon Record Office. Peter Sharland's will of 1829 – 1078/IRW/S/491
6. Cheriton Fitzpaine tithe of 1838 transcribed by R R Sellman, op cit
7. Exeter census
8. Mormon IGI
9. Ursula W Brighouse. Woodbury. A View from the Beacon. 1998, 132
10. Exmouth shipping report – Woolmer's Gazette 24 September 1831 p 3 col 3
11. Exeter Flying Post 14 December 1837 p 2 col 4
12. Exeter Flying Post 26 May 1842 p 2 col 5
13. Devon Record Office. Peter Sharland's will of 1842– 1078/IRW/S/492
14. Brighouse, op cit, 192
15. Mormon IGI
16. Helen Barrett, Our Heritage. A History of Kentisbeare and Blackborough, 1977, 34
17. Exeter Flying Post 15 February 1810 p 4 col 3
18. Knighthayes Estate Office, Tiverton. Box 9/14. Will of Thomas Row, 3 August 1805
19. Devon Record Office. Broadhembury parish registers
20. Fareham, Hampshire, census, 1851. HO107 1661 f 171
21. Sharland wills. Public Record Office
22. The Western Times 26 March 1860 p 5 col 3
23. Cheriton Fitzpaine census for 1851 – HO107 1887 f 456 p 12
24. Mormon IGI
25. Crispin Gill, Plymouth. A New History. Devon Books, 1993, 216
26. Exeter Flying Post 2 May 1844 p 1 col 3
27. In 1865 E & H Sharland, Fareham, Hampshire tanners owed Bodley's Foundry, Exeter, Devon, £21-0s-7d. Cheque paid in June. DRO Bodley ledger 67/5/22A
28. H P White. A Regional History of the Railways of Great Britain. Volume 2 – Southern England. David & Charles, Newton Abbot, 1969, 119-121
29. Mormon IGI
30. Loxbeare census, 1841. HO107 255 f 3 p 7
31. DRO. Loxbeare tithe apportionment
32. Loxbeare census, 1851. HO107 1889 f 381 p 5
33. Plymouth St Andrews census, 1851. HO107 1879 f 408 p30
34. Loxbeare census, 1871. RG10 2174 f 62 p 7
35. Mormon IGI
36. Cheriton Fitzpaine, census for 1851 – HO107 1887 f 456 p 12
37. Exeter Flying Post 7 September 1854
38. Cheriton Fitzpaine, census for 1861 – RG9 1474 f 48 p 7
39. Exeter Flying Post 19 March 1857 p 1
40. Will of Thomas Melhuish Comins Sharland. PROB.
41. Exeter Flying Post 24 August 1864 p 1 col 2
42. Western Morning News 2 January 1939

17

Rounding a hide

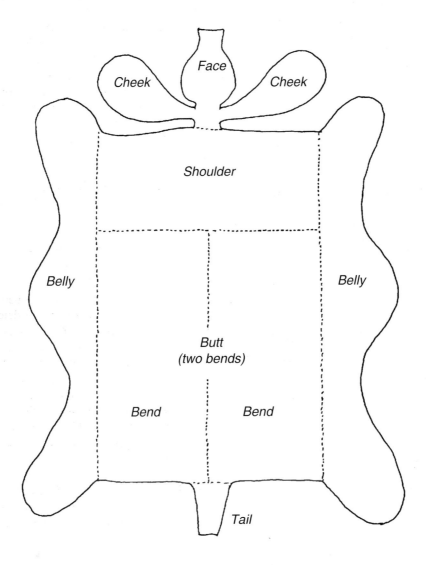

Parts of a cattle hide. After liming and the removal of flesh and hair the hide would be 'rounded' or cut into parts, as shown here.
• Butt. When divided into two, known as bends. The best part of the hide and used for sole leather and boot leather
• Shoulder. Used for straps and welts. A welt was a strip of leather sewn round the edge of a boot or shoe upper to serve as an attachment to the sole
• Belly. Used for dressed leather and handbags
• Face and cheek. Football studs, heel lifts, billiard cue tips and washers would be formed from this inferior hide, when tanned
• Tail. Used for the top piece on the heel of a shoe as it was the hardest part of the hide
Also see the glossary on page 150
Diagram courtesy Dick Pearce, South Molton and Shirley Bray, The South Molton Archive

Alphington

Alphington Tannery

Location	SX 919 903
Operational	to 1910 or later
Output	60 to 100 hides a week in 1821
Bark mills	two, steam powered by 1821
Tan pits	60 in 1792; 140+ in 1816
Staff	8 or more in 1851

Alphington tannery, only about a mile or so from the city of Exeter, was well placed to compete with the four tanneries there, and stood on the edge of the parish of St Thomas.

The yard, just south of the Alphin Brook, a tributary of the Exe, was well-established by the late 18th century. Samuel Dingle had been tanner in 1772 when his stock was advertised for sale. [1] He was succeeded by the Berry family. Mr Berry died in 1789 [2] and with Mrs Berry in possession the yard was offered to let in 1790. [3] She continued to rent the property in 1792:

'A TAN-YARD. To be Lett immediately, a very compleat Tan-Yard, a good Dwelling-houfe in it, with extenfive and convenient Buildings .. about 60 Pits, fupplied with a running stream of water, remarkable for giving the Leather a superior Colour .. situate in the parifh of Alphington about a Mile from Exeter, lately rented by Mrs Berry .. for further particulars apply to Mr John Luke, ironmonger, Exeter ..' [4]

William Berry was tenant by 1811, but had sublet the yard to a Mr Northam. [5] Berry, who also held the lease on Alphington Mills upstream, was bankrupt. [6] Following a case in the High Court, the tanyard and mills were for sale in 1815. The yard was by now extensive, with *'nearly 150 pits .. and a capital steam engine and bark mills ..'.* The premises belonged to Lord Courtenay. [7]

John Sanders was the next incumbent, in a partnership with Richard Wright which was dissolved early in 1819; [8] Sanders continued as sole trader – but not without upset. In 1821 his Newfoundland dog ran amok savaging members of the family and then, on the loose, biting a child in Ide and causing chaos among a flock of sheep near Haldon House. The dog was put down. [9] In the same year the Sheriff of Devon took possession of the yard and Sanders' stock and utensils were for sale, including 80 tons of bark. [10] This was now a relatively large establishment by Devon standards and 60 to 100 hides could be tanned in a week. Bridge Cottage as it was then known appears to have been erected just prior to the sale. [11]

As with Richard Reynolds at Shobrooke, who was bankrupted in 1821, Berry seems to have spent money extending the facilities in the years of the boom and Sanders suffered the consequences in the post-war slump. Steam engines at that date were expensive and not necessarily economical pieces of machinery; new residences came at a price. It would be fascinating to know where the Alphington and Shobrooke engines were manufactured. They were probably small beam engines and the nearest ironfoundries capable of manufacturing them were at Bristol, Neath Abbey and Hayle. Exeter foundries had not yet developed the necessary skills – at any rate, on present evidence.

The tannery may have remained unsold as a lease-holder was still sought in 1821. [12] In the same year James Wippell, an Alphington tanner, married. [13]

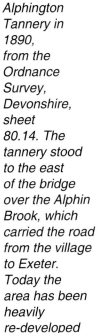

Alphington Tannery in 1890, from the Ordnance Survey, Devonshire, sheet 80.14. The tannery stood to the east of the bridge over the Alphin Brook, which carried the road from the village to Exeter. Today the area has been heavily re-developed

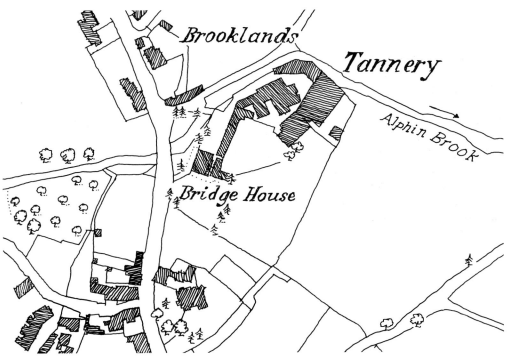

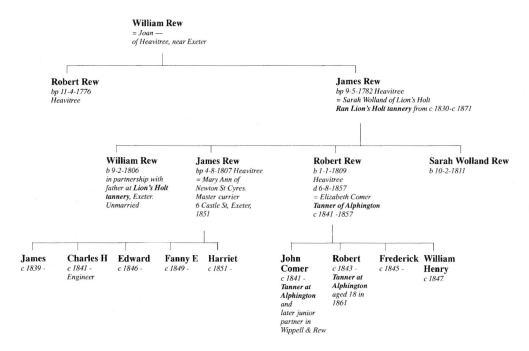

William Rew
= Joan —
of Heavitree, near Exeter

Robert Rew
bp 11-4-1776
Heavitree

James Rew
bp 9-5-1782 Heavitree
= Sarah Wolland of Lion's Holt
Ran Lion's Holt tannery from c 1830-c 1871

The Rew family, tanners of Exeter and Alphington. Tree derived from Heavitree and Alphington census returns and transcriptions of parish registers

William Rew
b 9-2-1806
in partnership with
father at **Lion's Holt
tannery**, Exeter.
Unmarried

James Rew
bp 4-8-1807 Heavitree
= Mary Ann of
Newton St Cyres.
Master currier
6 Castle St, Exeter,
1851

Robert Rew
b 1-1-1809
Heavitree
d 6-8-1857
= Elizabeth Comer
Tanner of Alphington
c 1841 -1857

Sarah Wolland Rew
b 10-2-1811

James
c 1839 -

Charles H
c 1841 -
Engineer

Edward
c 1846 -

Fanny E
c 1849 -

Harriet
c 1851 -

John Comer
c 1841 -
Tanner at Alphington and later junior partner in Wippell & Rew

Robert
c 1843 -
Tanner at Alphington
aged 18 in 1861

Frederick
c 1845 -

William Henry
c 1847

Robert Rew was here in 1837 when he wed Elizabeth, *'second daughter of Mr John Comer, Lake Barton'*, Newton St Cyres. [14]

In 1841, Robert Rew lived at Bridge Cottage with his family. The second tanner, James Wippell, was at Little Burn Cottage with his second wife Mary – his first wife died in 1829. [15] He himself died in middle age – in the 1840s – and Robert Rew, who was born at Heavitree in 1809, ran the Alphington Yard with eight men in 1851.
At home on census night were his wife Elizabeth, four sons and two servants. At this date, Thomas Wippell, probable son of James, was also at Alphington, employing six tanners. He may have been Robert Rew's junior partner. [16] Robert was the third son of James Rew who ran the tannery at Lions Holt, Exeter, from at least 1830 to about 1871.

Robert Rew died in 1857 [17] – aged 48 – and in 1861 his wife was listed as a farmer's widow. It is possible that Mrs Rew, like many other Devon tanners, also farmed. Her sons John C Rew, 20, and Robert Rew, 18, were either tanners or about to take up the trade. Thomas Wippell had taken charge of the yard [18] and headed a business that in 1866 was known as Wippell & Rew. [19] His junior partner was John C Rew.

The bark mill required a new waterwheel shaft, bosses and chairs for bearings in 1876. These were supplied by Bodley of Exeter. [20] In this period the tannery obtained some of its oak bark from the Fulford estates – from woods at Dunsford, Tedburn St Mary and Duryard, near Cowley Bridge, Exeter. [21]

The partnership was still active in 1881. Thomas Wippell had by now established his family in Bridge House, once the home of the Rews and John Rew, unmarried, lived next door. [22] Rew had left the partnership by 1891. On census night George

Foreknall and his family were staying with the Wippells at Bridge House. Foreknall was a leather merchant from Chesterfield in Derbyshire, which suggests Wippell's trade wasn't entirely local. His son, Thomas R Wippell, then 32, had entered the industry [23] and in 1897 the firm was trading as T Wippell & Son, tanners. [24] It was still operating in 1910, [25] by which time the elder Thomas had probably retired. He would then have been 83.

Today the site has been lost under recent developments and 20th century industrial buildings.

Alphington sources
1 Exeter Flying Post 24 July 1772 p 3 col 3
2 Exeter Flying Post 22 January 1789 p 3 col 2
3 Exeter Flying Post 9 December 1790 p 3 col 2
4 Exeter Flying Post 19 January 1792 p 3 col 4
5 Exeter Flying Post 4 July 1811 p 1
6 Exeter Flying Post 21 October 1811 p 4 col 2
7 London Gazette 22 August 1815; Woolmer's Gazette 17 August 1816 p 4 col 5
8 Exeter Flying Post 18 February 1819 p 4 col 3
9 Exeter Flying Post 11 January 1821 p 4 col 4
10 Exeter Flying Post 3 May 1821 p 4 col 5
11 Woolmer's Gazette 4 August 1821 p 4 col 5
12 Exeter Flying Post 22 November 1821 p 4 col 3
13 Exeter Flying Post 11 October 1821 p 4 col 1
14 Exeter Flying Post 7 December 1837 p 2 col 5
15 Alphington census 1841 – HO107 262\3 f 6 p 6, HO107 262\3 f 10 p 14; Exeter Flying Post 26 March 1829 p 2 col 4
16 Alphington census 1851 – HO107 1867 f 235 p 17, HO107 1867 f 255 p 30
17 Exeter Flying Post 6 August 1857 p 5 col 2
18 Alphington census 1861 – RG9 1390 f 116 p 31 entries 740 and 741
19 Post Office Directory of Devonshire 1866, 1277-8
20 The Mills Archive. Bodley drawing 9307 of 1876
21 DRO 1926D/FU/F7/22
22 Alphington census 1881 – RG11 2146 f 106 p 21
23 Alphington census 1891 – RG12 1684 f 89 p 7
24 Alphington census 1901 – RG13 2039; Kelly's Directory of Devonshire 1897, 1111; 1902, 1136
25 Kelly's Directory of Devonshire and Cornwall, 1910, 1143

Ashburton

Old Mill
Tanyard off Lawrence Street
Tanyard east of the church

Old Mill tanyard was operational in the Napoleonic period and appears to be the yard outlined in this notice of 1811:
'TO be SOLD or LET .. All those Capital YARN and WORSTED MILLS .. near the populous town of Buckfastleigh .. Also, All those TAN-YARDS, with convenient Pits, Drying-Houses, Bark Lofts .. adjoining the town of Ashburton, and the whole are near the turnpike road leading from Ashburton to Plymouth and Totnes ..' [1]

Ashburton had four tanyards in 1822. The address for the fourth was given as East Street, but its location has yet to be determined. W Mann, an Ashburton tanner who had started tanning in 1799, was looking for a partner in 1807; John Vere Mann was listed as a tanner at East Street in 1823 and in 1826 he married *'Grace, third daughter of Mr H Barons, late of Wisdom, Cornwood'*. William Mann died in 1832 and John V Mann in 1834. [2]

In 1839 there were three yards in the town. [3] Old Mill, which stood between Stone Park and the Chuley Road, later became Ashburton Brewery [4] and the old brewery buildings are today occupied by Rendells Auction Rooms.

The other two tanyards were closer to West Street. One was east of the church and the second off Lawrence Street. [5]

Even at the close of leather making in the town, the bark harvest continued in neighbouring woods, the bark possibly going to the major tannery at Newton Abbot – witness this notice from May 1848:
'Ashburton. The barking season is proceeding satisfactorily, a large quantity of trees and Forest wood will be taken down during the month, thus affording employment to a large number of labourers.' [6]
The practice continued after the Ashburton yards had closed – this report comes from May 1856:
'Ashburton. The bark season has commenced and affords employment to large numbers of labourers.' [7]

Lawrence Lane / Lawrence Street

Location	SX 7563 6977
Operational	to circa 1840
Bark mills	two, possibly water powered
Tan pits	3 limes, 19 handlers, 8 letches, 32 troughs

In 1812 John Higgins occupied the Lawrence Street tannery; he was also an associate of George Barne

of Tiverton, acting as his treasurer in committees in Exeter. [8] He died in 1825 [9] and we have a good description of his tannery which was auctioned in lots in 1826:

'Ashburton .. Two .. newly-erected Dwelling-Houses situate within the borough of Ashburton .. and also the Tan-Yard behind, attached to, and adjoining the same, consisting of two watering pools, 3 lime pits, 19 large handlers with drying lofts over, 8 letches, with drying lofts over, 32 troughs, and a steam boiler, and a counting-house, offices ..
Part of the above premises are held for the residue of a term of 1000 years, and the remainder on a lease for lives .. Trade .. carried on upon the Premises on a very extensive scale for a great many years by the late Mr John Higgins, deceased ..
Also to be Sold .. detached from but very near to the above Premises and to the town .. Ground containing about half an acre, commonly called the Bowling Green .. garden, barn, two bark-mill houses, and several large store rooms .. lately erected by the said Mr Higgins.' [10]

Lawrence Lane may then have been occupied by John Vere Mann, who was here in 1830, having moved from East Street. [11]

Lavington Evans, who earlier occupied a tannery in North Street, had moved to West Street by 1830 and was then at Lawrence Lane by 1839, when it was owned by Richard Harris. Lavington was the son of William and Sarah Evans, baptised at Ottery St Mary in 1785. The Evans brothers, tanners of Colyton were the sons of his brother Samuel, baptised in 1787. [12]

The tannery had probably closed by 1841.

Old Mill

Location	SX 7556 6941
Operational	to circa 1854
Bark mills	two, one water-powered, one horse-powered
Tan pits	3 limes and 83 tan-pits, under cover, (1848)
Staff	15 in 1851

Old Mill was for sale in 1813. Its name indicates it was on the site of an earlier fulling mill – Ashburton was a woollen manufacturing town in the eighteenth century: [13]
'Borough of Ashburton .. To be SOLD in FEE, by order of the assignees of John Ellis, all that Messuage and Tenement with the Yard, Courtlage, Garden and Outhouses adjoining, formerly used as a tanyard, called OLD MILL, situate near the Western end of the town of Ashburton and very well calculated for a tanner .. Apply to Mr Abraham, solicitor, Ashburton ..' [14]

John Rendell was the proprietor throughout the 1830s and he both owned and occupied Old Mill tannery in 1839, besides possessing other properties elsewhere in the town. [15] There was a ready market for local leather: Sixteen boot and shoe makers were active in the town in 1850. [16]

The tannery was put on the market in December 1848 and the sale notice provides some detail:

'Ashburton, Devon. To Tanners and Others. For Peremptory Sale, by Public Auction .. under the directions of the Assignees and Mortgagees of the Estate of Mr John Rendell ..

Lot 1. All that capital Messuage or Dwelling House, with the excellent Tan Yard, Drying Lofts, Bark Barn, Sheds and other premises situate at and called Old Mill, adjoining the town of Ashburton, now and for many years occupied by Mr John Rendell, Tanner. The Tan Yard contains 1 Water-pit, 3 Lime and 83 Tan-pits under cover, Drying Lofts in which 300 hides may be dried, improved Bark Mill, and Lifting Pumps, driven by a never-failing stream of water, and all other requisite buildings and conveniences for carrying on a large Trade in the centre of a good Bark country, and within a few miles of each of the South Devon Railway Stations at Newton, Totnes and South Brent. The Bark Barn will hold 100 Tons of Bark.

The Dwelling-House, which is very pleasantly situate, contains 2 Parlours, 2 Kitchens, and 8 Bed-rooms, Wash-house, Dairy, Cellar, and other convenient Offices; it fronts into a walled Garden well stocked with choice Fruit Trees. Near are Stables for 14 horses, Cow-houses and other outbuildings. The whole of the above premises are most substantially built, and in excellent repair. The Tan Yard is held for the residue of a Term of 2,000 Years ..

Lot 2. The Fee-Simple and Inheritance of the said Dwelling-house, Offices, and Bark Barn (subject to the said Term of 1,000 Years), including the said chief rent of 25s.

Lot 3. All those Five Cottages or Dwelling Houses and other buildings, with the Garden, Inclosed Yard .. containing altogether 1r 17p, situate near old Mill aforesaid, and now occupied by Mr Rendell and by John Penwill and others, as tenants ..' [17]

In 1851 Lavington Evans employed 15 staff – 12 men, two boys and a woman. He was aged 60 and one of his sons, Jonathan, aged 20, worked for him. [18] In 1853 Old Mill tannery was offered to let when occupied by a Mr Evans, very possibly Lavington. With its 83 tan pits under cover, it was larger than Lawrence Lane which only ran to 59. A bark mill was on site too, powered by a waterwheel. [19]

Old Mill probably ceased to operate at this time: in 1854 its equipment was to be sold:

'To Tanners. To be Sold on very reasonable terms. Two Bark Mills, one of them connected with a powerful Horse Pump. Also two excellent Stoves, with Pipes requisite for drying leather; and many other

articles used in the trade. Apply to Mr Evans, Tanner, Ashburton.' [20]

This notice appears to indicate that the pumps to the tanpits at Old Mill were worked by horse power.

In 1856 only Mr Furneaux of Higher Town was listed as a tanner and the other tanneries extant in 1839 had long closed. [21] Old Mill House was occupied by Elizabeth Rendell, a 'tanner's widow' in 1861, who lived with her daughter Elizabeth and grand-daughter Lucy. [22]

The branch railway didn't reach the town until May 1872, by which time both trade and population had declined. [23] It may be that the local bootmakers failed to modernise and Crediton boots and shoes, produced with sewing machines in small factories, undercut the hand-made products from the Ashburton cordwainers. And so the local market for leather dried up. The large tannery at Newton Abbot, which was on the main line railway, was also probably more efficient, and thus more competitive. But for a period, to the mid nineteenth century, Ashburton's tanneries no doubt helped to keep the town alive as the woollen industry faded out.

Tannery east from the church	
Location	SX 7559 6977
Operational	to circa 1840

The tannery by the church has gone too. A nearby recreation ground may be the site of its tan pits. Only the name 'Tanyard Cottage' on a door in an alley points to its past existence.

This tanyard was owned and occupied by Benjamin Parham in 1839, but had probably closed by 1841. [24]

Ashburton sources
1 Sherborne Mercury 28 January 1811
2 Sherborne Mercury 3 August 1807, Pigot's Directory 1823-24, The Alfred 3 October 1826 p 3 col 5, Exeter Flying Post 31 May 1832 p 2 col 4. John Vere Mann death. Exeter Flying Post 20 March 1834 p 3 col 3
3 Ashburton Tithe Map and Apportionment, 1839
4 Ordnance Survey Map, Devonshire, 1887, sheet 114.3
5 Ashburton Tithe Map and Apportionment, 1839
6 The Western Times 6 May 1848 p 6 col 5
7 The Western Times 10 May 1856 p 7 col 1
8 Exeter Flying Post 20 August 1812 p 4 col 5
9 Exeter Flying Post 3 March 1825 p 4 col 2
10 Exeter Flying Post 9 February 1826 p 1 col 3
11 Pigot & Co's National Commercial Directory, Devonshire, reprinted Michael Winton, King's Lynn, 1993, 45
12 Ibid; Ashburton Tithe Map and Apportionment, 1839; Mormon IGIs
13 Francis Pilkington. Ashburton – The Dartmoor Town. Devon Books, 1989, 24-28
14 Sherborne Mercury 11 October 1813
15 Pigot & Co's Directory, 1830; Ashburton Tithe Map and Apportionment, 1839;
16 Francis Pilkington, op cit, 79, from White's Directory

17 Exeter Flying Post 7 December 1848 p 1 col 4
18 Ashburton census, 1851, HO107 1871 f 339 p 2
19 Exeter Flying Post 26 May 1853 p 1 col 1
20 The Western Times 1 July 1854 p 1 col 5

21 Post Office Directory, Devon and Cornwall, 1856
22 Ashburton census 1861, RG9 1405 f 5 p 2
23 Francis Pilkington, op cit, 77-78
24 Ashburton tithe map and apportionment, 1839

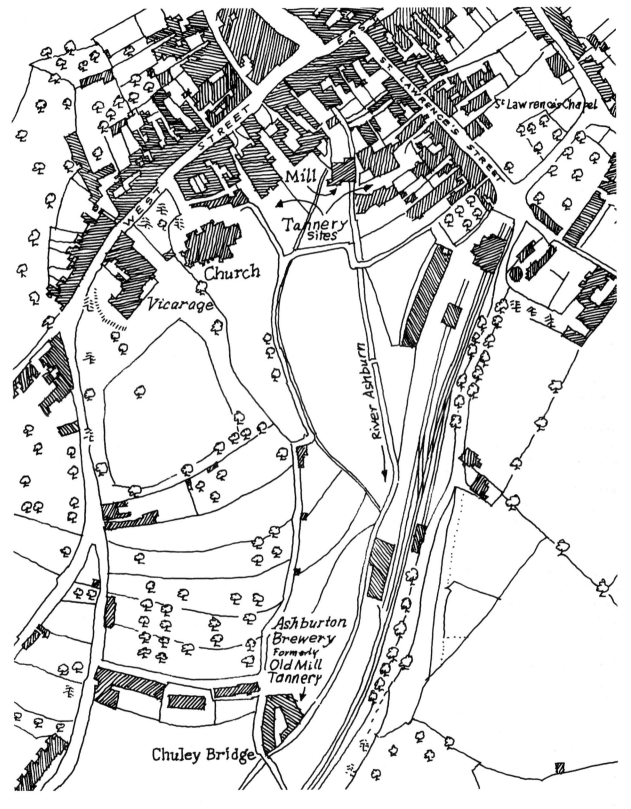

Ashburton, from the 1887 Ordnance Survey map, (25" to the mile, sheet 114.3). To the south the Old Mill Tannery, by Chuley Bridge, has become the Ashburton Brewery. To the north east of St Andrew's Church stood two other tanneries; that nearer the church was on ground now occupied by the Methodists and a third tannery was accessed from St Lawrence's Street, to the east of the River Ashburn. All three tanneries were extant at the time of the tithe survey. The tithe map was drawn up in 1839. The branch railway from Totnes arrived after the tanneries had closed

23

Axminster

Two tanneries have been identified in the parish and a third may have existed at Smallridge in the neighbouring parish of Chardstock, previously in Dorset. [1]

Westwater
Location	SY 2822 9927
Operational	to 1779
Bark mill	if it existed, water-powered

Westwater was an old-established tanyard: William Wyat, tanner here in 1559, was buried that year. [2] It was remote from the town, in the valley of the Yarty, a tributary of the Axe. A map of the parish, dated 1778, shows Westwater to be a separate entity from Higher, Lower and Middle Westwater farms. It was close to Lower Westwater, with a stream running by. [3]

In 1762 and 1764 Richard Haycraft, a tanner, woolstapler and leather dresser, insured a house, tanpits and drying house at Westwater together with other property including mills for £1000. [4] Westwater was to let in 1779:
'A TAN YARD, To be Lett, for a term of feven, fourteen, or twenty-one years ... that commodious TAN-YARD belonging to the late Mr Richard Haycraft, deceafed, lying at Weftwater, near Axminfter, Devon; together with a good dwelling houfe, a large orchard .. six or feven acres of very good ground .. apply to Mrs Sarah Haycraft, at Axminfter, the owner thereof .. March 3, 1779.' [5]
Sarah Haycraft had connections with Thomas Whitty, junior, of Axminster Carpets. [6] No more is known of the tannery. A house survives here, derelict in the 1970s but rebuilt in the 1980s.

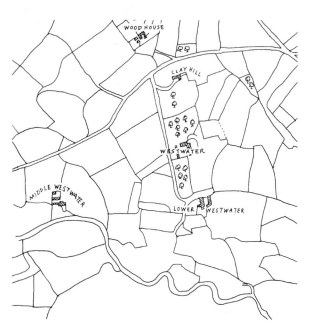

Westwater in 1838, from the Axminster tithe map. The track to Lower Westwater is now blocked off and that farm has a new entrance from the east. The road running through the map leads to Higher Westwater, off to the left; at the foot the river Yarty nears its meeting with the river Axe, off to the right

Lyme Street
Location	SY 2999 9844
Operational	to circa 1845

John Bunter Liddon was tanning at Axminster in the period 1793 to 1810. [7] A second Axminster tanner, Francis Colmer, was declared bankrupt in 1798. [8] They may have used the Lyme Street tanyard, then on the eastern edge of the town and it may have been this yard that was for sale in 1813:
'Old-Established TANNING BUSINESS IN THE MARKET-TOWN OF Axminster, to be disposed of ..' [9]

James Stocker, a tanner, wool dealer and tallow chandler of 'Lime Street' was listed in 1830 and James Stocker, possibly his son, married in the town in August 1838. [10] He was shown as leaseholder of the yard in the same year. [11] In 1841 James and his wife Elizabeth lived here with a baby daughter and two servants; Elizabeth was a widow, 42, and retired governess, living in St Sidwell, Exeter in 1851 and the tannery was no longer listed in directories. [12] Today Tanners Cottage survives in a rank with the tanner's house, the latter fronting Lyme Street.

Site of the early 19th century tannery at Lyme Street. When operational it would have been on the edge of the town. Lyme Street became gentrified in the Georgian era as large residencies were built nearby. The tanner's house is now known as The Laurels

Sources
1 Sherborne Mercury 21 October 1811 p 3 col 5
2 A H Shorter, DCNQ, from D&CRS transcriptions
3 Map of Axminster 1778, DRO 4377M/E2; OS 25" map of 1889, sheet 71.4
4 Stanley D Chapman, The Devon Cloth Industry in the Eighteenth Century. D&CRS, 1978, 3-4
5 Sherborne Mercury 15 March 1779
6 DRO 49/26/8/16
7 DRO 281M/T1172-1173 of 1793 and 281M/T1174-1175
8 Exeter Flying Post 15 March 1798 p 3 col 1
9 Sherborne Mercury 13 December 1813 p 3 col 5
10 Pigot & Co's Directory, 1830; Exeter Flying Post 9 August 1838 p 2 col 5
11 DRO Axminster tithe map and apportionment
12 Axminster census 1841, HO107 200/7 f 7 p 8

Axmouth

Borough House	
Location	SY 267 930
Operational	to circa 1868
Bark mill	power source not known
Tan pits	18 handlers, 6 troughs, 4 latches, 2 grainers, and 3 lime pits in 1830
Staff	possibly 10 in 1861

A harbour probably existed at Axmouth in the Roman period, at the southern end of the Fosse Way. In the medieval period shingle built up, partially blocking the mouth of the river Axe. The harbour was revived and operated commercially from 1803 to 1868: bark and hides were imported here for tanneries in the Axe valley

Twenty shillings were paid in 1207 to site a tannery outside the medieval port of Axmouth. [1] 600 years pass before the historical record re-emerges.

A relatively small tannery existed in the 19th century at the north end of the parish, bordering Musbury, and was run by Lydia Newbury, a widow by 1830, in which year the yard was offered to let:
'To Tanners .. To be Let, for a Term .. commodious Dwelling-House, with convenient offices; and attached thereto, a desirable Tan Yard, which contains 18 Handlers, 6 Troughs, 4 Latches, 2 Grainers, and 3 Lime Pits, with good Bark and Mill Houses, and Store Rooms; with a Labourer's Cottage adjoining – situate near the Turnpike Road leading to Lyme Regis and Axminster, and about a quarter of a mile from Axminster Turnpike Gate .. The premises may be viewed by applying to Mrs Newberry, of Musbury, the owner, and further particulars known of her ..' [2]

Borough House was part of an estate known as Great Bindon; in 1846 it was owned and occupied by Lydia Newbury and totalled a little over 11 acres; she leased a further five acres from John Ames, Esq. [3] By 1851 she was 64 and her unmarried son Thomas, 29, a tanner, was working the yard, possibly with one servant. [4] He was listed as tanner of Borough House, Axmouth, in 1856. [5]

Axmouth, a town in Leland's time, had declined to a village of 400 souls by 1800. The harbour was re-established in 1803 or thereabouts, by digging out some of the shingle beach and contructing a new pier, allowing smacks, sloops and schooners of up to 100 tons to berth. On the 18 September 1856 two vessels reported visiting Axmouth are of interest:
'Axmouth. .. Arrived 18th .. Celerity, Wood, master, bark laden ..; 21st .. Elizabeth, Pickard, master, hides and tallow.'

In 1868 the railway arrived and in January 1869 the pier was destroyed in a storm: the harbour ceased to function. The *Celerity* and *Elizabeth* were both carrying freight destined for local tanneries, and if not Axmouth and Musbury, then probably for the tanneries at Colyton. The hides may have come from overseas, brought coastwise from a deep-sea port such as Plymouth, Southampton or possibly Topsham. The oak bark was very possibly west country in origin, but not necessarily so. [6]

The situation at Borough House was largely unchanged in 1861: Lydia Newbery was head of the household but her son Thomas now employed 19 labourers and four boys, which, unless he was farming as well, suggests that the tanyard had expanded from its status in 1830. [7]

Thomas Newbery continued tanning in 1866 [8] but by 1871 he had relinquished his hold on the business. It seems he married in about 1865; his wife Catherine was born in Boston, Lincolnshire. By 1871 they had three offspring growing up at Borough House and Thomas had become a *'traveller in wine trade'*. [9] The Newberys were not found in the parish in 1881 and the tannery probably closed about 1865-6, when Thomas married.

Borough House has been renamed Musbury House, and stands near the boundary with Musbury parish. It is surrounded by trees and a walled garden and not visible from the public highway.

Axmouth sources
1. Pamela Sharpe, Population and Society in an East Devon Parish. Reproducing Colyton 1540-1840. University of Exeter Press, 2002, 130-131
2. Exeter Flying Post 20 May 1830 p 2 col 2
3. DRO – Axmouth tithe map and apportionment, 1846
4. Axmouth census 1851 – HO107 1862 f 653 p 10
5. Post Office Directory, Devon and Cornwall, 1856
6. W G Hoskins, Devon, Devon Books 1992, 326; The Western Times 27 September 1856 p 5 col 6
7. Axmouth census 1861 – RG9 1374 f 28 p 6
8. Post Office Directory of Devonshire 1866, 1277-1278
9. Axmouth census 1871 – RG10 2036 f 50 p 8

Bampton

Frog Street
and two other locations

According to 96-year-old John Staddon, interviewed in 1929, there were three tanners in Bampton in his time. [1] To a casual historian this seems an extravagant claim, but investigation shows that this was the case. William Periam, George Rowe and Henry Norman were all running yards in the parish at the beginning of the 19th century. [2]

A tannery 'adjoining the town ..' was for sale in 1800:

'To be Sold in Lots, by Public Auction. Lot 1. The Fee and Inheritance of an extenfive DWELLING HOUSE and large Garden, two orchards, and an excellent TAN YARD, with Linhays, Lofts, Drying-houfe, Pound-houfe, and Stable, and every requisite belonging to a tan yard, with a conftant fupply of water, containing by eftimation nearly two acres, pleasantly fituated adjoining the town of Bampton .. the prefent tenant's term will expire at Michaelmas 1802. Dated October 28, 1800.' [3]

With owners and tanners unidentified, the location of this yard is at present unknown. The only tannery clearly defined in the 19th century was at Frog Street.

Frog Street	
Location	SS 9560 2250
Operational	to 1851
Output	25 hides per week in 1822; 48 butts in 1851
Bark mill	water powered
Tan pits	48 in 1851

John Oxenham was tanner here in 1790; his brother William a fellmonger in the same street. [4] Thomas Farrant owned and occupied a tanyard in Bampton in 1810. [5] It is probable that this was the yard at Frog Street. It was for sale in 1822 – a year when there was a slump in the leather trade, following the Napoleonic Wars – and having recently been refitted was *'capable of tanning 25 hides a week'*. Oak bark was ground in a water-powered bark mill and this yard then clearly belonged to Farrant. [6]

The tannery seemingly remained unsold and Thomas Farrant was still here in 1841; his wife Elizabeth ran a girls' school on the same premises with 17 boarders aged between 8 and 15. [7] This suggests the tanyard wasn't generating enough income for the family to survive on. The Bampton tithe apportionment lists the Farrants as owners of the Frog Street property and the associated tithe map shows a leat running to the bark mill. [8] The leat has gone – eliminated when

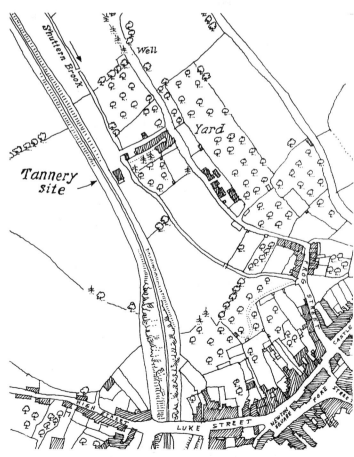

The Frog Street tannery site in 1890. From the Ordnance Survey sheets 24.11 and 24.15

The Frog Street residence and tannery buildings in 2004, with the Shuttern Brook in the foreground. The building on the left once served as a drying loft

The roofless bark mill building standing between the Shuttern Brook and the course of the old railway in 2004. The leat ran behind this building and is shown on the tithe map of c 1840

the Exe Valley Railway was constructed and took its course in 1884. The bark mill survives today, within the grounds of a private house, roofless and with the suggestion of a wheelpit on the southern wall.

Farrant was listed as tanner in 1844, and paying rates on his yard in 1846 but died in 1847. [9] Samuel George Farrant briefly ran the yard, in partnership with Charles Williams, from 1847 to 1849. He left his estate to his brother-in-law John Trowey Periam, a lime merchant. Through his marriage to Maria Periam, Farrant had also taken on a grocer's and a draper's shop. [10] At Frog Lane, the boarding school continued under the direction of the widowed Elizabeth Farrant and her 25-year-old daughter Ellen. [11] In the same year – 1851 – a Mr Farrant offered the tanyard to let:

'.. with Immediate Possession. A TAN YARD, in full work, containing 48 pits, and capable of tanning 48 butts per week; situated in a first rate bark district, with an unlimited supply. The bark mill driven by a never-failing stream of water. For further particulars apply to Messrs W and J Hassell, Leather Factors, Bristol; or to Mr Farrant, Bampton, Devon'. [12]

It probably ceased trading, as there are no further records of tanning in the town, although an Edwardian photograph exists showing a cart in Castle Street loaded high with oak bark, destined for a tannery elsewhere. The Frog Street premises are now known as 'The Old House' and the house and walled garden survive with the roofless bark mill and drying lofts, the latter converted to a residence.

Other sites

Knowle or Knowles was a possible tannery site in the 18th century. The tanner William Periam was here in 1780 and was listed as operating a yard in 1793. He later moved to Higher Arthurshayne. [13] In 1806 premises he leased were for sale:
'TAN-YARD, BAMPTON, DEVON. To be SOLD by Auction .. All thofe moft Desirable FREEHOLD PREMISES, late in the occupation of Mr W. PERIAM, Tanner, comprifing a commodious TAN-YARD .. together with a comfortable dwelling-houfe .. ' [14]
The Frog Street tannery site almost adjoins Higher Arthurshayne, and may thus have been Periam's yard.

George Rowe occupied a Bampton tanyard owned by William Style in 1800. [15] His tannery was on the market in 1803:
'Bampton, Devon. To be Sold in Fee, and entered on at Lady-day next, all that Meffuage or Tenement and Garden with large and convenient Tan-Yard behind the same, and all neceffary and convenient Outbuildings for carrying on the Tanning Bufinefs, situate in or near the town of Bampton, aforefaid, now and for many years paft in the occupation of Mr George Row, tanner ..' [16]
In 1820 this yard was owned and occupied by James

Carter. [17] While it stood close to the town its location has yet to be identified.

A yard which evidently wasn't Frog Street was on the market in 1833, owned by Mr Trenchard:
'To Tanners, Bampton, Devon. To be Sold, or Let .. a compact TAN-YARD, consisting of 49 Tan-pits, with the necessary Limes, Drying Loft, Bark Sheds, &c .. together with the Dwelling-House, Walled Garden and Orchard, situate at Bampton ..
The stock may be taken at a valuation, or the owner will work out the same as his successor may work in.
.. Bampton is allowed one of the most eligible situations for the supply of Bark in the West of England .. Apply (if by letter post paid) to Mr Trenchard, (the Proprietor) at Bampton ..' [18]
Was this the tannery occupied by Henry Norman in 1805, or was this George Rowe's yard, once owned by the Style family?

Bampton sources
1   Tiverton Gazette 17 September 1929
2   William Periam, tanner, Bampton, 1793 – British Universal Directory; tanyard for auction in 1806, 'late in the occupation of Mr W Periam, tanner' – Sherborne Mercury 6 January 1806
    George Rowe occupied a house and tanyard owned by William Style in 1800 – DRO land tax assessments; tan yard for sale, Bampton, 'now and for many years paft in the occupation of Mr George Row, tanner' – Exeter Flying Post 1 September 1803 p 2 col 3; House and tanyard in Bampton owned and occupied by G Rowe in 1805 – DRO land tax assessment.
    Henry Norman occupied a house and tanyard owned by William Joyce, in the parish, in 1805 – DRO land tax assessments
3   Sherborne Mercury 3 November 1800

Frog Street
4   Indenture of 23 October 1790 in private hands
5   Mr Thomas Farrant. House and tanyard at Bampton. Occupied by himself. Land Tax Assessment 18s 8d DRO - Land Tax Assessments, Bampton
6   Woolmer's Gazette 16 March 1822 p 3 col 4
7   Bampton census 1841 – HO 107 202\5 f 5 p3/4
8   DRO Bampton Tithe Map and Apportionment, 1842 – 37 = Cottage, Outhouse, Yards, Garden and Orchard 0-3-28; 38 = Lower Mead and Bark house. Meadow 1-1-15; 43 = Orchard 1-1-30; 326 = Higher Mead. Meadow 3-2-26; Total = 7 acres 1rod 19 perches Owned and occupied by Thomas Farrant
9   Pigots General Directory, Devonshire, 1844; DRO – Bampton. Highway rate books, 1269A/Ps 3-4 Exeter Flying Post 30 September 1847 p 2 col 6
10 DRO 1044 Badd2/43/9, 1044 Badd2/T4/57; White's Directory of Devon, 1850
11 Bampton census, 1851 – HO107 1890 f 10 p13
12 Exeter Flying Post 3 April 1851 p 1 col 1

Other sites
13 Personal communication. Tom McManamon, 1-2005; British Universal Directory, 1793
14 Sherborne Mercury 6 January 1806
15 George Rowe occupied a house and tanyard owned by William Style in 1800 – DRO land tax assessments
16 Exeter Flying Post 1 September 1803 p 2 col 3 also Exeter Flying Post 10 October 1805 p 4 col 3
17 DRO land tax assessments
18 Woolmer's Gazette 5 October 1833 p 1 col 1

Barnstaple

Bear Street
Boutport Street
Rackfield or Pilton Bridge

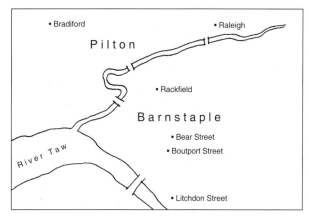

Barnstaple, like Exeter, had commercial advantages over its hinterland and was thus attractive to tanners. Together with Pilton the town boasted port facilities through which hides, oak bark and valonia could be imported and leather exported. Neighbouring districts were rich in oak woods and cattle breeding had been carried on for centuries: hides and oak bark were also obtainable locally. And the town held regular market days. In 1821 Barnstaple was exporting timber and bark. [1]

Excavations made in the 1980s on land behind 27-28 Joy Street led to the discovery of pits dating from the post-medieval period associated with both metal working and tanning. Tanning had been undertaken here on a small scale compared with the 19th century operations at Rackfield. [2]

Barnstaple was operating with at least three tanneries for much of the 19th century and there were others functioning during the Georgian era – one in Litchdon Street and one by Vicarage Street. The latter was lost in 1844 when the churchyard at St Mary Magdalen was developed. [3] A further two tanneries were active in Pilton.

Introduction
1 Rev Daniel Lysons, Magna Britannia, 1822, ccxcvii
2 Archaeology in Barnstaple 1984-1990. North Devon Rescue Archaeology Unit, p17, p 28
3 W F Gardiner, Barnstaple: 1837-1897. 1897, 86

Bear Street	
Location	SS 559 333
Operational	to 1910 or later
Bark mill	probably horse powered
Tan pits	12 layers, 28 handlers, 5 latches and 3 lime pits – in 1845

Bear Street was probably an old-established yard – it was less than 100 yards beyond the site of the medieval East Gate and surprisingly central within the expanded 19th century town.

John Baker was tanner at Bear Street in 1844. [1] Evidence indicates that he had run this business since the end of the 18th century. With his death at the end of 1844 or early in 1845, the yard was offered at auction and the notice gives details of the facilities:
*'Barnstaple .. an excellent and long-established Tan Yard, with four large Drying Lofts, very large Bark Shed, Store Rooms, Bark Mill and Offices.
The Pits consist of 12 Layers, 28 Handlers, five Latches, with Pumps in each and Three Lime Pits. There is an abundance of room in the yard for an increase of Pits ..
The Dwelling-house adjoins the Tan Yard and consists of two Front Parlours, Kitchen, Pantry, Wash-house, and Cellar; five Bed-Rooms with two Attics .. a suitable resident for a respectable Family. The Premises .. were late in the occupation of Mr John Baker, the Proprietor, by whom the business has been carried on for nearly a half a century, and whose decease alone causes them to be offered for sale.'* [2]

At some time before 1849 Samuel Adams moved here. He was a Crediton man, brother to Edward Adams who founded a dynasty of tanners and bootmakers in that town and to John Adams whose family operated yards in Great Torrington and Petrockstowe. [3] Samuel had married Mary Ann Hamlyn Norrish at Moretonhampstead in 1833. [4] His early career is not known, but he very possibly learnt the business at Crediton, initially.

One of the major hazards in 19th century tanneries was fire and it occurred at Bear Street at the end of December 1849, not long after Samuel had established himself here:
'Alarming fire. On Saturday, the inhabitants of Barnstaple were alarmed by the intelligence of a fire breaking out in the back [bark?] store of Mr Adams, tanner and currier, Bear-street. The West of England and Parish fire engines were soon on the spot, and commenced playing on the burning roof, while a number of persons were employed in taking steps to prevent the fire spreading to the adjoining building. Very soon the large stock of dry bark was one mass of fire; and as the floor gave way the burning materials were mingled with the coals in the cellars beneath. The engines for the first hour were well supplied with water from the pumps of the surrounding dwelling houses, but on the wells being exhausted, they could not be kept in quarter work. Adjoining the burning building was [sic] the currying shops, containing oil, tallow, and other inflammable materials and also the coach manufactures of Mr Symons and Mr Gibbons; serious apprehensions were entertained for their safety, but happily through the exertions of the firemen and the bystanders the fire was confined to the place it broke out. As evening approached the fire increased in intensity, the flames shooting very far above the tottering walls. And from the coals being ignited the heat in the street was scarcely sufferable.

Some of the surviving tannery buildings at Bear Street in 2007. Note typically louvered upper storey

Bear Street sources
1 Pigot & Co's Directory, Devonshire, 1844
2 The Western Times 5 April 1845 p 1 col 1
3 See Crediton tanyards; for Great Torrington see for example census for John Adams in 1851 – HO107 1894 f 545 p 76 and his son Richard – HO 107 1894 f 512 p 11; for Samuel Adams see Barnstaple census 1851 – HO 107 1892 f 216 p 22 and 23
4 Mormon IGIs: Samuel Adams married Mary Ann Hamlyn Norrish 11 April 1833 at Moretonhampstead
5 Exeter Flying Post 3 January 1850 p 8 col 3
6 Barnstaple census 1851. HO 107 1892 f 216 p 22 and 23
7 Barnstaple census 1861. RG9 1489 f 24 p 4
8 Post Office Directory of Devonshire 1866, 1277
9 Samuel Adams, tanner, died 17 January 1872 Executors: his widow Mary Ann Hamlyn Adams and Samuel Norris Adams, tanner, son. Estate value £8000
10 The Post Office Directory of Devonshire and Cornwall, Kelly, 1873
11 Barnstaple census 1881. RG11 2244 f 136 p 48 [George]; Bishop's Tawton census 1881. RG11 2251 f 47 p 20. Taw Vale Parade built 1846: Julia and Jonathan Baxter, Barnstaple Yesterday. H J Chard & Son, Bristol, 1980
12 Kelly's Directory of Devonshire and Cornwall, 1902, 1136, Kelly's Directory of Devonshire and Cornwall, 1910, 1143

At about seven o'clock the walls were, with ladders and poles, thrown on the burning materials which had the effect of lessening the draught and smothering the fire to some extent. Throughout the night the firemen remained throwing water over the smouldering mass. The calamity is supposed to have been caused by the pipes of a stove in the coal cellar becoming overheated. The premises and stock in trade was [sic] partially insured in the West of England Fire Office.' [5]

It was as well that Adams had some insurance. He was not destitute and by 1851 was employing seven men. [6] Ten years on, aged 62, his staff numbers were much the same – seven men and one boy. His sons Samuel Norrish, 21, and George, 18, were employed in the business. [7] Nearby competitors were Samuel Rice at Pilton Bridge and John Sanders at Boutport Street, both with similar-sized yards.

In 1866 the Bear Street tannery was trading as S Adams & Son. [8] Samuel Norrish Adams ran the yard in 1871 – his father had retired. The following year Samuel Adams senior died, leaving an estate valued at about £8,000. [9]

The concern now came to be known as S & G Adams, tanners, Bear Street, Barnstaple: Samuel N Adams had enlisted his brother George as partner. [10] In 1881 Samuel and his family had a house at Newport, on the eastern outskirts of the town. George was living at fashionable 1 Taw Vale Parade. [11]

By 1902 this business had developed into S & G Adams & Co, [12] clearly a successful operation, still extant in 1910. Remarkably, buildings associated with the tannery remain on site, occupied by Archway Appliances in 2005: the entrance to the yard is opposite Tarka Books.

Rackfield or Pilton Bridge

Location	SS 5584 3360
Operational	to 1910 or later

W F Gardiner, historian of 19th century Barnstaple, writing in 1897, indicated that the Rackfield Tannery was established in 1827. [1] But there are indications it was in existence before that date. The following sale notice appeared in 1807:
'.. To Tanners, Leather-Dreffers, Fellmongers .. Dwelling House, with offices, yards and drying grounds fituated at Pilton Bridge .. now in the occupation of Mr Samuel Bembridge the younger, the proprietor .. furnifhed with ware-rooms, lofts, kiln, pits, furnaces ..'
Bembridge was also proprietor of a water-powered leather mill at Rawleigh, in Pilton. [2]

Water was available at this tannery as it stood alongside the leat from the river Yeo to Town Mills. Nearby was the large 'Rackfield' which in earlier centuries was laid out with lines of tenters used to dry and stretch the woollen cloth fulled in Barnstaple's tucking mills.

Rackfield Tannery was owned or occupied by William Sanders in 1843; he also appears to have operated the nearby yard in Boutport Street [3] but other evidence suggests that the Smyth family operated here from at least 1844 to 1850 or later and then again from the 1870s. [4] This family also successfully ran the tan yard at Swimbridge throughout the Victorian period, from at least 1841 to 1910, and the Barnstaple operation was a secondary but by no means insignificant development. [5]

Rackfield Tannery, Barnstaple, in 1927, looking south west. To the right of the tannery is the leat running to Town Mills, top, right of centre. On the extreme right is the locomotive and carriage depot of the Lynton and Barnstaple narrow gauge railway. Almost all of the site now lies under the Barnstaple ring road

James Rice was tanner, employing seven men and two boys in 1861. [6] In 1869 John and Samuel Sanders moved from Pilton and established a fellmonger's and woolstapler's yard across the leat. [7] The firm, S Sanders & Son, was still listed as fellmongers at Pilton Bridge in 1907. [8]

As noted earlier the Smyth brothers had re-established the Swimbridge connection by 1873. In 1886 the tannery was the first business in Barnstaple to possess a telephone. [9] The company was still listed here in the 1910 trade directory but not in 1919. [10] An aerial view of Barnstaple taken in 1927 shows quite an extensive tannery, with tan pits visible, to all intents still looking operational; it may have been run from Swimbridge and thus not listed in Kelly's. [11]

At some point in the twentieth century most of the buildings were demolished and the tan pits filled in. The yard was redeveloped for use by the Post Office. [12] Then towards the end of the twentieth century Mermaid Cross was constructed as part of Barnstaple's ring road and almost all of the site and most of the nearby landmarks were obliterated.

Rackfield or Pilton Bridge sources
1. W F Gardiner, Barnstaple: 1837-1897. 1897, 86
2. Sherborne Mercury 27 July 1807
3. Michael Bone, Barnstaple's Industrial Archaeology. Exeter Industrial Archaeology Group, University of Exeter, 1973, 20; DRO - 1843 tithe map of town
4. William G Smith, Pilton Bridge – Pigot's General Directory, Devonshire, 1844; William G Smyth, Pilton Building – White's Directory, 1850; Smyth Brothers, tanners, Rackfield, and at Swimbridge – The Post Office Directory of Devonshire and Cornwall, Kelly, 1873
5. See Swimbridge tannery text
6. Barnstaple census 1861
7. Margaret Reed, Pilton: its past and its people. Vineyard, 1985, 101-102; Mike Bone & Peter Stanier. A Guide to the Industrial Archaeology of Devon, Association for Industrial Archaeology, 1998, 21
8. Kelly's Directory of the Leather Trades, 1907, 55
9. Michael Bone, op cit, 20
10. Smyth Bros, Rackfield, Barnstaple – Kelly's Directory of Devonshire and Cornwall, 1897, 1111; Smyth Bros, tanners, Rackfield, Barnstaple – Kelly's Directory of Devonshire and Cornwall, 1910, 1143. No entry found for 1919 edition
11. Aerial photograph of 1927 also showing the locomotive depot of the Lynton and Barnstaple Railway. Shown as Rackfield Tannery on 1906 Ordnance Survey map
12. Michael Bone, op cit, 20

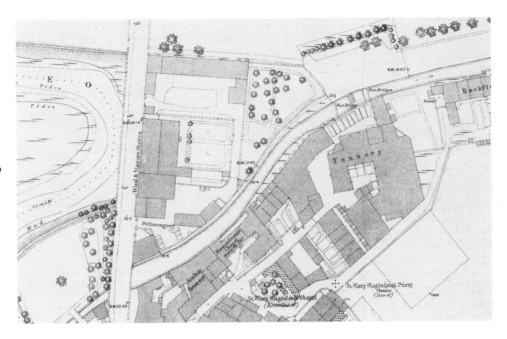

Rackfield Tannery in 1889. At the end of Boutport Street and situated alongside the leat to Town Mills. The road running north led to Pilton Bridge and Pilton. From the 1:500 Ordnance Survey map, sheet 13.2.20.

Boutport Street

Location	SS 558 332
Operational	to circa 1870
Output	40 hides a week in 1831

The Boutport Street tannery was situated in the centre of town, near the junction with Queen Street and not far from the High Street and Butchers Row. Next door to the yard was the Horse and Groom public house. [1] As with Bear Street, this location seems to imply an early foundation.

John Leworthy Davis was a Barnstaple tanner who married in 1827 and was running the Boutport Street yard in 1830. It was for sale or lease in 1831:

'.. Dwelling-House, Tan-Yard, and Garden, together with the Warehouses, Lofts, Bark Shades .. The tan yard is capable of tanning 40 English Hides a week, and the currying business having been carried on since July last, every necessary article is in place, and there is an excellent opening in the town for a Currier.
The whole of the premises are in good repair, and now in possession of Mr J L Davis, to whom Letters may be addressed .. and all particulars known .. possession may be had immediately ..' [2]

Davis was in debt and probably had no option but to dispose of the business. [3]

William Sanders was tanner here in 1844. [4] It was probably he who lost valuable bark, part of a rick stored on the marsh near the quay in October 1836, damaged in a flood following a violent gale and high tide. [5] Barnstaple suffered an outbreak of cholera in 1849 and Mr Sanders was the first individual in the town to die of the disease. [6] Not altogether surprisingly it seems the tannery was out of commission in 1850. [7] By 1856 the yard was functioning again with

John Sanders controlling operations. [8] It is assumed that he is the John Sanders of 'Sanders, John & Son, woolstaplers & fellmongers', a firm associated with Pilton, [9] although Sanders was born in Salcombe Regis. Aged 40, he was employing eight men in 1861. [10]

Joseph Edward Baylis arrived in Barnstaple in 1866 from one of the country's leading glovemakers and proceeded to organise Sanders' business in Pilton: Sanders moved out of town and became a farmer at East Down. [11] The Boutport Street yard was listed as in the hands of tanner A Ballment in that year, but may have closed by 1873. [12] In addition to tanning, there had been a currier's workshop on the premises. By 1890 the building fronting onto Boutport Street was trading as 'Seldon's Leather Warehouse'. It was apparently still in existence in 1980 as a car showroom. [13]

Boutport Street sources
1 Julia and Jonathan Baxter. Barnstaple Yesterday. Over 160 Photographs of Barnstaple from the 1860s onwards. H J Chard & Sons, Bristol, 1980, photo 143
2 Exeter Flying Post 1 March 1827 p 4 col 2, Pigot & Co's Directory, Woolmer's Gazette 9 April 1831 p 1 col 3
3 Exeter Flying Post 24 February 1831 p 2 col 2
4 Pigot & Co's Directory, Devonshire, 1844
5 Woolmer's Gazette 15 October 1836 p 3 col 3
6 Michael Bone, Barnstaple's Industrial Archaeology. Exeter Industrial Archaeology Group, University of Exeter, 1973, 20
7 White's Directory of Devonshire, 1850
8 Post Office Directory, Devon and Cornwall, 1856
9 Margaret Reed, Pilton – Its Past and its People. Vineyard, 1985, 101-102
10 Barnstaple census, 1861
11 Margaret Reed, op cit, 101-102
12 Post Office Directory of Devonshire 1866, 1277; The Post Office Directory of Devonshire and Cornwall, Kelly, 1873; White's Directory Devonshire, 1878, 1090, lists the tannery but this reference is almost certainly to Rackfield
13 Julia and Jonathan Baxter, op cit. Photo 143

Bickleigh
Higher Brithayes
Millhayes

The parish had two tanneries in operation in the late 18th century – Millhayes, in the Exe valley, by Bickleigh Bridge, which was at work at least by 1786, and Higher Brithayes, in the Burn valley, which may have ceased to function after 1792.

Higher Brithayes	
Location	SS 962 075
Operational	to circa 1790
Tan pits	number unknown

This site is well away from Bickleigh village, in the Burn valley, on the way to Butterleigh. George Barne senior was a Bickleigh tanner in 1764 when devisee of the will of Butterleigh tanner John Martyn. This may imply that there was a neighbouring tannery at Butterleigh, its site yet to be identified. [1]

William Braddick may have run Higher Brithayes, as he was described as Bickleigh tanner in 1785, but by then he had interests in property in Bampton, Tiverton, Branscombe and Newton Poppleford. [2] Late in the 18th century it was run by George Barne, who also farmed at Coombe, Butterleigh, nearby. Barne was a major figure in local affairs – he was later a member of Tiverton Corporation, churchwarden at Butterleigh, where his brother John was rector, [3] and was to become a partner in Dunsfords' and Barne, the Tiverton bank, later known as Dunsford & Co. [4] More an entrepreneur than tanner, Barne attended and later chaired a number of meetings of Devon tanners in Exeter, when the industry was threatened by government taxes on leather or exportation of bark. [5]
The tannery was offered to let in 1792:
'To be LETT from Michaelmas next, for a term of 14 years, or fuch term as fhall or may be agreed upon, All that Tenement or Farm called HIGHER BRITHAYS, fituate in the parifh of Bickley, about four miles from Tiverton, ten from Exeter, four from Cullompton .. confifting of a good dwelling-houfe, convenient out-houfes, and A TAN-YARD, and about 80 acres of arable, meadow and pafture land, now in the poffeffion of Mr George Barne, tanner; all in high order. For which purpofe a furvey will be held at the Bell-Inn ..' [6]

George Barne's father died in 1788. [7] It seems George then inherited enough to establish a tannery and build a residence at New Place, in Westexe, Tiverton. [8] Nicholas Braddick, a Bickleigh tanner, died at Bradninch in 1847, aged 70. He was possibly the last tanner here. [9]

For the last 150 years or so Higher Brithayes has served as a farm. Farming ceased just after the millennium and evidence of a tanyard is now probably lost under concrete hardstandings. The nearby river Burn may have powered a bark mill at or near Lower Brithayes at one time, although a tributary might have provided a leat nearer to the tannery.

Millhayes	
Location	SS 938 075
Operational	to circa 1846
Tan pits	54 handlers, 13 troughs, 12 bloomers, 10 latches – in 1846
Bark mill	possibly water-powered
Staff	9 in 1841

Richard Jarman, the tanner here until his death in 1843, was the son of Robert and Mary Jarman, and was baptised in the village on 13 December 1797. [10] On his father's death in 1821 he inherited £400. His uncle John, the previous Bickleigh tanner, died in 1829 and Richard was already running the tannery when he married Susan Upham on 2 November 1830. [11] By 1841 the household included two female servants and six male workers or servants. In Bickleigh nine journeymen tanners were recorded on census night. [12] Millhayes was owned by the local landowner, Sir Walter Palk Carew, and formed part of the 124-acre Clamour Cleave estate, which Jarman farmed. [13]

Aged 46, Richard Jarman was clearly not in good health when he wrote his will early in August. He died three days later having named his executors as Susannah Jarman, his wife, and John Barne, a banker of Tiverton. John was son of George Barne. Jarman's wealth was estimated at under £3000. Quite an extensive and extended family comes to light: his sister Mary Ann had married Henry Copplestone and was living in Bristol. He was not friends with his brother-in-law. Mary Ann was to receive £50 on condition Henry could not access it. Richard's younger sister Esther had married and emigrated to Van Diemen's Land – now Tasmania – and was left £50 *'in case she shall return to England'.* [14]

Following Richard's death, Mrs Jarman advertised the tannery to let:
'To Tanners. Bickleigh – Devon. To be let by Private Contract for a Term of 14 years .. Tan Yard with a comfortable House and Premises, with about 6 acres of Rich Marsh Land.
The yard has been successfully worked by the late Mr R Jarman and his Uncle, for the last 60 years, and consists of 54 Handlers, 13 Troughs, 12 Bloomers, 10 Latches &c, with two excellent Lofts, all in thorough repair, with a constant supply of water .. The taker can also be accommodated with 40 ton of good dry Bark. To view and treat for the same, apply to Mrs Jarman, on the Premises.' [15]

Millhayes in 2004
Some of the outbuildings survive from the days when there was an operational tannery here. The tan yard stood alongside Bickleigh Mill, seen on the left

Millhayes in 2004
The tanner's house is also still extant and visible from Bickleigh Mill car park, across the bridge over the mill's tail race. It adjoins the tanyard buildings on the south side

Millhayes in 1842.
The tannery stands to the south east of Bickleigh Bridge and is next door to Bickleigh Mill. The surveyor has even indicated the tan pits, evidently not under cover in this yard. The mill leat from a weir on the Exe and its overflow are clearly indicated. It is possible that the tannery utilised the leat water to run a bark mill. The New Inn is now The Trout Inn.

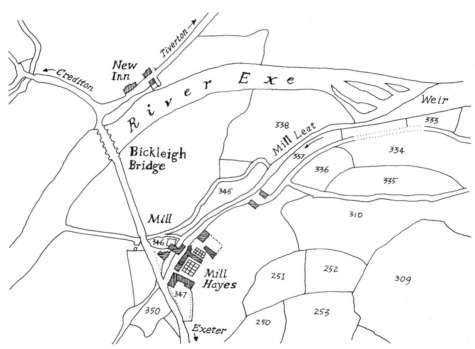

She may not have had any takers. No other Bickleigh tanners are recorded in the local trade directories and in 1851 Susan Jarman was listed as a farmer's widow, working 250 acres with four labourers, and servants. [16]

In 2004 it is perhaps remarkable that the tanner's house, garden and range of tannery buildings have survived largely unchanged over 150 years, although the tan pits have no doubt been filled in. The leat from the Exe supplying Bickleigh Mill runs close to the complex and may have provided water for the pits and to power a bark mill.

Bickleigh sources

1 DRO 49/9/391/64a and b
2 Knightshayes Estate Office, Tiverton, Chest 49 [1785]; Will of William Braddick. KEO, Tiverton. Chest 49. 27 August 1793
3 Jill Neusinger, A History of St Matthew's Church, Butterleigh, undated but c 2000, 15 and 18-19; Georgian Tiverton, D&CRS, 1986, 135
4 Pigot's General Directory, Devonshire, 1844

Exeter Flying Post 6 May 1858 p 5 col 5 [death of Henry Dunsford]
5 Oak bark exportation: Bristol Mercury 30 August 1790; Tax on leather production: Exeter Flying Post 20 August 1812 p 4 col 5, Exeter Flying Post 29 May 1817 p 1 col 3
6 Exeter Flying Post 19 February 1789 p 3 col 1
7 Exeter Flying Post 18 September 1788 p 2 col 4
8 Pigot's General Directory, Devonshire, 1824
9 The Western Times 13 February 1847 p 5 col 1
10 Mormon IGIs
11 DRO 1078/IRW/J/65: will of Robert Jarman; and will of John Jarman; Exeter Flying Post 11 November 1830 p 2 col 3 – R Jarman's marriage; Jarman a trustee regarding transfer of a mortgage – Knightshayes Estate Office, Tiverton, Box 9. 9 October 1835
12 Bickleigh census, 1841 – HO107 224\1 f 6 p 5
13 DRO – Bickleigh tithe map and apportionment 1842. Item 347 = 'Mill Hays House, Buildings, Tanyard, Offices & Garden'
14 DRO – Richard Jarman's will of 2 August 1843 – 1078/IRW/J/64
15 Exeter Flying Post 2 April 1846 p 2 col 6
16 Bickleigh census, 1851 – HO107 1888 f 21

Bideford

Westcombe	
Location	SS 4495 2691
Operational	before 1768 to 1910 or later
Tan pits	17 handler pits, 3 layer pits, 4 latch pits, 2 lime pits, 2 water pits, 1 mastering pit – in 1861
Staff	5 in 1851, 4 in 1871

The tanyard at Westcombe was active in 1768 when offered for sale at auction. It included a mill house. Tanning never became a major industry in Bideford and in the notice to prospective buyers the site was recommended for alternative uses such as a *'Brewery, the Malting Trade or the Woollen Manufacture'*.[1] Such proposed usage suggest that at least there was an adequate water supply. Nevertheless tanning continued here on a small scale into the 20th century.

A Bideford tanyard was on the market in 1790: *'.. a very eligible object to tanners, as a confiderable bufinefs has been carried on therein for 60 years .. For further particulars enquire of Mifs Buckingham on the premifes'*.[2] This may refer to Westcombe, but there was also a small tannery at Meddon Street.

Joseph White ran Westcombe in 1830. In 1841 it appeared to be in the hands of his wife Elizabeth and 20-year-old son, William White.[3] William was certainly tanner in 1844.[4] A decade later, George Long, a Torrington man by birth, was in charge of the yard, employing five apprentices. Elizabeth White may have been the owner as she was then listed as 'landed proprietor'.[5] Long continued the trade at Westcombe through the 1850s and 1860s. The premises were auctioned in 1861 and the auction notice gives a detailed description:

'.. To be Sold .. all those two very desirable Dwelling Houses with the Garden, Orchard, Tan-yard, Tan-pits .. situate at Westcombe .. in the respective occupations of Mr George Long, Tanner and Currier, and Mr William P White.
Each of the Dwelling-houses comprises Parlour, Kitchen, back-kitchen, Wash-house, Pantry, four Bedrooms .. The Garden and Orchard contain one acre of land or thereabouts. That part of the Premises used for tanning and currying purposes comprises 17 handler pits, 3 layer pits, 4 latch pits, 2 lime pits, 2 water pits, 1 mastering pit, beam shed, mill house, bark store, bark mill, drying house, stove room, currier's workshop, warehouse, two store rooms .. The Premises are conveniently situated and well adapted for carrying on the business of a Tanner and Currier, for which they have been used during the last 45 years, and are supplied with a never-failing stream of water .. '[6]

The notice suggests Westcombe was established in 1816 – but it was quite clearly extant in 1768. Long

Westcombe: the building with the iron roof, centre, may be the old drying house. The tall building was probably a 19th century steam-powered flour mill

was unable or unwilling to expand the business and aged 50 in 1871, he was still employing no more than four men and a further servant at his residence.[7] At some time after 1873 John Whitlock Narraway came to Westcombe. His stay was brief – he was here in 1878[8] but gone by 1881 when George Lee was running the yard. The premises now stood next door to a small factory – a shirt collar manufacturer employing 350 staff.[9] Narraway was still in town and was listed as tanner of Honestone Street in 1890.[10]

A further change had occured by 1891. James Prouse, a bootmaker, of 20 High Street, Bideford, had become proprietor.[11] His son, George, was a law student in 1901 and a second son, John, had taken up tanning, aged 20, possibly given charge of Westcombe while his father remained in the High Street.[12] By 1907 Prouse was also at High Street, Torrington. The tannery was in production in 1910 with Prouse still the owner.[13] It stood at the east end of what was then Belvoir Lane – now Westcombe – by a small stream, which would have provided the water for the tanpits and may have powered the bark mill.[14] Today the site is used by local refuse vehicles.

Bideford sources
1 Sherborne Mercury 23 November 1768
2 Sherborne Mercury 18 January 1790
3 Pigot & Co's National Commercial Directory, Devonshire, 1830; Bideford census 1841 – HO107 242\8 f 8 p 10
4 Pigot's Directory, Devonshire, 1844, 16
5 Bideford census 1851 – HO107 1895 f 60 p 16
6 The Western Times 17 August 1861 p 1 col 5
7 Post Office Directory, Devon and Cornwall, 1856; Post Office Directory of Devonshire 1866, 1277-1278; Bideford census 1871 – RG10 2200 f 59 p 15
8 John W Narraway, tanner and currier, Westcombe, Bideford. White's Directory 1878
9 The Post Office Directory of Devonshire and Cornwall, Kelly, 1873; Bideford census 1881 – RG11 2258 f 58 p 17
10 Narraway, John Whitlock, 8 Honestone Street, Bideford White's Devonshire Directory 1890
11 Bideford census 1891 – RG12 1786 f 57 p 17
12 Bideford census 1901 – RG13 2160 f 130 p 30
13 Kelly's Directory of the Leather Trades, 1907, 55, 66; Kelly's Directory of Devonshire and Cornwall, 1910, 1143
14 Ordnance Survey 25" = 1 mile map, sheet 19.6 of 1889

Bow

There was at least one tannery at Bow in the 18th century:

'Tanners. Run Away, on Thursday Morning, the 4th Day of this inftant January, from his Mafter, Mr. George Packer, tanner, of Bow-Nymet-Tracey, in the County of Devon, SAMUEL BOWDON, His Apprentice. He is about 21 Years of Age, Dark Complexion, Five Feet high or thereabouts, with black straight hair. He wore away a round Tan Jacket and Leather-Breeches .. also eloped at the fame Time, from the faid Mr. Packer, JOHN PETHRICK, a yearly Servant, about 40 years of Age, Five Feet Four inches high ..' [1] This may have been a yard at Bow Town; its location has yet to be pinpointed.

An extraordinary exodus took place in the period 1850-1870 – thirty or so labourers born in the parish, most with their families, re-established as workers in Bermondsey tanneries, in London [see appendix].

Halse	
Location	SS 7327 0159
Operational	to circa 1889
Output	60 to 100 hides a week in 1821
Bark mills	steam powered by 1865
Tan pits	number unknown
Staff	20 in period 1861-1881

By 1805 Samuel Wreford was tanning at Bow and almost certainly at Halse: he married a daughter of Mr Reed of Efford at Shobroke in that year. [2] Wreford was one of 16 Devon tanners appointed to a committee in 1812 at Exeter tasked with the generation of a memorandum to the Board of Trade on the undesirability of the new leather tax the government was introducing. [3]

James Lee Sanders, who had been tanning at St Thomas's, Exeter, in 1813 [4] was re-established at Bow by 1828. His waggoner was injured in

Looking north west: Tannery House, left, and Colliton, right. The now demolished Halse tannery site is represented by Tannery House. Colliton or Collaton's was the tanner's residence

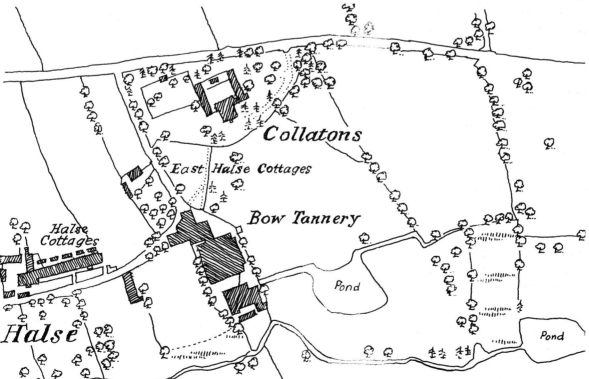

Bow Tannery in 1889, from the Ordnance Survey map. The cottages for tanyard workers have since been demolished. Tannery House now stands on the tanyard site and Collatons, or Colliton – the tanner's house – remains a residence. To the north east is Grattons, the house to which Samuel Wreford retired

an accident and later died. [5] It is possible he was Wreford's partner. But by 1841 Wreford had retired, aged 55, to Grattons, an estate just north east of the tannery at Halse – Sanders had taken possession of the tannery and was living at Colliton, the house overlooking the works. [6] Halse tannery included a terrace known as Halse Cottages. 17 tan yard labourers were living here in 1851. [7]

John Stanlake, the tannery foreman at Bow for no less than forty years, died in October 1854. His gravestone is in Bow churchyard. [8] His employer, may have lost his wife in the same year:
'Bow. The handsome painted window just put up in Bow church, was placed there by J L Sanders, Esq, of Colleton, Bow, as a memorial window to his late wife.' [9]

By 1861, James Lee Sanders, aged 75, had retired and was living at Grattons. Samuel Price, aged 33, had taken on the tannery and was now living at Colliton. Price had been born at Rull, an East Worlington farm, and in 1861 employed 20 staff at Halse. [10] Although Sanders had retired the business was run under the banner 'Sanders and Price'. Power for milling bark and for working the tan pit pumps was provided by a steam engine and in the 1860s repairs were carried out to their engine by staff of Bodley's Old Quay Foundry and Engine Works, Exeter. [11]

Price was still in control in 1881 and still employed 20 hands. [12] He may have retired when aged 59, for in 1887 it seems the tannery closed. [13] Samuel Price, like James Lee Sanders before him, had an only child – a daughter – and so really had no one to pass the tannery on to. It was a time when the industry was changing and the country tannery may have begun to prove uneconomic. By 1889 Price had died and his representatives instructed auctioneers to sell the plant and machinery belonging to the tannery. It then included:
'Steam Boiler, 6 Horse Power high pressure Beam Engine, Butt and Belly Rollers (by Huxham and Newhalls); Bark and Valonia Mills, Myrabolan Mill, several hundred feet of Steam Piping, Liquor and Water Pumps, 4 hand Pumps, 3 brass Butt Rollers, Zinc Beds for Butt and Belly rolling, Glue Press with iron screw .. Dog cart, 30 cider casks ..' [14]

Both Colliton and Grattons survive today but the tannery has been demolished and Tannery House stands on the site. The rank of workers' cottages has also gone. A memorial to Samuel Wreford of Grattons and members of his family can be seen on the north wall of St Bartholomew's church, Nymet Tracey.

Bow sources

1. Exeter Flying Post 11 January 1787 p 3
2. Exeter Flying Post 16 May 1805 p 4 col 2
3. Exeter Flying Post 20 August 1812 p 4 col 5
4. Exeter Flying Post 27 May 1813 p 4 col 2
5. Exeter Flying Post 28 February 1828 p 2 col 5 and 13 March 1828 p 2 col 5
6. Bow tithe map and apportionment, circa 1840 Bow census, 1841. HO 107 250\12 f 6 for Sanders; HO 107 250\11 f 18 p 30 for Wreford
7. Bow census, 1851. HO 107 1886 f 294 p38
8. The Western Times 21 October 1854 p 5 col 2
9. The Western Times 11 November 1854 p 7 col 6
10. Bow census, 1861. RG9 1471 f 4 East Worlington. Census, 1851: HO 107 1891 f 239 p 9 and IGI: Samuel Price was baptised 18-10-1827
11. Devon RO. Bodley journals 67/5/2/1 folio 1409
12. Bow census, 1881. RG11: 2228 f 5 p 4
13. Barbara Carbonell and Mary Wauton, Thirteen Centuries in Bow alias Nymet Tracy with Broadnymet, Devon, 1949, 23-24
14. The Western Times 19 March 1889 p 1 col 3

Grattons or Grattan, home of the Wreford family, when Samuel had retired from running the tannery at Bow

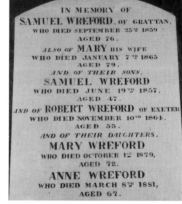

IN MEMORY OF
SAMUEL WREFORD, OF GRATTAN,
WHO DIED SEPTEMBER 25th 1859
AGED 76.
ALSO OF MARY HIS WIFE
WHO DIED JANUARY 7th 1865
AGED 79.
AND OF THEIR SONS,
SAMUEL WREFORD
WHO DIED JUNE 19th 1857.
AGED 47.
AND OF ROBERT WREFORD OF EXETER
WHO DIED NOVEMBER 10th 1864.
AGED 55.
AND OF THEIR DAUGHTERS,
MARY WREFORD,
WHO DIED OCTOBER 1st 1879,
AGED 72.
ANNE WREFORD
WHO DIED MARCH 8th 1881,
AGED 67.

Wreford memorial on the north wall inside Bow or Nymet Tracey church

Bradninch

Bindles	
Location	SS 993 024
Operational	to circa 1824
Output	35 hides a week in 1822
Tan pits	watering pit, three lime pits, 24 handlers in 1824

In the medieval period several tanners operated from Bradninch. In the late 14th century Reginald Tannere, Adam Catour and others, like their Tiverton competitors, obtained their hides in Exeter, 10 miles away. The city consumed rather more beef than the Bradninch parishoners. [1]

A well-established tannery existed here in the 18th century. William Segar was tanner in 1702. [2] The tanyard was located just west of the bridge crossing the Culm at Hele or Devon Valley Mill. Upstream, three water grist mills owned by Francis Gwynn of Ford Abbey were on lease to Abraham Elliot in the 1760s and the tannery was also his concern at this time. In 1770 the lease on the grist mills site was purchased by Thomas Dewdney and William Matthews who established the paper mill which is still in production in 2004, albeit after considerable rebuilding and expansion over the intervening years. [3]

William Martyn was the tanner in years preceding 1782: he was by then bankrupt. [4] Thomas Sharland was running the yard in the first years of the 19th century [5] but Joseph Bowden was also tanning at Bradninch in 1802. [6] By 1812 Robert Drew was tenant at Bradninch: he later claimed he had tanned in the parish since about 1798. Drew served on the committee of tanners chaired by George Barne of Tiverton to prepare a memorandum to the Board of Trade regarding a new leather tax. [7] With John Drew, a yeoman, he bought a house and 30 acres of land at Bindles in 1817, from the estate of John Francis Gwynn. [8]

The tanyard was offered to let in 1816, 1821, 1822 and 1824. The 1821 notice provides output and identifies the site:
'Tan Yard to be Let. Bradninch .. capable of tanning 30 hides per week .. all of which premises are called or known by the name of Bindles and are situated in Bradninch aforesaid and Broadclist and now in the occupation of Mr Robert Drew as tenant thereof ..' [9]

By 1821 Robert Drew was in trouble. Like a number of his competitors in the years after Waterloo, he had experienced difficult trading conditions and was in debt. With help from his family he kept the business going in a small way but on 28 June disaster struck. The paper mill at Hele, adjoining his house, caught fire. The mill was completely destroyed and so was Drew's house and his stock-in-trade. He was uninsured; he was already pressed for money. Destitute, he published a lengthy appeal to the public in the local press. He stated that he had been a tanner at Bradninch for *'upwards of twenty five years'* and that he had a wife and nine children to support. [10] The tanyard, across the road from the mill, appears to have survived and the paper makers may have then held the lease, as interested parties were asked to contact John Dewdney, probably a relation of Thomas Dewdney, in a notice to let in 1822:
'Tanyard .. Bradninch, Devon .. to be let .. capable of tanning 35 hides per week .. an extensive Shed, Linhays .. new-built House, and Offices attached, with a Stable, Barn, and Courtlage .. at the option of the tenant, 33 acres of excellent Arable, Meadow and Pasture Land, including an excellent Orchard .. apply .. Mr John Dewdney, Bradninch ..' [11]

Robert Drew was still tenant in 1824 when a further notice was published, giving an indication of the tannery's facilities. While there is no clear statement that the bark mill was water powered, it would be reasonable to suppose that it may have been:
'TAN-YARD. TO be LET for a Term, with immediate Possession, a TAN-Yard, situate in the town of Bradninch .. consisting of a Watering Pit, three Lime Pits, 24 Handlers, and a spacious Drying Loft over, with a sufficient number of Layers, a Turf Frame, and a never-failing stream of Water; Bark-house, Leather-house, Linhays, and Stable; — and a roomy convenient DWELLING HOUSE and GARDEN.
For viewing, apply to Mr Drew, on the premises; and to treat for the same, to Mr Bowden, at Culmstock ..' [12]

The yard probably closed. It may be that no one was willing to take on a small tannery, no doubt in close competition with two others at Cullompton and the near neighbour at Beare in Broadclyst. The site was redeveloped as a court or square of cottages: housing for the paper mill workers. These buildings have since been demolished and a car park now stands here.

Bradninch
1. Maryanne Kowaleski, Local Markets and Regional Trade in Medieval Exeter, Cambridge University Press, 1995, 302, citing mayor's court rolls, 1389/90 m 49
2. William Segar, tanner, married at Clyst Hydon – A H Shorter, D&CNQ, from transcribed parish register, D&CRS
3. Paddy Nash, Memories from the Mill. Privately published 2001, 9
4. Exeter Flying Post 19 July 1782 p 3 col 3 and 21 October 1784 p 3 col 3
5. Betty Carnall apprenticed to Thomas Sharland. DRO 1978A/9/14-16/11a-b
6. DRO 53/6 Box 5
7. Exeter Flying Post 20 August 1812 p 4 col 5
8. DRO 146B/T63-64
9. Exeter Flying Post 3 May 1821 p 1 col 3
10. Exeter Flying Post 5 July 1821 p 4 col 4
11. Sherborne Mercury 10 June and 29 July 1822
12. Exeter Flying Post 27 May 1824 p 1 col 3

Bridestowe

Tanyard Court
Location   SX 513 892
Operational   from at least 1650 to c 1843

Bridestowe may well have possessed an established tannery by the early 17th century: a field 'Tanners Meadow' was noted in 1650 [1] and was still so named in 1844, adjacent to Tanyard Hill. These two pastures formed part of the tannery property in the nineteenth century, owned by J G Newton Esq. [2]

18th century tanners included William Sloley in 1738, Alexander Woodrow in 1741 and Arthur Edgecumbe in 1789. [3]

Offered to let in 1796, the property was described as: *'.. a very good Tan-Yard now in work, a good Dwelling-houfe and gardens, convenient outhoufes and ground thereto belonging, in the parish of Bridestowe, adjoining the Turnpike Road, five miles from Oakhampton [sic], ten miles from Launcefton .. For further particulars apply to Mr John Newton of Bridestowe, where the taker may depend on having good Encouragement in taking the fame.'* [4]

Activities continued here into the 19th century as tanners John Bevan and James Palmer of Bridestowe dissolved their partnership in 1836, Bevan retaining control of the business. [5] The yard was occupied by a Mr Cottle in 1844, but may have ceased work in that decade: Bevan may have remained the tenant, but was bankrupt in 1848. [6]

Tanyard Court, a cul-de-sac west of the church and close to the river, indicates the site. There may have been water power here but the 1796 lease notice gives no information relating to machinery or the number of tan pits in situ, or indeed the output of the yard. New housing largely occupies the site today.

Bridestowe sources
1   D Richard Cann, The Book of Bridestowe, Halsgrove 2002
2   DRO – Bridestowe tithe map and apportionment, 1844
3   Cann, op cit, 122; A H Shorter, The Tanning Industry in Devon and Cornwall, 1550-1850. Devon & Cornwall Notes & Queries, Volume XXV, 1952, 10-16, from D&CRS transcriptions from parish registers
4   Exeter Flying Post 14 July 1796 p 2 col 3
5   Exeter Flying Post 12 May 1836 p 3 col 5
6   DRO – Bridestowe tithe map and apportionment, 1844
    Owner: John Gubbins Newton Esq
    Occupier: – Cottle
    59 = Tanyard Meadow. Pasture 2-0-13
    60 = Tanyard Hill. Pasture 4-3-38
    16 = Tanyard Higher Field Arable 5-1-25
    23 = Tanyard, Garden, Courtlage and House 1-0-23
    Total 13-2-29;
    Bevan's bankruptcy: Exeter Flying Post 8 June 1848 p 3 col 7

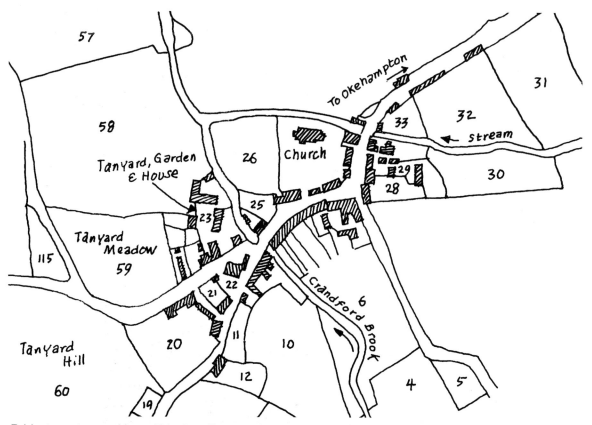

Bridestowe tanyard lay within the village and was still recorded as a tanyard in 1844, when the tithe map was surveyed. Tanning ceased, it seems, in the same decade

Broadclyst

Beare	
Location	SS 987 013
Operational	to circa 1905
Output	200 hides in 1875
Bark mill	water-powered but steam power here by 1875
Staff	10 or 12 in 1861-1875

Broadclyst was quite a sizeable tannery by Devon standards, capable of processing 200 hides a week in 1875. [1] It was located at Beare and water supplies came from a stream-fed reservoir to the east of the Exeter – Cullompton turnpike road. When the M5 Motorway was constructed in the 1970s, the tannery, which lay in its path, was largely demolished. [2] The tanner's residence – Beare House – survives.

William and Emanuel Boutcher were the Broadclyst tanners in 1786. [3] As at several other country sites, tanning was combined with farming: William Boucher Gould – the son of John Gould and Ann Boutcher – was farming at Broadclyst in 1851 and living at Crabtree House [4] but was recorded as tanner when he died an untimely death 'after a short illness' in 1853 at the age of 37. [5] Gould, who had married Sarah Wish in 1839, had tanned here from at least 1841.[6] Gould's brother-in-law, William Trump Wish, who came from a well-established local farming

family, [7] took control of the tanyard and ran it until 1875 or so. He was also farming: with 50 acres and 14 men and two women in 1861. Allowing him four labourers for the farm, 12 staff may have worked in the tannery at that date. [8]

The business expanded under Wish: in addition to water power, he also had a 10-horse power steam engine at work in 1875. In that year he offered the business to let and the complex here included ten cottages for labourers. [9] William Wish died on 10 October 1877, leaving an estate valued at £20,000. [10] Wish was also related by marriage to John Trump who ran the tannery at nearby Whimple from about 1879. [11] William Cock was tanner here in 1883 and the yard was in the hands of the Beare Tanning Co in 1897-1902 but had probably closed before 1906. [12]

Broadclyst sources
1   Exeter Flying Post 29 September 1875 p 1 col 2
2   Ordnance Survey map, Devonshire. 25" = 1 mile, sheet 69.1 of 1889
3   DRO 1148 Madd/2/L15/448-453
4   Broadclyst census 1851. HO107 1866 f 78 p 12
5   Exeter Flying Post 5 May 1853 p 8 col 6
6   Broadclyst census 1841. HO107 210/3 p 6
7   The Wish family trace back to 1660 at Broadclyst. [IGI]
8   Broadclyst census 1861. RG9 1385 f 15 p 7
9   Exeter Flying Post 29 September 1875 p 1 col 2
10   William T Wish's will: Executors Emma Ann Wish, widow; Thomas Wish, brother, and Edward Richards Wish
11   Mormon IGIs
12   Kelly's Directory of Devonshire and Cornwall, 1897, 1111; 1902, 1136, and not listed: 1906 edition

The tannery in 1889 – it has since been demolished and part lies inder the M5 Motorway.
It stood to the north of the Exeter-Cullompton turnpike which has been improved since the Ordnance Survey map was drawn. To the south of the turnpike can be seen the reservoir or pond, now dry, which provided the water power for the bark mill

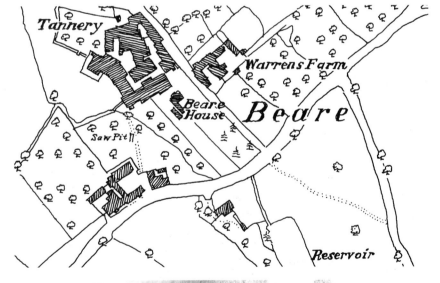

Houses at Beare in 2004; the remaining structures on the tannery site. The M5 Motorway runs beyond the trees

Broadhembury

Dulford

Location	ST 0707 0590
Operational	to circa 1832
Bark mill	water-powered
Tan pits	72 in 1794

There were tanners here in the 18th century: William Hussey in 1725, Andrew Payne in 1735 and William Shiles in 1775-1785. Shiles was the son-in-law of Richard Cross of Duryard, Exeter, and insured Godford Mills at Awliscombe in 1782. [1]

The mill at Dulford, by the turnpike road from Honiton to Cullompton, was owned by the Shiles family in the late 18th century. It was an estate which included Hayne Farm, just upstream. [2] A leat from the River Weaver ran to Hayne Farm. Here it powered a waterwheel before running at a lower level to Dulford Mill, where it turned the overshot waterwheel for the flour mill. Adjoining was a bark mill and a courtyard of barns nearby may have enclosed a set of tan pits, and provided stores for oak bark. Alternatively the tan pits may have been located at Hayne, thought to be the site of the 'Higher Tan-Yard'; the following sale notice of 1792 provides the evidence:
'Lot 1. The Tan-yard, called the HIGHER TAN-YARD .. fituate in the parifh of Broadhembury .. late in the poffeffion of Mrs Shiles, a bankrupt ..
Lot 2. .. all that Grift Mill called Dilford Mill in the poffeffion of William Shiles, fituate in Broadhembury aforefaid, with the bark mill thereunto adjoining ..
Lot 3. The Benefit of a certain Leafe .. GODFORD.
Lot 4. .. GODFORD MILLS ..in the poffeffion of the faid Elizabeth Shiles and fituate in Awlifcombe ..' [3]

A Georgian miller's house survives at Dulford and the farm house at Hayne dates from the same period. In 1794 this notice appeared:
'At Dilford in Broadhembury ..To be Let .. A good .. TAN-YARD, with 72 pits, large drying kiln, a commodious dwelling-houfe, a walled garden, large drying linhays, ftables, outbuildings .. Mr David Phillips, builder, Exeter ..' [4]

Edward Sharland was tanner at Broadhembury in the period 1809-1825, when the proprietor was Mr Anning. [5] Sharland then moved to Hampshire to run a tanyard at Fareham. A member of the Shiles family re-established here but the property was offered to let in October 1831:
'To be Let, at Dulford .. a very good Dwelling-House, a Tan Yard .. together with a Farm .. adjoining the Turnpike Road; .. now in the possession of Mr Henry Shiles ..' [6]
In 1832 the tanyard was the property of the owner of Dulford House. [7] The leats still ran in 2006.

Broadhembury
1 A H Shorter, D&CNQ; DRO 1148Madd/2/L15/415; Exeter Flying Post 17-3-1775 p 2 col 2; DRO 530M/T72; Royal Exchange FIP 84764, 29 October 1782
2 DRO – Broadhembury tithe map and apportionment
3 Sherborne Mercury 2 July 1792
4 Sherborne Mercury 22 September 1794 p 2
5 Exeter Flying Post 17 November 1808 p 1 col 2
6 Woolmer's Gazette 22 October 1831 p 1 col 4
7 The Western Times 21 April 1832 p 1 col 5

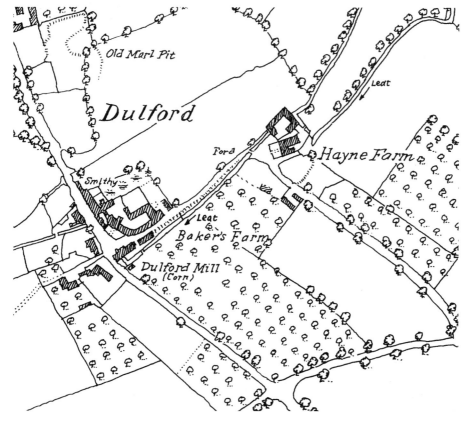

Broadhembury in 1889. A leat ran to Hayne Farm where there was a waterwheel and a lower leat ran to Dulford Mill, powering a second overshot waterwheel. The bark mill apparently adjoined Dulford Mill in 1792 and Hayne Farm probably represents the Higher Tan Yard of that date. Baker's Farm may be the site of a lower tanyard. Hayne Farm and Dulford Mill formed one estate in the early 19th century and the farmhouse at Hayne dates from the Regency period. From the Ordnance Survey, 25" = 1 mile, sheet 57.8

Broadhempston

Forder Green

Location	SX 789 675
Operational	until c 1850
Output	100 hides a week in 1840

Forder Green was very probably an established tanyard by the late 18th century. In 1801 William Francis, the tanner here, was advertising for journeymen. [1] He was still short staffed in 1805 and 1809:
'*To JOURNEYMEN TANNERS. Wanted a steady MAN to work at the beam. Conſtant employment and good wages will be given by William Francis, Broadhempſton, near Totnes, Devon. Dated October 7, 1805.'* [2]

In 1811 Francis offered the property for sale:
'*Tan-Yard. To be Sold by Private Contract, The Fee-simple and Inheritance of a Modern-built Dwelling-House, with an Extensive and Newly-built Tan-Yard, well-supplied with water, and now in full work; with spacious outbuildings of every description, and four cottages for labourers, Walled Garden, and (with or without) 35 Acres of excellent Orchard, Meadow, Arable, and Pasture Land; situated in the parish of Broadhempston .. in an exceeding good bark country .. For further particulars apply to William Francis, the proprietor .. Broadhempston April 13, 1811.'* [3]

A member of the Francis family put the yard up for sale again in 1834:
'*To be Sold in Fee or Let for a Term of Years, a Valuable Tan-Yard, replete with every convenience together with an excellent Dwelling-house and Estate consisting of 35 acres of rich Land. The situation is desirable from its proximity to the navigable River Dart and to three considerable market towns, also from its being in a good bark neighbourhood. As the owner is about to decline business the premises will be disposed of at an immense sacrifice. Apply to Mr Francis, Broadhempston, Ashburton ..'* [4]

William Wilcocks was tanner in 1841, [5] probably as tenant of John Thuell, who was listed as owner and occupier at that time. The estate totalled 46 acres. [6] John Thuell was bankrupt in 1847: he was a tanner but also a partner with William Jeffery in woollen mills at West Mill, Buckfastleigh and at Buckfast. [7] Thuell was mentioned as a former occupant when the premises were advertised to let in 1856, when in the possession of William Mann. He may well have been related to the Mann family, tanners in Ashburton in the early 19th century. But it is clear from the following notice that tanning had ceased in the late 1840s or early 1850s:

'*Broadhempstone, Devon. To be Let, by Tender, for a Term of three, seven or fourteen years .. Farm, situate at or called Forder Green, with the four*

cottages adjoining, in the parish of Broadhempstone, formerly in the possession of Mr Thuell and now in the occupation of Mr Wm Mann.
Excellent dwelling house and offices, with walled and kitchen gardens, greenhouse, pound house .. There is also on the premises a Tan Yard, formerly laid out on the most approved plan, and capable of tanning 100 hides per week, with lofts, bark linhays .. tanning business, which a few years since was carried on there on an extensive scale ..' [8]

The tanpits were still open to the elements in June 1858:
'*On Monday evening a little boy, son of Mr John Waycott, tailor, of Forder Green .. returned from school, and went out to pick strawberries. Night came on and he did not return. Search was made for him and on Tuesday he was found drowned in an old tan pit.'* [9]

There is no evidence that leather was made here later in the century. Today a large residence survives with walled gardens. On the site of the tannery are 19th century farm buildings, seemingly purpose built. However one relic survives mounted by the barns – a bell, which seems more appropriate for a Victorian tannery than a farm. A small stream runs by, no doubt once providing the water for the tan pits.

Broadhempston sources
1 Sherborne Mercury 4 May 1801
2 Sherborne Mercury 28 October 1805; Exeter Flying Post 24 August 1809 p 1 col 4
3 Sherborne Mercury 15 April 1811
4 Sherborne Mercury 27 January 1834 p 4 col 6
5 Broadhempston census 1841
6 DRO – Broadhempston tithe map and apportionment. 1841. Items included 591 House and Shrubbery, 588 Tan Yard and Lofts, 589 Kitchen Garden, 590 Walled Garden, 586 Forder Green Cottage, etc
7 The Western Times 12 June 1847 p 1 col 3, 14 August 1847 p 1 col 5
8 Exeter Flying Post 13 March 1856 p 1 col 1
9 The Western Times 19 June 1858 p 7 col 1

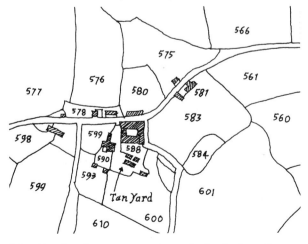

The Forder Green tanyard was indicated on the Broadhempston tithe map of 1841. Farm barns now stand on the site

Buckerell

Hamlet

Location	SY 144 999
Operational	to circa 1842

Buckerell sources
1. Woolmer's Gazette 30 August 1823 p 7 col 4
2. Buckerell tithe and apportionment, 1845. 'Part of Farmery, Tan Yard &c'. Total 14a 1r 3p, including a house and garden, item 477, 0-3-27
3. Exeter Flying Post 6 October 1842 p 2 col 6

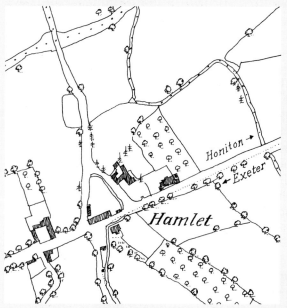

Tanyard site in 1889, east of the triangle of roads

What was once the old Roman road from Honiton to Exeter – later the turnpike, then A30 trunk road – ran straight past the tannery. It has now been superseded by a new dual carriageway. William Cockram was the Buckerell tanner in 1816; in 1823 he occupied a house, tanyard and 13 acres here, when the property was advertised to let. [1]

The tanyard has long since gone but in 1845 a small estate of 14 acres here was known as *'Part of Farmery, Tan Yard &c'*, owned and occupied by Christopher Flood, Esq in 1845. [2] It is probable that it had already closed by then: Henry Hawker, the Buckerell tanner and fellmonger had died in 1842 when his house and lands totalling 15 acres were offered to let. [3] While a small stream, a tributary of the Otter, may have supplied sufficient water for the tan pits, and the communications were good, the business may have struggled to compete with other nearby tanyards at Honiton and Ottery St Mary.

Buckfastleigh

Tannery off Chapel Street

Location	SX 7370 6620
Operational	1806 to 21st century
Output	not known
Bark mill	water-powered
Staff	8 in 1851

One family effectively controlled the Buckfastleigh tannery throughout the 19th century – the Hamlyns. Like their contemporaries in Newton Abbot, the Vicarys – they ran two businesses: wool combing and woollen manufacture and a tanning industry. The tannery was bought in 1806 and wool combing commenced the same year. [1]

Joseph Hamlyn, born in South Brent, was the first of the tanners [2] and his offspring included three sons and two daughters. His second son John was baptised at the Weslyan Methodist chapel in 1816 and his brother William followed in 1822. [3] Joseph's daughter Maria appears to have married John Furneaux, a woolstapler and farmer; [4] later the two families operated in partnership.

Buckfastleigh was functioning with three woollen mills in the Victorian period and a further two mills were at Buckfast. Of these five mills, the Hamlyns bought Town Mill and from 1842 leased West Mill; they also owned Higher Mill in Buckfast. [5]

In 1851 Joseph, now aged 69, had retired; his son John was listed as a serge manufacturer employing 83 women, 37 men, four boys and eight girls. William Hamlyn ran the tannery with six men and two boys, but also farmed 108 acres with a further 20 labourers. William had a rival, Thomas Furneaux, aged 60, farming and tanning with three men and two boys. At Jordan Street, Higher Town, John Furneaux ran a woolstapling business with 36 hands and a further eight labourers farming. [6] The town's river, the Mardle broke its banks in November 1852:
'.. At Buckfastleigh rivers came down torrents, the streets were flooded .. the waters broke into the tan-yards of Messrs Hamlyns, but no injury to any extent has been sustained ..' [7]

By 1853 John and William had formed a company known as Hamlyn Brothers. [8] The company ran the tannery and the woollen mills and in 1861 had 270 staff on the payroll. There were setbacks. One of the woollen mills suffered a fire in 1858. [9] In 1861 an employee, a 12-year-old lad, James Edmonds, was killed when his apron got entangled with a working water-wheel shaft in an old wash house and his head was dashed against a wall. [10] And in 1865 William died, in his early forties. He left an estate worth nearly £25,000. [11]

His tannery was in Higher Town, well supplied with water from the Mardle and upstream from the woollen mill. [12] John Hamlyn was living at Park

View House, Chapel Street, in 1871 and his brother's widow, Mary was at Maiden House, Market Street. Her two elder sons, James, 23, and John, 21, were both wool merchants and tanners. Her son Joseph, 20, was learning the woollen business and his brother William, 18, was likewise involved in tanning. [13] There were also two members of the Furneaux family tanning in the town in 1873. [14]

Two years later the company took over a woollen mill at Horrabridge which had been established by Gill, Rundle and Bridgman of Tavistock, in about 1840. [15]
John Hamlyn built Fullaford House in 1876, perhaps to rival John Furneaux's Harewood House, built in 1868. [16] Business was still good and the company traded with firms in Yorkshire: Edward Brooks, a Bradford woollen spinner, was staying with John Hamlyn on census night in 1871. [17] Agents and offices had been established at Bradford and Manchester by 1878. [18]

In that year John Hamlyn died. He left £100,000, but with no heirs to inherit. Executors included his elder brother Joseph, of Torquay; John Furneaux and William Hamlyn's four eldest sons, James, John, Joseph and William. [19]

William's sons continued to run the business, with Joseph, his third son, focusing on the tannery. [19] Because the business lasted so long in the family's hands there are no sale notices to indicate its size and production. However the report of a major fire here in 1882 gives some idea of the scale of this Buckfastleigh concern:

'.. Loss of £5000. About mid-day on Saturday a fire which caused the most intense alarm, and resulted in the destruction of property of great value, broke out upon the extensive premises of Messrs Hamlyn Bros, wool staplers and tanners, of Buckfastleigh. The firm is well-known in the West of England in connection with the woollen industry but it seems they also carry on business on a moderately large scale as tanners, the latter department having been established about fifty years. Outside the tannery which is separated from the factory by several hundred yards, lay four huge stacks of bark, each 40 feet in height, and weighing altogether upwards of a thousand tons. It was the accumulation of two years, the last year was the most successful season for bark, and was valued between £5000 and £6000 as it stood. To protect it from the elements the exposed sides of the ricks were packed with furze. Shortly before the dinner hour on Saturday the rick next the tannery, by some means not yet ascertained ignited, when a conflagration ensued .. fed by a strong south-west wind the flames spread rapidly until all four ricks were enveloped .. The whole of Messrs Hamlyn's employees, in number about 500, were out and at it in a 'twinkling of an eye' after the alarm had been raised – some dipping water from the stream in buckets, some emptying the leather and other valuable property from the warehouses .. On arrival of the town engine and fire brigade they found abundance of water at hand, and speedily set to work. They were joined by two fire brigades from Ashburton and one from Totnes, the telegrams despatched to these towns asking for help having brought the engines to the scene of the fire in remarkably good time, attached as each was to four swift horses ..

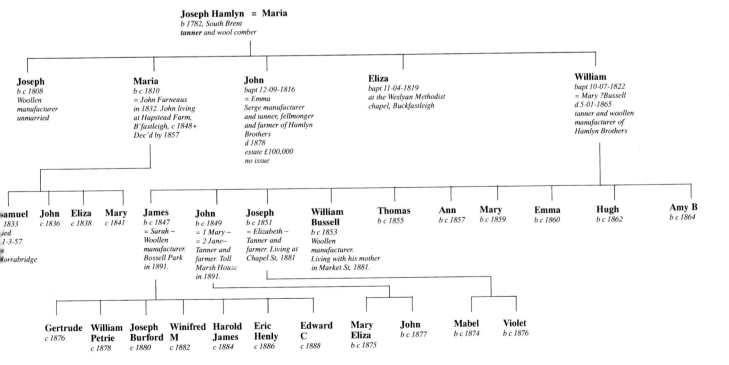

The Hamlyn family of Buckfastleigh in the 19th century: tanners and woollen manufacturers

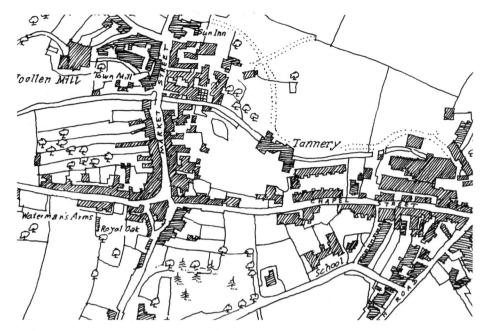

Buckfastleigh in 1887. The tannery stands to the north of Chapel Street and may have extended west to Market Street. Above it on the river Mardle are the Town Mill and the Sherwell Woollen Mill. Downstream is the Town Woollen Mill. From the Ordnance Survey 25" = 1 mile map, sheets 114.10 and 114.11

The members of the firm, fully alive to the emergency were here there and everywhere, advising what should be done, controlling what was being done, or giving a word of encouragement to the bands of willing helpers around them. Saturday afternoon, Saturday night and all yesterday the fire continued to rage ..' [21]

It is interesting that the bark stores were so large that they were in the open, merely protected by furze on their weather sides. And clearly the telegraph, in speeding the messages for help, was a significant factor in helping to stop the fire from spreading to other premises.

The conflagration may have induced Hamlyn Bros to reduce their operations and Greendown Farm and Town Farm, long owned and operated by members of the company, were offered to let in the same year. [22] But they recovered and in 1887 the family provided financial support for the construction of the town hall. [23] In 1889 Hamlyn Bros employed 700 hands; their rivals John Berry & Sons had a further 400 working for them. As at North Tawton blue serge was manufactured in the Buckfastleigh mills for use by navy personnel. [24]

At the end of the century the wool trade was declining in the west, and the Horrabridge Mills became redundant and were demolished. [25] In 1920, Hamlyn's Mill was sold to the Co-operative Wholesale Society for £270,000. Fellmongery continued in the town and Axminster Carpets was still tanning British sheepskins here in 2003. [26]

The Vicary family had provided employment to many in Newton Abbot and North Tawton in the 19th century. Here too, in Buckfastleigh, the Hamlyn family played a major part in providing work for many of the townspeople for a century and more.

Buckfastleigh sources

1   Sandra Coleman, The Book of Buckfastleigh. A Time for Remembering 1930-2002. Halsgrove 2003, 85; DRO tithe map and apportionment, 1839 - item 1108, 'Tan Yard', owned by Joseph Hamlyn
2   Buckfastleigh census, 1851
3   Mormon IGIs
4   A John Furneaux married Maria Hamlyn at Buckfastleigh, 1832; Maria is probably daughter of Joseph and Maria Hamlyn, and sister to William and Joseph jnr
5   Sandra Coleman, op cit, 85
6   Buckfastleigh census 1851 – HO107 1874 f 307 p 47, HO 107 1874 f 337 p 42, HO107 1874 f 331 p 31
7   Woolmer's Gazette 13 November 1852 p 7 col 4
8   Exeter Flying Post. Report on the entertainment of tannery workers at Hamlyn Bros. 18 August 1853 p 4 cols 2 and 3; Hamlyn Brothers, tanners, Buckfastleigh, Ashburton Post Office Directory, Devon and Cornwall, 1856
9   Exeter Flying Post 23 December 1858 p 5 col 5
10 The Western Times 7 September 1861 p 7 col 3
11 Will of William Hamlyn. Died 5 January 1865
12 Ordnance Survey map of Devonshire, sheet 114.11, 25" = 1 mile, of 1889
13 Buckfastleigh census, 1871 – RG10 2096 f 56 p 1, RG10 2096 f 63 p 16
14 The Post Office Directory of Devonshire and Cornwall, Kelly, 1873
15 Helen Harris. The Industrial Archaeology of Dartmoor. Newton Abbot 1992
16 Sandra Coleman, op cit, 51 and 118
17 Buckfastleigh census, 1871 – RG10 2096 f 56 p 1
18 Harrod's Directory
19 Will of John Hamlyn, woollen manufacturer, tanner and general dealer of Buckfastleigh. Died 21 June 1878
20 Buckfastleigh census 1881 – RG11 2177 f 39 p 25, RG11 2177 f 59 p 15, RG11 2177 f 75 p 1, RG11 2177 f 75 p 2
21 The Western Times 10 January 1882 p 3 col 6
22 The Western Times 24 February 1882 p 4 col 1
23 Sandra Coleman, op cit, 21
24 Kelly's Directory, Devonshire, 1889
25 Helen Harris, op cit
26 Sandra Coleman, op cit, 87, 90

Buckland Monachorum

Coombe

Location	SX 501 661
Operational	from at least 1694 to c 1831
Bark mill	water powered
Tan pits	32 handlers, 12 vats, 'and letches in proportion' (1817)

The house at Coombe

At least two locations in the parish suggest themselves as sites of tanneries, although they may merely be properties owned by tanners: John Martyn, a Buckland tanner was recorded as 'of Milton' when buried in 1685. [1] In 1688 John Dunning the elder, tanner of Ludbrook, was involved in property at Lower Didhams, to the south west of the village. [2] Didhams features again in papers relating to tanner Elize Dunrith in 1692. [3]

The tanyard that survived into the nineteenth century was at Coombe, to the east of Milton Combe, itself south of Buckland Monachorum village. According to an advertisement of 1794 *'the bark has been ground by a Water Mill for a century past'*. [4]

Sampson Dawe was a tanner of Buckland in 1738; [5] it was either he or a relative of the same name who was referred to in the 1794 notice in the Sherborne Mercury:
'A TAN-YARD. To be LET - for a term of 16 years from Lady-day next .. All that capital YARD known by the name of COOMBE in the parifh of Buckland Monachorum .. together with an excellent ESTATE, about 70 acres ..The tanyard is .. all under cover, of a planched floor, drying places and bark lofts over the fame .. about eight miles from Plymouth and Plymouth Dock and fix miles from Taviftock .. and near the turnpike road leading to each, and a fine country for hides and bark .. the above was lately the refidence of Sampson Dawe, deceafed ..' [6]

The tannery was later worked by a further member of the Dawe family – Sampson Dawe, possibly the third tanner of this line, as it was for sale in 1817:
'An Auction will be held .. for Selling the Fee-simple and Inheritance of all that Messuage and Tenement
called Coombe situate in the parish of Buckland Monachorum .. in the possession of Mr Sampson Dawe, the proprietor; containing 33 acres of very excellent meadow and pasture land, with orchards .. There is .. A very valuable Tan-Yard, now in full course of working; consisting of 32 handlers and 12 vats, and letches in proportion, (the whole under cover,) with a capital bark-mill, worked by a stream of water, which runs through the yard ..' [7]

It was possibly tanner T Brown who bought, or maybe leased the property. In July 1822, by which time he was established at Buckland, he married Elizabeth Turner, second daughter of the late Mr James Turner, at Colebrooke. Three years later, in September, he was assaulted:
'On the night of Saturday se'nnight, about nine o'clock, as Mr Brown, tanner, of Buckland Monachorum, was returning on horseback from Plymouth, he was stopped near Hartley Gate, by a footpad, dressed in black, who jumped from a hedge, where stood another man, and, seizing Mr Brown by the collar, demanded his money, and threatened to murder him if he made any noise; but happily at that moment the approach of horses was distinctly heard, and "murder" being loudly called, the villain quitted his hold, and made off, leaving a large bludgeon in the hands of Mr Brown.' [8]

A Thomas Brown was tanner at Plympton from at least 1844 to 1857 and died in 1871, leaving £2000. [9] He may have bought the Plympton tannery when it was for sale in 1831. [10] By 1842 Coombe Farm, with the tanyard, was leased by owner John Toll to another Dawe – Joseph Dawe, who owned the neighbouring farm, Lower Helling Town. As farmer and miller at Hellingtown he has been declared bankrupt in 1824 but owned the estate in 1842. [11] It is not clear when Coombe tanyard closed. Today all real trace of it has gone. A small tributary of the Tavy still runs by the estate.

Buckland Monachorum sources
1 A H Shorter, The Tanning Industry in Devon and Cornwall, 1550-1850. Devon & Cornwall Notes & Queries, Volume XXV, 1952, 10-16, from Devon & Cornwall Record Society transcriptions: Buckland Monachorum parish register, 1685
2 Plymouth & WDRO 178/20 – 1688
3 Plymouth & WDRO 178/11 – 1692
4 Sherborne Mercury 17 February 1794
5 Plymouth & WDRO 178/35 (a-b); 36 (a-b) – 1738, 1740
6 Sherborne Mercury 17 February 1794
7 Sherborne Mercury 31 March 1817 p 1 col 3
8 Exeter Flying Post 15 September 1825 p 4 col 3
9 Pigot's Directory, Devonshire, 1844, 135; White's Directory, 1850; Plympton census, 1851. Fore Street HO107 1877 f 393 p 9; Post Office Directory, Devon and Cornwall, 1856; NDRO 178B/M/T115 of 1857; Will – died 9 August 1871
10 Sherborne Mercury 4 July 1831 p1
11 DRO Buckland Monachorum tithe map and apportionment – item 1291 House and Garden, 1296 Tan Yard. In all Coombe Farm totalled 33a 3r 23p; Exeter Flying Post 21 October 1824 p 1 col 4

Cheriton Fitzpaine

West Upham
Lower Waterhouse

Locations	SS 8810 0838 and
	SS 8825 0820
Operational	until about 1870
Bark mills	water powered
Tan pits	25 layers, 40 handlers,
	12 latches in 1823
Staff	36 in 1851

West Upham farm buildings in 2005

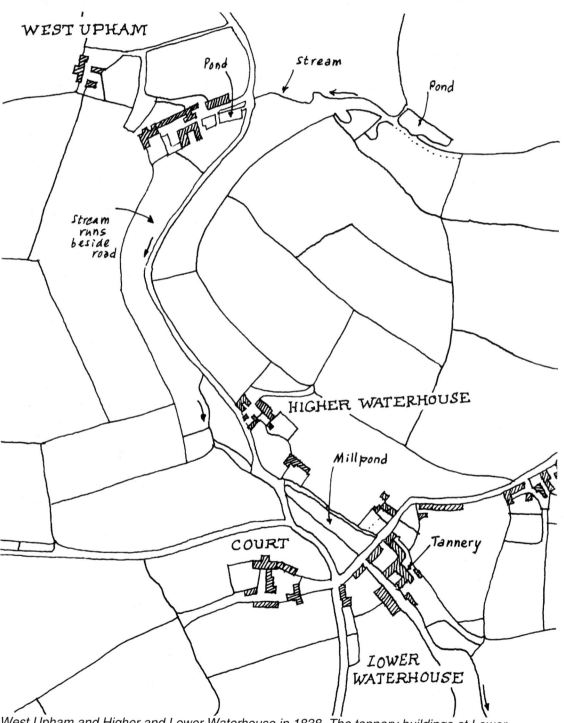

West Upham and Higher and Lower Waterhouse in 1838. The tannery buildings at Lower Waterhouse had been largely demolished by 1886 – see the Ordnance Survey map, 25" = 1 mile, sheets 44.16 and 55.4 – and Upham Lodge, built in 1898, now stands on part of the site. While there was also a tannery at West Upham, it is not clear which buildings it utilised

These two tanyards both possessed water-powered bark mills, were near one another on the same stream, and for a time were worked as one unit. They were over a mile from Cheriton Fitzpaine village.

Peter Sharland was a Cheriton tanner by 1808 and was almost certainly based at Lower Waterhouse. Thomas Rowe, later a tanner in Alphington, was born in Cheriton and apprenticed to him at that time. [1]

West Upham was for sale in 1823 when it was owned and occupied by William Drake:
'TO TANNERS. TO be LET by Tender, for a Term of 14 or 21 years, from Lady-day next, all that well-constructed Tan-Yard, Farm and Premises, situate in the parish of Cheriton Fitzpaine, Devon, now and for many years past in the occupation of the owner, Mr. Thomas Drake, who is about to remove therefrom.
The Tan-Yard consists of 25 layers, 40 handlers, and 12 latches (nearly the whole of which is covered by drying lofts, &c) with limes, soaks, and watering pits in proportion, a bark mill turned by water, and every other necessary appendage.
Near the Yard is a handsome DWELLING-HOUSE, consisting of a hall, 2 parlours, 6 bed-rooms, and all necessary offices.
The farm consists of about 120 acres of excellent arable, meadow, pasture, and orchard grounds, all now in a high state of cultivation.
There are also THREE neat COTTAGES for Labourers, newly built, near the Yard ..' [2]

West Upham was probably bought by William Sharland, Peter Sharland's son, in 1824, for in 1838 he owned and occupied Lower Waterhouse, West Upham and South Coombe, in all about 222 acres, together with a number of cottages – Fursdons, Moors, Gates and Moxey's – leased out to tenants. South Coombe was a farm to the east. The tithe map and apportionment of the time shows buildings and cottages at Lower Waterhouse. It is also clear from the map that the available waterpower here was of a greater order than that at West Upham.[3]

William's business was successful and by 1851 he had retired to Exeter. [4] In 1850 he and his only son Thomas M C Sharland had operated from Lower Waterhouse as Sharland & Son. [5] But in 1851 Thomas was in sole charge of the Cheriton tanneries. He was then aged 38, and farmed 225 acres with 10 labourers and had a further 36 engaged on tanning operations. His younger brother Henry assisted. The brothers lived at Lower Waterhouse. [6]

Thomas married his cousin Ann Sharland. She died young – probably in childbirth – at 1, Peamore Terrace, New North Road, Exeter on 15 September 1852, aged 34. [7] A tablet on the south wall, Cheriton Fitzpaine church, commemorates her:
'Sacred to the Memory of Ann, the beloved wife of Thomas Melhuish Comins Sharland, of Lower Waterhouse in this parish ..'
A year or so after Ann's death, Thomas offered South Coombe and West Upham to let. [8] His father William died in 1855 and Thomas himself passed away in 1863, aged 50, leaving an estate worth £45,000. [9]

The estate was offered for sale in 1864, in six lots:
'To Tanners and others .. Sell by Auction, extensive and substantial Tanyards, Dwelling Houses, Cottages, and several good Farms, now let to respectable tenants .. late the property of Mr T M C Sharland, deceased .. The tanpits will contain from eight to nine thousand hides and the drying and bark sheds are of ample dimensions with good water power, and well supplied with bark of excellent quality.
Lot 1 – A very compact and highly productive Farm called 'West Upham' containing 110a 2r 17p of watered meadow, arable land, and orchard, which is let to Mr Francis for a term of fourteen years, from 29 September 1854. With this lot will be sold a good Dwelling House, Tanyard .. offices, bark mill by water power, extensive ponds .. seven acres of meadow and .. orchard .. and also Eleven Cottages and Gardens ..'
Lot 3 – A genteel dwelling house, the late residence of Mr Sharland .. with this lot will be sold a capital tanyard, bark barn, drying sheds and bark mill by water power, mill pond, and all conveniences for a tanning trade, also five cottages and 19a 2r 19p of first-class meadow and pasture land .. having been occupied by the late Mr Sharland and his father, where a handsome fortune by the trade was made by them, and it affords a good opportunity for a man of capital and energy to do the same ..' [10]

The tanyards were still extant in 1869 but most of the structures at Lower Waterhouse had been swept away by 1886 [11] and Upham Lodge, built in 1898, stands on part of the site. The neighbouring 'Old Tannery' is thought to have been a store. In the garden of Upham Lodge granite cobbling survives under topsoil. Some of the tan pits were also extant when the present owners moved in; oak bark residues and an elephant hide were discovered here. The pits have since been sealed with clay. Nearby stood a row of cottages for the tannery workers; all since demolished. [12]

Cheriton Fitzpaine sources
1 DRO 1481A/PO 708/79 of 1811
2 Exeter Flying Post 12 June 1823 p 1
3 DRO. Cheriton Fitzpaine tithe map, apportionment, 1838
4 Exeter census, 1851
5 White's Directory of Devon 1850
6 1851 census Cheriton Fitzpaine, HO107 1887 f 456 p 12
7 The Western Times 18 September 1852 p 4 col 5
8 The Western Times 2 September 1854 p 1 col 1
9 Will of Thomas M C Sharland. PROB
10 Exeter Flying Post 24 August 1864 p 1 col 2
11 The Western Times 16 April 1869 p 1 col 2; Ordnance Survey map 1886, 25" = 1 mile, sheets 44.16 and 55.4
12 Professor Anderson, personal communication, September 2006

Chudleigh

Exeter Street	
Location	SX 869 796
Operational	until circa 1869
Bark mill	horse powered

Leather was being produced in the town at the beginning of the 18th century: William Caseley was tanner in 1707. [1]

John Westwood was Chudleigh tanner in 1743 [2] and either he or a relative of the same name was running the business in the 1780s. Westwood was by then evidently a successful businessman, owning several vessels: he sent one of his apprentices away to sea, aged 20, for seven months. Unfortunately the lad was press ganged and ended up serving on a government guard ship for a further six months. [3]

Tanning may have also been carried out in Ideford Coombe. Mr Burd was living and possibly working there at the end of the eighteenth century. [4]

A catastrophe struck the town on 22 May 1807. A fire which took hold in a baker's yard in Culver Street – now New Exeter Street – was spread by strong winds to neighbouring thatched roofs. Soon the centre of Chudleigh was ablaze; all the traders' premises were destroyed in no more than four hours, including the tannery which had been established in Exeter Street. [5]

The town tanyard, presumably rebuilt following an insurance claim, was for sale in 1823:
'Chudleigh. To be Sold .. convenient Dwelling-House with an excellent Tan Yard in the centre of the town of Chudleigh together with Drying House, Drying Loft, Pound House, Bark Linhays, Stable, Store-room &c .. NB These premises have lately been put in complete repair .. have a never failing stream of water, and lie in the midst of a country abounding with oak timber .. for viewing the Premises apply to Mr Geo. Pulling, Chudleigh.' [6]

By 1830 John Berry had a well-established operation here: in a summary of the town's trade it was noted that he was running *'a considerable tannery business'*. [7] Berry had been baptised at Moretonhampstead in August 1781. [8] His wife Mary bore him at least four children: the eldest was John, baptised at Broadhempston in February 1812. He followed in his father's footsteps and became a tanner; the second son Joseph, baptised in Broadhempston in 1818, became a currier.

John Berry was still head of the family firm in 1851, aged 69, but no doubt helped by his son John, aged 39. They lived at Old Exeter Street. [9] The tannery was actually sited in the 'v' between Old Exeter Street and New Exeter Street, earlier Culver Street,

just before they merge. Water for use in the tanpits probably came from the potwater leat, the town's water supply, which ran partly as a leat and was partly piped from a spring on Haldon hill. It entered the town via Old Exeter Road and had been flowing from at least some time in the 16th century. A slaughterhouse adjoined the yard, useful no doubt for the tanners, with ready access to hides. Now a small housing development stands on the site. [10]

It would be of interest to know if John Berry, John Westwood's apprentice in 1743, was related to the 19th century tanners. [11] Throughout the 1850s John Berry was listed as the Chudleigh tanner, but at some stage the son must have taken over. [12]

John Berry senior was no longer living by 1861. His widow continued to live in Exeter Street with two daughters, one unmarried, and the other married with three children, all born in London. [13] John Berry junior carried on at the tannery, wrongly listed under Chulmleigh in the 1866 directory. [14] He died in February 1870. [15] Mrs Prudence Berry, his widow, was listed as tanner in that year, [16] but in October the tanyard plant was offered for sale and included a *'capital horse-power bark mill'*. [17] While there was apparently enough water to supply the tan pits, the one stream offering any power, accessible in Chudleigh – the Kate Brook – was already directed to the leats of three corn mills. So the horse mill would have been essential for grinding the oak bark.

It is probable that following the sale of the yard by Prudence Berry, leather production ceased at Chudleigh. A site in the centre of town was not an ideal place for a tannery. The centre has since been somewhat redeveloped and any evidence of the yard in Old Exeter Street/Exeter Street has now gone.

Chudleigh sources
1   Devon & Cornwall Record Society: transcriptions from Chudleigh parish register. Bondsman nominated by Caseley.
2   DRO 3009A-99/PO/18/84 of 1743
3   DRO 3009A-99/PO 14/628 of 1798
4   DRO 3009A-99/PO9/76 of circa 1800
5   Anthony Crockett, Chudleigh: A Chronicle. Devon Books, 1985, 94-95; Mary Jones, History of Chudleigh, 1875, 61
6   The Alfred 6 May 1823 p 1 col 2
7   Pigot's General Directory, Devonshire, 1830
8   Mormon IGIs
9   Chudleigh census 1851. Old Exeter Street. HO107 1870 f 472 p 57
10 Personal communication – John Moore of Chudleigh Knighton, 16 March 2005; A Chudleigh Chronicle, 111
11 see 2
12 White's Directory 1850, Slaters Directory 1852, Post Office Directory, Devon and Cornwall, 1856
13 Chudleigh census, 1861 Exeter Street – RG9 1402 f 85 p 19. Joseph Berry lived nearby as currier and shopkeeper
14 Post Office Directory of Devonshire 1866
15 Exeter Flying Post 23 February 1870 p 5 col 6
16 Devon Directory, 1870
17 Exeter Flying Post 5 October 1870 p 1

Chulmleigh

Ford	
Location	SS 671 158
Operational	until circa 1865
Staff	4 in 1861

Chulmleigh's tanyard was at Ford, well away from the town and the old road from Exeter to Barnstaple. The present house is thought to date from 1779, and was very probably the tanner's residence. [1] Earlier in the century – between 1731 and 1747 – John Tanner was making leather in the parish. [2]

Ford was indicated as the location of the yard in 1811, when the then tanner, Samuel Wreford, employed Elizabeth Violet, aged 10, as an apprentice. [3] In August 1812 Wreford was present at the meeting of tanners held at the London Inn, Exeter, where a committee was appointed, under the chairmanship of George Barne of Tiverton, to lobby the Board of Trade over Devon tanners' concerns at the new duty on leather. [4]

Samuel's son Samuel had been born in 1805 or thereabouts and he too became a tanner. In November 1840 he married Grace Howe Sheere at St Mary Lothbury in the City of London. [5] She was a Devonian, baptised in 1803 at Huish, near Hatherleigh. [6] But the London wedding appears to indicate that the Wrefords were a cut above the average west country yeoman.

The Ford estate totalled 63 acres in 1840: the tanyard is not noted in the tithe apportionment nor is there an indication of a mill on the associated tithe map. [7] Both Wrefords, father and son, were tanning here in 1841. [8] Two streams meet at Ford and a water-powered bark mill may have existed on site but there is no clear evidence on the ground today.

By 1851 the younger Wreford was farming 76 acres and employing eight labourers. Samuel was recorded as 'master tanner and farmer'. A tanner's servant, four farm servants and a house servant shared the household with Grace Wreford and her three daughters. John Wreford, thought to be Samuel's younger brother, a master currier in the town, with an address in South Molton Street, was no doubt using leather manufactured at Ford. [9]

Samuel was still at work in 1856. [10] But he, like a number of 19th century tanners, died relatively young. His wife Grace was a widow by 1861: in this year she was running the tanyard with three men and a boy. The farmland appears to have been leased out. [11]

Ford Farm was offered to let in 1866, Grace's brother-in-law John handling the arrangements. The evidence suggests that tanning had ceased

The house at Ford, the residence of the Wreford family, tanners, in the 19th century

at Chulmleigh as, almost as an afterthought, the newspaper notice added: '.. *a good Tan-Yard can be Let with the farm, if required'.* [12] And in 1870 John Wreford was no longer a currier, but instead ran an ironmonger's shop in the town. [13]

By 1871 Grace Wreford had retired to Fore Street, John Wreford had retired and Ford was occupied by farmer John Bendle. [14]

A second tannery may have existed west of Bonds Farm. The farmer there found stone, mortar and rubble when digging a sheep dip. He had been told the farm, at SS 6842148, was once a tannery. [15]

Chulmleigh sources
1 Personal communication from owner Catherine Sherlock in 2004
2 John Tanner, tanner, employed a bondsman in 1731 – A H Shorter, from Devon and Cornwall Record Society transcriptions from parish sources; John Tanner, tanner, Chulmleigh, took on William Milford as apprentice tanner in 1847 – DRO 4678/PO10/34
3 DRO 4678A/PO17/10 of 1811
4 Exeter Flying Post 20 August 1812 p 4 col 5
5 Exeter Flying Post 12 November 1840 p 2 col 6
6 Mormon IGIs
7 DRO – Chulmleigh tithe map and apportionment, 1840
8 Chulmleigh census 1841 – HO107 260\7 f 4 p 1
9 Chulmleigh census 1851 – Ford Farm. HO 107 1891 f 292 p 2; South Molton Street. HO107 1891 f 301 p 20
10 Post Office Directory, Devon and Cornwall, 1856
11 Chulmleigh census 1861 – Ford Farm. RG9 1485 f 48 p 14; South Molton Street. RG9 1485 f 44 p 5
12 Exeter Flying Post 12 September 1866 p 1 col 1
13 Devon Directory 1870
14 Chulmleigh census, 1871
15 Note from Sue Watts, The Historic Environment Section, DCC, November 2006, citing report by Mr Simpson, 26 May 1993

Colyton

Puddlebridge/Purlebridge
Hamlyn's or Baker's Tannery
Tanneries below Chantry Bridge

J & F J Baker & Co's tannery at Colyton is the last in all Britain to use high quality oak bark processing. [1] An oak bark tannery can be seen at the National History Museum, St Fagans, Cardiff, but Colyton is the last real, live, working tannery in the country.

Puddlebridge or Purlebridge	
Location	SY 2135 9522
Operational	17th century

17th century records indicate a tannery at Puddlebridge on the River Coly. Purlebridge, a mile or so west of Colyton, is possibly the location. John Reede was tanning here in 1611; [2] Thomas Roade was a Colyton tanner in 1618 [3] and a second John Reed followed the same trade in the town in 1651. [4] Aaron Reed's will of 1691 includes a reference to a tan works at Puddlebridge. Yet another John Reed, his son, was to inherit the tanyard while the implements of trade were to go to his daughter Rebekah. [5]

A further 17th century Colyton tanner, Nicholas Hoare, was one of 105 men from the town implicated in the Monmouth Rebellion. Whether he worked for the Reeds or had a separate yard elsewhere is not known. [6]

Records for the 18th century are sparse. Aaron Wishlade was involved in the business in the period 1709 - 1716. [7]

Snook's Tannery or Chantry Tannery	
Location	SY 246 941
Operational	closed before 1898
Bark mill	water powered

The tanyard here was owned by John Snook in 1841, [8] and he was listed variously as a gentleman, solicitor or surgeon – in the latter case, possibly his son – of Colyton, in the period 1833-1851.

Snook's yard was to let in 1833:
'.. A convenient TAN-YARD, with a modern and commodious DWELLING-HOUSE and Offices, Garden, &c, situate in the town of COLYTON, in the county of Devon. The Yard not only possesses the usual requisites of drying lofts, store rooms, &c but has the advantages of a constant supply of spring and river water, by the latter of which the bark mill is worked, a surrounding neighbourhood affording bark, and a great facility for obtaining raw goods .. Apply if by letter, post-paid, to Mr. J. SNOOK, Colyton, Devon.' [9]

And in 1851 the yard was for sale, but with two orchards and a flour mill, lately a lace factory:

'To millers and Others. Freehold Property at Colyton .. Sell by Auction .. Lot 1. All those Premises originally built for Flour Mills, having a new iron water-wheel with a constant supply of water; and also the convenient Mill House.. adjoining together with the Cottage and Garden .. These Premises have recently been used as a Lace Factory, but can be reconverted into a Flour Mill .. immediate possession can be had. 2. – All that convenient Dwelling-House and Offices, with Garden in Front, and Tan-Yard, Drying Lofts, and large Kitchen Garden at the back, now in the occupation of J. S. Snook, Esq, Surgeon. 3. – A small orchard adjoining Lots 1 and 2, with a frontage to the road on the South of about 70 yards. 4. – A small Orchard .. contiguous to Lot 2, known as the Higher Orchard, and bounded by the river and mill stream .. For viewing the Premises, application may be made to Mr Snook, senr. .. Solicitors, Sidmouth.' [10]

No tanner is recorded here after 1851; the flour mill has survived into the 21st century, converted. Certainly Snook's yard had closed by 1898:
'.. Snook's tannery, and Beed's, each had its day. The Col spared half her flood to feed their pits; But competition hasten'd their decay, And trade, like fashion, hither flits, Today, 'tis with us, and to-morrow quits ..' [11]

Baker's Tannery	
Location	SY 2425 9418
Operational	at work in 2007
Bark mill	water powered
Staff	22 in 1851, 28 in 2004

'There is a tannery belonging to Mr Roper on a very extensive scale', reported Pigot in 1830. [12] This was probably the yard that survives today. The tannery's promotional leaflet states that it stands on the site of a Roman tanyard, but the evidence for this statement has not been forthcoming and one authority suggests the history of the yard goes back 400 years. [13]

Thomas Beed owned and occupied what is now known as Baker's tannery in 1841. At that date the premises included a second yard immediately below Chantry Bridge, together with a second house and garden. In all the estate covered nine acres. [14] The downstream yard was disused by 1889 and may have served as saw mills in 1881. [15]

By 1850 two brothers who originated in Ottery St Mary had settled in Colyton – Robert Buncombe Evans and William Nathaniel Evans. In 1851 they were living in Cuckoo Street with their two married sisters, Mary Meech and Sarah Hall, six nephews

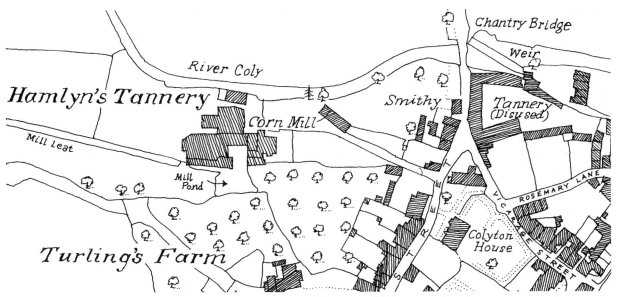

Hamlyn's Tannery, later Baker's Tannery, to the left of centre, with its associated water-powered corn mill, and a second tannery, downstream from Chantry Bridge, disused in 1889. Taken from the Ordnance Survey of Devonshire, 25" = 1 mile, sheet 83.3. Snook's tannery was the next site downstream

and nieces and three servants. The Evans brothers employed 22 men in their tannery at that date. [16] Tanning was, it seems, in their blood – their uncle Lavington Evans ran one of the Ashburton tanneries in the period 1823-1851. They appear to have leased Baker's tannery. William Evans married in 1853 [17] but in 1860 they were bankrupt. [18] The yard was offered to let in 1861:

'To be Let, by Private Contract, with Immediate Possession, all that desirable Tannery, situated in the town of Colyton, Devon, late in the occupation of Messrs Evans, tanners. It comprises a Dwelling-House and Offices, Garden and Lawn, together with a Tan Yard, Drying Shed, Mill House, with cast iron Drying Room over, and every other requisite, in

which the business of a tanner can be conveniently carried on .. It is well situated for obtaining a good supply of bark from the immediate neighbourhood, and is within one mile of the Colyton Railway Station of the London and South Western Railway ..' [19]

Between 1862 and 1866 W Baker moved in, although by 1873 John Baker was listed at Hamlyn's Tannery and also had premises at Chard in Somerset. He was here in 1883 as well. [20] By 1902 the firm was trading as J & FJ Baker & Co Ltd, the business that survives today. Bakers then undertook tanning and curriering and also ran a steam flour mill.

A water-powered flour mill building is still extant

Lime pits covered up and under cover at Baker's Tannery, Colyton

18' x 4' undershot waterwheel by Hawker of Chard. Photograph by Alan Stoyel

within the complex, although it has been gutted of machinery, excepting the waterwheel. Animal foodstuffs were still being milled as recently as the 1960s using electrically powered grinders. [21]

In 2004 the managing director was Andrew Parr and he ran the establishment with 28 employees. [22] The waterwheel used to work the paddles of the tan pits and grind the oak bark was cast by Joseph Hawker of Chard in 1856 and is an 18' by 4' undershot type. [23] Hides come from Exeter, and are mainly from oxen or heifers. Bark is taken from coppiced oaks from the Forest of Dean, Cumbria and Wales. Valonia, imported from the Mediterranean, is also used in the production of hard leathers for orthopaedic and surgical use. Leather for saddlery is softer and only uses the tannin from the oak bark. [24]

Colyton sources

1 J & F J Baker & Co publicity leaflet 2004. The only other oak bark tannery in the country in the 21st century was at Grampound Road, Cornwall, which closed in 2002
2 A H Shorter, D&C N&Q, from D&CRS transcriptions from Colyton parish registers
3 DRO 281M/T106 of 1618
4 DRO 281M/T62-64
5 Pamela Sharpe, Population and Society in an East Devon Parish. Reproducing Colyton 1540-1840. University of Exeter Press, 2002, 130-131
6 Colin Haynes, The Most Rebellious Town in Devon. Coly Publications, 2003, 18-19
7 DRO 281M/T348-349, T350, T351-3, T354, T355
8 DRO Colyton tithe map and apportionment, 1841 – items 894, 895 and 923
9 Sherborne Mercury 29 April 1833 p 4 col 4
10 Woolmer's Gazette 1 March 1851 p 1 col 2
11 G E Evans, Colytonia: A Chapter in the History of Devon. Being some account of the Old and George's Meeting, Colyton, from 1662 to 1898. Liverpool 1898, 121
12 Pigot's General Directory, Devonshire, 1830
13 J & F J Baker – The Tannery Shop leaflet, repeated by Tim Williams, Express & Echo, 3 October 1990; R M L Cook, Second Report of the Industrial Archaeology Section, TDA 103, 1971, 248-250
14 DRO Colyton tithe map and apportionment, 1841 – items 871, 872, 873, 874 and 892
15 Ordnance Survey map, Colyton, Devonshire sheet 83.3, 25" = 1 mile, of 1889; Colyton census 1881 – RG11 2129 f 28 p 9: John George Hann, saw mills, employing 28 staff
16 Colyton census 1851 – HO 107 1862 f 531 p 19
17 Exeter Flying Post 27 October 1853 p 8 col 6
18 Exeter Flying Post 25 July 1860 p 5 col 3
19 Exeter Flying Post 8 January 1862 p 1 col 1
20 Post Office Directory of Devonshire 1866, The Post Office Directory of Devonshire and Cornwall, Kelly, 1873, White's Directory, Devonshire, 1878, 1090, Kelly's Directory, Devonshire, 1883, 784
21 Kelly's Directory, Devonshire, 1902, 1136 [and 1906 and 1910 editions]; R M L Cook, op cit
22 Western Morning News magazine 28 February 2004
23 Derrick Warren. Joseph Hawker and the development of the crawler tractor. SIAS Bulletin 72, August 1996, p 16
24 Tim Williams, op cit; Western Morning News magazine 28 February 2004; R M L Cook, Second Report of the Industrial Archaeology Section, TDA 103, 1971, 248-250

Baker's Tannery, Colyton. Looking east

Baker's Tannery, Colyton. Looking west. The old corn mill was on the left, next to the bark mill

Suspender pits on the first floor at Baker's Tannery; frames carrying the hides are raised and lowered slightly by water power

Crediton

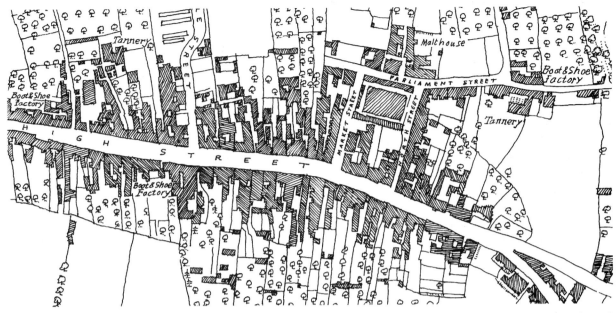

Crediton High Street from the Ordnance Survey, Devon, sheets 67.2 and 67.6. Off image to the left is St Lawrence's Green. The parish church is off to the right. On the left is the tannery in the High Street with a boot and shoe factory virtually adjoining. Another boot and shoe factory stands on the south of the street. The Parliament Street tannery also has a boot and shoe factory nearby

East Town
Parliament Street
High Street

Woollen cloth was Crediton's staple industry in earlier times. One family who had made a success of the trade was Northcote of nearby Newton St Cyres. [1] By the mid 18th century Crediton was failing to compete – the great fire of 1743 which destroyed some of the town may have contributed – and gradually the manufacturers of boots and shoes came to replace the weavers, spinners and fullers here. [2] Consequently there was a demand for leather: tanneries in the vicinity such as those at Sandford, Shobrooke and Bow now had increased opportunities at market and premises in the town were either expanded or established to cater for the demand.

One individual who bridged the changing trading patterns was Stephen Shute, who combined woolstapling and cloth manufacture with tanning. He must have been one of Crediton's leading citizens in the mid eighteenth century. In 1751 he held stock valued at £2000 in warehouses in London – at Cottons Wharf, Southwark; in Sherborne Lane and at Cateaton Street. In 1753 his London stock was insured for £1600 and in 1758 his stock and property in Crediton totalled £1,750. His brick and slated residence was at East Town. Fourteen other houses or tenements in the vicinity, together with several barns, linneys and warehouses were insured by Shute. It is reasonable to suppose that his tannery was the one established at East Town. [3]

George Elston was the first to develop wholesale boot and shoe manufacture, starting in 1830. He found markets for shoes beyond the immediate hinterland of Crediton and developed an export trade too. In the following decade Crediton's wholesale trade became firmly established. John Elston then furthered development, beginning in 1840. [4] He was able to revolutionise manufacture. Charles Singer, an American citizen, patented his lock-stitch sewing machine which made the process of stitching ten times faster. [5] This reached Crediton in 1858. Boot manufacture expanded further and the town was known as a centre of the shoe trade in the west country, some referring to it as a second Northampton. [6]

Samuel Squire Gimblett arrived in Crediton in 1859. *'The cause of his coming was singular. In the early part of 1853 he was shipwrecked while on his way to Australia with a large quantity of boots; these were lost, and a considerable time elapsed ere more English-made goods were received by him when he began business in Ballaratt, Melbourne. Here he resided until the latter part of 1856, when he returned to England with the intention to manufacture goods for export. He at first settled in Plymouth where he carried on the business of an exporter. Thinking a change desirable, he had nearly decided to start for Wellingborough, Northamptonshire, and it was simply through the delay of a post that he was led to select Crediton, which, for the town and neighbourhood, has been acknowledged as a fortunate occurrence .. The style of boots worn by the miners of Australia was vastly different from that of English wear and he laid himself out to suit the Australian tastes .. This consisted almost wholly of mens boots, most of which were heavily nailed or braded. The Colonial trade*

increased at a rapid rate, the firm took new and more commodious premises, got together a good staff of workmen, and became rooted to the town ..
From 1859, which was the date of Mr Gimblett's starting here, the sewing machine got rapidly into general use, so that but little difficulty arose in preparing the various 'uppers' for the new class of work .. Low rents and cheap labour very materially assisted the masters here .. The greatest share of the home trade was commanded by Mr John Elston .. Mr Gimblett was still confining his attention to the Australian trade, as boots .. were then allowed to enter the colony free of duty, which was not the case some years later ..' [7]

Others have recorded Gimblett as a Cornishman. In fact he was born in Exbourne, the son of an agricultural labourer. He was apprenticed to Edward Baker, a Gunnislake cordwainer in 1841 [8] and in 1846 married Mary Ann Mole. Four of his daughters were born at Calstock. [9] Gimblett was probably making boots in this mining town before he left for Australia in 1853, allegedly shipwrecked on the way. In 1851 his first wife had died and his three-year old daughter Hannah was living with maternal grandparents. Her younger sister Emma was lodged with a Gunnislake stonemason. Daughter Jane, a year old, was with paternal grandparents in Exbourne. [10] Samuel was away up country and in the same year he married his second wife, Dee Hambly, a Cornish lass, in the Bristol registration district. Their daughter Mary Ann was born the following year in Calstock. [11] What led Gimblett to Australia? A William Hambly, probably a Cornishman, was mining in Victoria, possibly at Ballarat, where gold was discovered in 1851. [12]

By 1857 there were 31 boot and shoemakers listed in Crediton. [13] Gimblett, a master shoe maker in 1861, then employed 11 men. Twenty years later, aged 59, and married for the third time, he was employing 83 men, 20 boys and 37 women. [14] His second wife Dee had died in 1873 and Samuel had married Josephine Staples in 1876. She died, aged 59, in 1882. [15]

In all three or four businesses were operating as small factories by the 1880s, and no doubt requiring a significant quantity of leather. [16] Gimblett's business was later run by his son Samuel R H Gimblett. In 1891 he lived at 110 High Street, near the Adams, tanners – Richard at 99-100 High Street, William at 104 High Street and Edward at 105 High Street. [17]

Samuel Gimblett senior married Annie, his fourth wife, at Christchurch, Hampshire, in 1893 and in 1901 had retired to Teignmouth. [18]

Raw materials were to hand. A great market was held each April in Crediton's High Street, where many of the local breed of Red Rubies were traded. [19] In the surrounding countryside many farms had pockets of woodland, some of it coppice, some of the coppices

no doubt of oak. [20] If there was a limitation, it was water. Mills on the River Yeo such as Bere Mills, Four Mills and Fordton Mills were already in the hands of millers and sailcloth makers. The tanneries had to rely on the Litterburn, a small stream that rose in a spring at the Green at the west end and ran down the valley to the church. It was eventually culverted when the town's sewer was laid. [21]

By the 19th century there were three tanneries in Crediton. Keagles and Pring had had a business at 22 High Street, but it had closed by 1815. [22] The Litterburn would probably have been inadequate for water power and the Crediton tanneries appear to have relied on horse- or oxen-powered bark mills.

East Town	
Location	SS 836 001
Tan pits	36 handlers, 2 watering pits, 7 latches, 4 limes and 2 grainers in 1821 77 pits in 1847
Operational to	1855

George Melhuish had expended capital on a tannery at East Town but by 1821 had been bankrupted in the process:
'To be Sold by Auction, by order of the Assignees of the Estate and Effects of George Melhuish of Crediton, Devon, bankrupt, the following Dwelling House, Tan-Yard and Lands. Lot 1. The Fee-Simple and Inheritance of all that Dwelling-House containing an Under-ground Cellar, and a Dining-parlour, Drawing-room, Counting-house, Hall, Kitchen, and every requisite office on the ground-floor; five good Lodging-rooms on the first floor; and four Garretts over; with two Walled Gardens, a Cellar and Stable; and a TAN-YARD containing 36 handlers, of which 24 are under cover, 2 watering pits, 7 latches, 4 limes, 2 grainers, 2 watering pits, 2 drying lofts (one 72 feet in length and the other 27 feet in length and 19 feet in breadth), 2 store rooms, a mill house (in which there is an excellent patent bark mill) .. waggon linhay .. barn capable of containing at least 80 tons of bark .. all adjoining in the East Town of Crediton and have been recently altered and fitted up at a very great expense .. The Tan-yard is well supplied with the most excellent water; and there is at all seasons of the year an abundant quantity of bark to be procured in the neighbourhood, and at a moderate price .. the yard has been lately planted, on an improved principle and it being the only yard within several miles of the market town of Crediton .. Lot 3. The Fee-simple and Inheritance of all that Brick Yard .. with a Brick-Kiln therein, and Buildings thereon, situate adjoining to the town of Crediton, lately in the possession of the said George Melhuish ..' [23]

This was not the only tanyard in the vicinity: Samuel Roberts had built or extended a second tannery, in Parliament Street, in 1790. [24] Melhuish had seemingly reached terms with his creditors, as he was offering his tanyard to let in 1824, although he was still the subject of bankruptcy proceedings in 1825. [25]

By 1839 Melhuish's tannery was leased by John Francis and was offered for sale. '.. *The Premises are Fee-Simple .. situate in the East Town of Crediton fronting the New Road lately made into the town and are now in the occupation of Mr John Francis, as tenant ..*' [26] In July 1840 '.. *A stable belonging to Mr Francis, tanner, in East-street, was discovered to be on fire .. the flames spread with alarming rapidity .. the Engines belonging to the West of England, West Middlesex and Sun Insurance offices were soon on the spot, and every exertion was made to subdue the flames, but .. eight houses in addition to the premises of Mr Francis, were entirely destroyed ..*' [27]

Thomas Melhuish was looking for a new tenant in 1846. Expansion had taken place since 1821. When offered to let – from Midsummer 1847 – there were: '.. *77 pits, partly under cover, with moveable Pumps, &c. The connection between Crediton, Bristol and London, by the Railroad, (the Terminus of the Exeter and Crediton Railway being near the Yard), and the valuable neighbourhood for collecting bark, give Crediton superior advantages for carrying on the Tanning Trade.*' [28] Because of conflicts of interest over broad and narrow gauge, the railway remained unopened until May 1851.

Francis was apparently still here in 1850. [29] In 1853 the tanner was Mrs Haycraft. Thomas Melhuish, Esq, of Poughill, retained the ownership. [30] Operations must have then ceased, for in 1858 the Hayward Schools were constructed on this site and Crediton was reduced to running two tanneries. [31]

Parliament Street

Location	SS 834 004
Operational	1790 - circa 1914
Staff	13 in 1871

Plan of the Parliament Street yard in 1889. OS 1:500 map, sheet 67,2.24. Note tan pits in a courtyard and the boot and shoe factory opposite

This tannery was reputedly established by Samuel Roberts in 1790. Philip Moggeridge bought the

concern and worked the yard until he died in 1837. John Francis, who had been leasing the East Town tanyard, was the next owner. [32] His firm was listed as Francis and Son, variously of Parliament Street, Belle Parade or Bell's Parade, and was here from the early 1850s to at least 1873: Francis employed 13 men in 1871. [33] From Francis and Son, the tannery came into the hands of William Snell. Snell was described by T W Venn, the Crediton historian, as: '*a gentleman whose not too amiable physiognomy and sporting grey bowler springs unbidden to the mind at the mere mention of his name.*' [34] John and William Snell were listed as tanners of Parliament Street in 1897 and 1910, but were not listed after the First World War. [35] Their goods appear to have been sent away by rail as the following report from 1887 implies:
'.. *Thomas Labdon, a carter in the employ of the London & South Western Railway .. was in the act of loading a quantity of leather at Messrs Snell's tannery, Parliament-street, when he slipped off the trolly, pitching heavily on his shoulder and dislocating his collarbone.*' [36]
The tanyard was later cleared and the site used for council offices; these in turn gave way to the library. [37] The existence of the yard is commemorated in the nearby residential block 'Tannery Flats'.

High Street

Location	SS 8297 0044
Operational to	1964
Staff	15 in 1881

The High Street tannery frontage in 1858, one of Crediton's earliest surviving photographs. The cart on the left has brought a consignment of oak bark

Edward Adams, the Crediton tanner. Portrait by William Widgery, 1856, courtesy of the Royal Albert Memorial Museum & Art Gallery, Exeter

According to T W Venn the High Street tannery was founded by Edward Adams in 1792. [38] That is unlikely: Edward Adams was baptised in Crediton, the son of Richard and Mary Adams, on 22 February 1790. [39] The yard may have been established by Edward's father, or it may have begun work at a later date. What is certain is that Edward Adams married Ann Coles at Crediton on 19 September 1819 [40] and probably set up shop in the High Street sometime thereafter, initially as a currier but later as a tanner and currier. Edward and his family were here in 1841, listed as next to Porch Court. [41] In 1851 he was aged 61, and it was apparent that his two sons Edward, 28, and Richard, 24, had followed him into the trade. [42]

By 1881 Edward senior was a widower and Edward junior and Richard ran the tanyard in partnership, employing 15 men. Richard lived at 100 High Street; Edward at 105. They in turn had sons who followed them into the business: William, Sydney and Walter, sons of Edward, were all currier's assistants at that date, as was Edward, Richard's son. [43]

This was a tanning family – Edward's elder brother John, baptised at Crediton in 1786, moved to Great Torrington. In 1851 he held premises in South Street, where he employed four men in tanning and currier's work. [44] In the same year John's son Richard was a tanner and currier of New Street, Torrington and his grandson George Doe Adams was another Torrington tanner by 1881. [45] It is thought Edward's younger brother Samuel may also have taken up the trade, in Barnstaple.

A portrait of Edward Adams survives in the collection at Exeter's Royal Albert Memorial Museum & Art Gallery. [46] T W Venn, commenting on the oil painting by Widgery, found Adams: '.. of ponderous proportions, yet carried that full weight in the councils of the town ..' [47]

His sons had dealings with Samuel Squire Gimblett who settled in Crediton in 1859. [48] He first established a boot and shoe factory in the recently built Victoria Buildings in East Town. Later he re-established next door to the Adams' tannery: tram lines physically linked the two businesses, with leather being delivered from Adams' premises to Gimblett. Gimblett died in 1906, aged 86, and his works, then run by his son, closed not long after. [49] Photographs survive of Gimblett's workers and of Adams' High Street frontage, with bark being delivered. The latter image is one of the earliest surviving Crediton photographs, dating from about 1858. [50]

William Herbert Adams, like Gimblett a Congregationalist, succeeded his father, Edward junior and Richard Adams, and Venn observed that:

'In the time of William Herbert Adams (3rd generation) trade was good, and we ourselves can remember the long train of 'ladder carts', sometimes stretching from the Green to Porch Court [by the tannery] waiting to off load their bark into his lofty sheds'. [51] William Herbert Adams was tanner at 106

High Street by 1910. [52]

The bark harvest in mid May was vital to Crediton, and as at Bow, the local memory is of the queues of horses and carts laden with oak bark. The old ways lasted at the High Street tannery well into the 20th century and indeed in August 2003 Stanley Britton of Withleigh mentioned that he used to take bark into Crediton in the 1940s where he'd *'get quite a bit of money for it .. the better the weather the better the result'.* [53]

Bruce Adams was the last of the Crediton tanners and the fourth generation of the family. He'd kept the business running by supplying speciality leathers, [54] possibly using chrome processing, but the works closed in 1964. Practically all the boot and shoe makers in the town had long since closed and with them went the tanners' business.

Crediton sources
1   Monument to Sir John Northcote in Newton St Cyres church; Crediton. The Official Publication of the District Council, 1910: '.. the staple industry of Crediton was the spinning of woollen goods and serge ..' p 13
2   Charles Luxton, Kyrton aforetime. Privately published 1949; Crediton, The Official Publication of the District Council, 1910: '.. the chief industry today is shoe making There are two boot factories .. besides two tanneries..'
3   Stanley D Chapman, The Devon Cloth Industry in the Eighteenth Century. Sun Fire Office Inventories. Devon & Cornwall Record Society, 1978, 39-40
4   The Trade of Crediton, V. The Western Times 14 November 1882 p 7 col 3
5   Trevor I Williams, A History of Invention from Stone Axes to Silicon Chips. Time Warner, 2003, 123
6   The Trade of Crediton, V
7   The Trade of Crediton VI. The Western Times 28 November 1882 p 3 col 4
8   Calstock census 1841 – HO107 133\2 f 10 p 12
9   Mormon IGIs; Crediton census 1861. RG9 1472 f 78 p 36; Exbourne census 1851 – HO107 1885 f 747 p 5
10   Calstock census 1851 – HO107 1901; Exbourne census 1851 – HO107 1885 f 747 p 5
11   Mormon IGIs
12   Jim Faull. The Cornish in Australia, Melbourne 1983
13   Billing's Directory 1857
14   Crediton census 1861 – RG9 1472 f 78 p 36; Crediton census 1881 – RG11 2229 f 29 p 6
15   Mormon IGIs
16   Ordnance Survey map, Crediton, 25" = 1 mile, 1889
17   Crediton census 1891 – RG12 1760 f 24 p 2-4
18   Mormon IGIs; West Teignmouth census, 1901
19   Photograph of market in: C Albert Labett. Albert Labbett's Crediton Collection. Obelisk Publications 1987
20   DRO. Crediton tithe apportionment 1842: this covered Crediton Hamlets as well as Crediton town
21   C Albert Labbett, op cit, 1987
22   T W Venn, History of Crediton, vol II, privately published [typescript] 1966, 108
23   Exeter Flying Post 19 April 1821 p1 col 3
24   T W Venn, op cit, vol II, 1966, 244
25   Exeter Flying Post 22 July 1824 p 1 col 3; Exeter Flying Post 21 April 1825 p 1 col 2
26   Exeter Flying Post 31 January 1839 p 2 col 3
27   Woolmer's Gazette 11 July 1840 p 3 col 2
28   Exeter Flying Post 3 December 1846 p 2 col 5
29   White's Directory of Devon, 1850, 276
30   Exeter Flying Post 3 February 1853 p 1 col 1
31   Charles Luxton, op cit, 1949

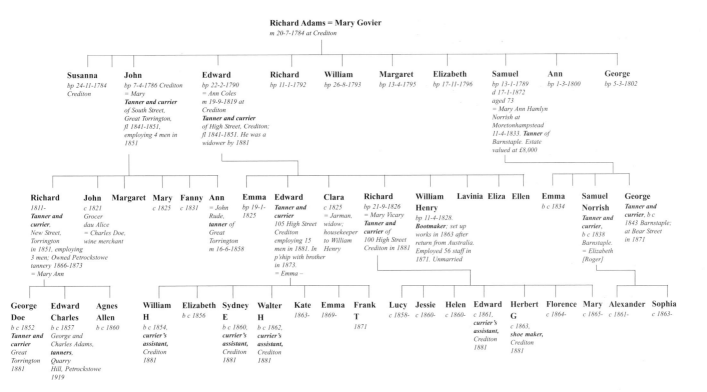

Richard Adams = Mary Govier
m 20-7-1784 at Crediton

Susanna	John	Edward	Richard	William	Margaret	Elizabeth	Samuel	Ann	George
bp 24-11-1784 Crediton	*bp 7-4-1786 Crediton* = Mary **Tanner and currier** *of South Street, Great Torrington, fl 1841-1851, employing 4 men in 1851*	*bp 22-2-1790* = Ann Coles *m 19-9-1819 at Crediton* **Tanner and currier** *of High Street, Crediton; fl 1841-1851. He was a widower by 1881*	*bp 11-1-1792*	*bp 26-8-1793*	*bp 13-4-1795*	*bp 17-11-1796*	*bp 13-1-1789 d 17-1-1872 aged 73* = Mary Ann Hamlyn Norrish *at Moretonhampstead 11-4-1833.* **Tanner** *of Barnstaple. Estate valued at £8,000*	*bp 1-3-1800*	*bp 5-3-1802*

Richard	John	Margaret	Mary	Fanny	Ann	Emma	Edward	Clara	Richard	William Henry	Lavinia	Eliza	Ellen	Emma	Samuel Norrish	George
1811- **Tanner and currier**, *New Street, Torrington in 1851, employing 3 men; Owned Petrockstowe tannery 1866-1873* = Mary Ann	*c 1821 Grocer dau Alice* = Charles Doe, *wine merchant*		*c 1825*	*c 1831*	= John Rude, **tanner of Great Torrington** *m 16-6-1858*	*bp 19-1-1825*	**Tanner and currier** *105 High Street Crediton employing 15 men in 1881. In p'ship with brother in 1873.* = Emma –	*c 1825* = Jarman, *widow; housekeeper to William Henry*	*bp 21-9-1826* = Mary Vicary **Tanner and currier** *of 100 High Street Crediton in 1881*	*bp 11-4-1828.* **Bootmaker**; *set up works in 1863 after return from Australia. Employed 56 staff in 1871. Unmarried*				*b c 1834*	**Tanner and currier**, *b c 1838 Barnstaple.* = Elizabeth *[Roger]*	**Tanner and currier**, *b c 1843 Barnstaple; at Bear Street in 1871*

George Doe	Edward Charles	Agnes Allen	William H	Elizabeth	Sydney E	Walter H	Kate	Emma	Frank T	Lucy	Jessie	Helen	Edward	Herbert G	Florence	Mary	Alexander	Sophia
b c 1852 **Tanner and currier** *Great Torrington 1881*	*b c 1857* **George and Charles Adams, tanners,** *Quarry Hill, Petrockstowe 1919*	*b c 1860*	*b c 1854, currier's assistant, Crediton 1881*	*b c 1856*	*b c 1860, currier's assistant, Crediton 1881*	*b c 1862, currier's assistant, Crediton 1881*	*1863-*	*1869-*	*1871*	*c 1858-*	*c 1860-*	*c 1860-*	*c 1861, currier's assistant, Crediton 1881*	*c 1863, shoe maker, Crediton 1881*	*c 1864-*	*c 1865-*	*c 1861-*	*c 1863-*

The Adams family, tanners and curriers of Crediton, Barnstaple, Great Torrington and Petrockstowe

100 High Street in 2005, now a bookshop. Home of Richard Adams in 1881 and later of Bruce Adams

Samuel Gimblett and his workers at the rear of 111 High Street. His premises were connected to Adams' tannery by a tramway

32 T W Venn, op cit, vol II, 1966, 244
33 Post Office Directory, Devon and Cornwall, 1856; Billings Directory 1857; Post Office Directory of Devonshire 1866, 1277; The Post Office Directory of Devonshire and Cornwall, Kelly, 1873; T W Venn, op cit, 1966, 65-66; Crediton census 1871 – RG10 2161 f 36 p 23
34 T W Venn, op cit, vol II, 244
35 Kelly's Directory of Devonshire and Cornwall, 1897, 1111; Kelly's Directory of Devonshire and Cornwall, 1910, 1143; Kelly's Directory of Devonshire and Cornwall, 1919, 1116
36 The Western Times 22 February 1887 p 7 col 6
37 Express and Echo 21 August 1976
38 T W Venn, op cit, vol II, 1966, 244-245; C Albert Labett. Albert Labbett's Crediton Collection. Obelisk Publications 1987
39 Mormon IGI
40 Mormon IGI
41 Crediton census for 1841 – HO107 215/5 f 5 p 4
42 Crediton census for 1851 – HO107 1887 f 76 p 4
43 Crediton census for 1881 – RG11 2229 f 27 p 2
44 Great Torrington census, 1851 – HO107 1894 f 545 p 76
45 Great Torrington census for 1851 – HO107 1894 f 512 p 11; census for 1881 – RG11 2257 f 38 p 9
46 Information from John Modin, curator, January 2004
47 T W Venn, op cit, vol II, 1966, 244-245
48 The Trade Of Crediton VI: The Western Times 28 November 1882 p 3 col 4
49 T W Venn, op cit, vol II, 1966, 244-245
50 C Albert Labbett, op cit, 1987
51 T W Venn, op cit, vol II, 1966, 244-245
52 Kelly's Directory of Devonshire and Cornwall, 1910
53 Conversation with Stan Britton of Quirkhill, August 2003
54 T W Venn, op cit, vol II, 1966, 244-245

Cullompton

Crow Green
Lower King's Mill
Court tannery

Crow Green	
Location	ST 0195 0698
Bark mill	water powered in 1816
Tan pits	47 in 1816
Operational to	1969
Staff	48 in 1881, over 100 in 1958

James Whitby, a Cullompton tanner, and his colleague Davis, a dissenting teacher, together with the ironfounder George Bodley of Exeter, patented an improved bark mill in 1801. [1] Tanning had been a Cullompton industry at least since the sixteenth century – it was a good location for animal hides and oak bark, was on the Bristol to Exeter highway and had more recently been linked to Honiton by a turnpike road.[2]

Towards the end of the Napoleonic wars Whitby ran the tanyard at Crow Green, located less than ideally for the townspeople, but by a stream, at the south west end of the town:
*'CULLOMPTON .. TO TANNERS. TO be SOLD by Auction, at the White Hart Inn, in Cullompton .. Lot 1.—The fee-simple and inheritance of a convenient TAN-YARD, containing 42 pits, exclusive of 5 lime-pits, with necessary buildings, and a capital patent bark-mill, worked by water: together with a Dwelling-house, and outbuildings adjoining; situate in Crow-green, in Cullompton, late in the occupation of Mr. James Whitby. — Also a rich Meedow [sic], called WASHBROOKE, or CROW GREEN MEADOW, adjoining to the Tan-Yard ..
Lot 2.— .. a dwelling-House and Garden, called the GATEHOUSE .. in the occupation of Mrs Whitby ..'* [3]

Daniel Sellwood may have been the next tanner here: certainly he was established in Cullompton in 1821 when he married Mary, eldest daughter of John Binford Esq, of Burnrew Lodge, Willand. [4] John Sellwood, possibly Daniel's father had tanned in Cullompton in 1801. [5]

A fire at the tannery in 1831 was devastating:
'.. The rapidity of the flames baffles description, and the town engines being drawn out were found in such need of repair, as to be for all effective purposes useless. Thus had the devouring element almost full scope, human exertions, though perilously rendered, being of little avail, and 21 houses and tenements were destroyed. The loss has consequently been very great, particularly among the poorer classes, by whom this part of the town was occupied, and who have lost their all ..' [6]

This disastrous fire has been forgotten as an even more savage inferno destroyed over a hundred Cullompton houses in 1839.

Wheat was the cause of further trouble for the Sellwoods in 1847. Daniel was a maltster as well as

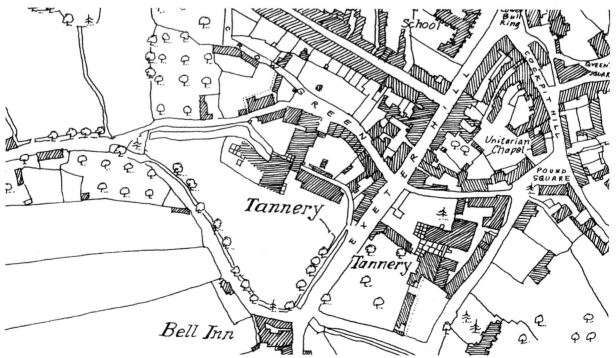

Crow Green tannery stood astride the main road through Cullompton, later to become the A38 but since downgraded. The leat can be seen by the tannery buildings to the left of Exeter Hill. The tail race ran alongside the road, and the channel can be seen today, before rejoining the stream by the Bell Inn. The tannery buildings on the right of Exeter Hill have been redeveloped as a Somerfield supermarket

The Crow Geen tannery site. The Somerfield supermarket and car park occupy the main site. Across the road the antiques store stood by the mill leat and was water powered. There were lime pits here too

Daniel Sellwood's house at 5 Pound Square, vacant in 2004. This was the house attacked by the mob in 1847

a tanner and certainly would have traded in barley, if not wheat. The high price of wheat resulted in mobs rioting and looting in Exmouth, Torquay, Taunton and Cullompton. In Cullompton, a mob of women and children having attacked two houses:
'.. proceeded thence to the house of Mr Sellwood, tanner, in the Pound Square. The charge brought against Mr Selwood was that some time since he bought 2000 bushels of corn for the purposes of speculation. The attack on the house was conducted with the greatest violence scarcely a pane of glass was left whole – more than 200 being destroyed, while serious injury was done to the furniture of the apartments exposed to the fury of the mob. The stones were thrown chiefly by children, and women it is said were the principal ringleaders ..' [7]

Sellwood and his family, were still at Pound Square in 1851. The household included four adult daughters, all unmarried, a younger son and three servants. Daniel Sellwood was now 57. [8]

In 1862 the firm had become Sellwood and Sons and Bodley's foundry in Exeter undertook repairs to the waterwheel powering the bark mill and to the tannery pumps and liquor valves. A new 30" plate bark mill was supplied in 1865.[9]

Two years later another fire broke out at the tannery: 'Early on Saturday morning the premises occupied by Messrs Sellwood, tanners, were discovered on fire, which was raging from the base to the roof of the warehouse, in which was stored eight hundred pounds worth of valonia, a quantity of bark, and a valuable stock of leather. The bark mill and boiler house were adjacent to the warehouse, and immediately beyond the former are two newly erected warehouses, used for storing and preparing leather. These warehouses contained several thousand pounds worth of leather in various stages of manufacture, and, being entirely of wood and glass, would soon have fallen prey to the devouring element but for the strenuous efforts of the firemen. There were four fire engines present – the West of England, under the direction of Mr Frost; the Royal Farmers, under the control of Mr James Bidgood; and the two Volunteer Engines, superintended by Mr J Forster and Mr John Blackmore. Happily the fire was confined to the building wherein it broke out; but how the fire originated is a mystery, though it is thought to have happened accidentally. The loss is estimated to reach over £2,000, and the property destroyed is insured in the West of England Fire Office. One or two firemen had very narrow escapes through the falling of a wall; and several of the townspeople who went to assist at the fire had a ducking in the tan pits. These pits were frozen over; but the heat from the fire soon melted the ice, and not thinking of this, in they went. They were safely got out. Mr Mortimer, tanner, has kindly offered the use of his machinery to the Messrs Sellwood; and it is believed that the hands in their employ will not be deprived of their customary labour.' [10]
Richard Mortimore ran the tannery at Lower Kings Mill, to the north east of the town.

Daniel Sellwood died in April 1859 and his wife Mary then directed the business with her eldest son, Binford Sellwood. [11] In 1871 Mary ran the household at Pound Square; her unmarried sons Binford, 36, and Frank, 28, managed the tannery but were also farmers. [12] In October 1867 they formed the partnership 'Sellwood Brothers' [13] and they employed 45 men and three boys in 1881: quite a large concern, providing employment in the town. [14]

Their mother died in January 1876. Binford Sellwood died on 6 February 1888. Like his brother, the Rev. Charles Sellwood, he was committed to the Anglican church and was a firm supporter of the Temperance movement. The church was a major benefactor of his estate. Binford's trustees were advised that in 1888 the tanning trade in the west country was in a poor way for *'want of purchasers'*. [15]

Early in the 20th century Sellwood Brothers became a limited company. [16] Fire, having caused two 19th century conflagrations here, was again a most destructive agent in 1958:
'Cullompton's worst fire for 100 years burnt out a tan-yard in a matter of minutes last night – and put more than 100 men out of work .. the yard, Sellwood's Ltd, was one of Cullompton's biggest employers and was one of the highest rated buildings in the town. It employed 8 per cent of the town's labour. Mr H R Tremlett, managing director of Tremlett's of Exeter and Sellwood's Ltd .. watched the building melting and collapsing – and remembered 1949 when his Exeter factory was burnt out.' [17]

From 1964, Tremlett's, who had taken over Sellwood's tannery sometime previously, concentrated their operations at Cullompton but the end came in 1969 when the leather side of the business was sold to a company in Beverley in Yorkshire, the largest tanners in Europe. [18]

One of the buildings survives as an antiques warehouse near a Texaco garage. Other parts of a site that had developed into a factory now lie under a Somerfield supermarket and car park.

In the 20th century the tannery reportedly made sole leather for shoes and some of its output was exported to Russia. [19]

The building once housing the water-powered bark mill. Now an antiques showroom

The scene the day after the 1958 fire. Photograph courtesy Syd Staddon

Sellwood's Tannery on fire in 1958. The chimney indicates steam power was being used in the main tannery in the 20th century. Photograph courtesy Syd Staddon

Lower King's Mill

Location	ST 0290 0797
Operational to	1875

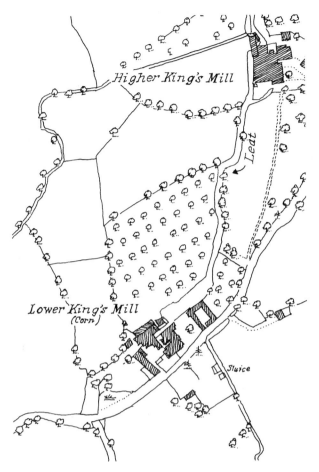

Lower King's Mill was a fulling mill in the 17th century, then a corn mill, a tannery from circa 1830 to 1875, and it then reverted to milling grain. Taken from the 25" = 1 mile Ordnance Survey maps of 1889, sheets 46.14 and 57.2

Higher and Lower King's Mill are served by a leat from the river Culm and stand to the north east of the town, past the railway and M5 Motorway. In the 17th century they were both tuck or fulling mills, serving the local woollen industry. [20] By 1771 the Higher Mills were producing paper, as they still do today, although entirely re-developed. The Lower Mill was operating as a corn mill in 1790. [21]

By 1830 Richard Mortimore lived at Lower Mills. He was a tanner and farmer and the premises were extended for use as a tannery until 1875. [22] No less than 18 labourers were employed in 1851: twelve at the tannery and six on the 130-acre farm.[23] A decade later the tannery was run with nine staff and the farm, now 160 acres, employed ten. The mill was grinding wheat with a further man and a boy and five servants took care of Kingsmill House. [24] R Mortimore & Son ordered a new *'zinc rolling bed'* from Bodley Brothers of Exeter in January 1865, and while the firm was recorded as millers in the iron-founders' journal, this item is one associated with tanning. [25]

When Sellwood's tannery at Crow Green suffered a major fire in 1867, Richard Mortimore offered his competitor the use of his machinery. [26] He died in July the following year, leaving an estate valued at £6000. [27] Richard, his son, took on the tannery and the mill, but it seems not the farm. His wife Mary, who came from Steyning in Sussex, bore him at least six children. [28] But he outlived his father by only six and a half years, dying in February 1875. Richard's estate was also £6000 [29] and his widow retired to Cullompton town. [30] Tanning ceased and the mill continued to grind wheat. [31]

Below: Lower King's Mill in 2004. The house is believed to date back to the 16th century in part

Court Tannery

Location	ST 0226 0782
Operational to	circa 1903

Charles B, or Biddlecombe Ewens as he was sometimes known, was the eldest son, as far as can be established at present, of John B Ewens, a bleacher, dyer and girth web manufacturer of Bridport. [32] Charles moved to Cullompton in about 1845 or 1846 and ran one of the town's inns. He is listed as a victualler in the 1851 census. Joannah, his wife, was a widow and 13 years his senior. [33] Charles then turned to fellmongering, Joannah remained a landlady, and his son Thomas, aged 14, assisted in this new venture. [34]

Either through his wife's family, or through his own Bridport connections, Charles seems to have come into money. By 1871 the family was living in Court House and the tannery at Court was established, Charles employing no less than 21 men, including his son Thomas. [35] The tannery stood at what was then the north end of the town, behind Court House. It was very probably steam powered and quite a large

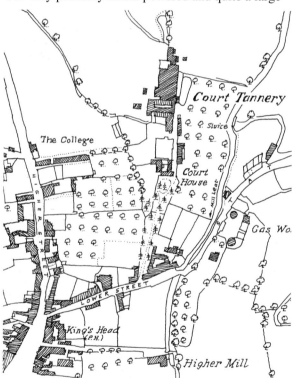

Court Tannery, Cullompton, in 1889. From the 25" = 1 mile Ordnance Survey map of 1889, sheet 57.2. Higher Mill should not be confused with Higher King's Mill. They were separate sites

establishment judging by the Ordnance Survey map of 1889. What water there was came from a small stream running past the north side of St Andrew's Hill. [36] The firm was operating as C B Ewens & Son in 1883 and survived into the twentieth century, but had closed, it seems, by 1906. [37] Charles was still an employer in 1901, aged 78, and living now with his

second wife, Maria, 44. [38] Court House, the tanner's residence, survives as an old peoples home.

Cullompton sources
Crow Green
1   Patent 2537 of 1801
2   Letter & Papers of Reign of Henry VIII, IV ii, 5510(16), cited in Medieval Archaeology, 1957, vol 1, 114 fn 57 [A Cullompton tanner pardoned following burglary: stealing kerseys from John Lane's house]
3   Exeter Flying Post 4 July 1816 p 2 col 3
4   Exeter Flying Post 28 June 1821 p 4 col 2
5   DRO 2404A/PO 147/6 – date: 1801
6   Exeter Flying Post 30 June 1831 p 2 col 5
7   Exeter Flying Post 20 May 1847 p 3 col 4
8   Cullompton Census. PRO – HO 107 1888 f 309 p 16
9   DRO Bodley journals 67/5/2/1 folios 133-138, 1109-1112
10 Exeter Flying Post 9 January 1867 p 7 col 5
11 DRO Daniel Sellwood's will 15 March 1858
12 Cullompton census, 1871. PRO – RG10 2167 f 48 p 22
13 DRO 74B/ME 94; The Post Office Directory of Devonshire and Cornwall, Kelly, 1873
14 Cullompton census, 1881. PRO – RG11 2233 f 53 p 21
15 DRO 74B/ME 94, The Western Times 10 February 1888, p 7 col 6
16 Kelly's Directory of Devonshire and Cornwall, 1919, 1116 Kelly's Directory of Devonshire and Cornwall, 1926, 1265
17 Western Morning News 18 October 1958
18 Western Morning News 28 October 1969
19 Personal communications from Muriel Coxhead and Peter Force, of Cullompton, November 2004-January 2005

Lower Kings Mill
20 Two tuck mills, Kingsmill, Cullompton, 1609-1664 – DRO 19 B/W/L/6/34-5
21 Kingsmill paper mills, Cullompton, 1771, 1777 DRO 1926B/W/L/6/36, 95; Sherborne Mercury 8 November 1790 p 1
22 Pigots General Directory, Devonshire, 1830, Pigots General Directory, Devonshire, 1844, Post Office Directory, Devon and Cornwall, 1856; Exeter Flying Post 6 October 1875 p 1 col 1
23 Cullompton census 1851 – HO 107 1888 f 225 p 15
24 Cullompton census 1861 – RG9 1477 f 86 p 9
25 DRO Bodley, ironfounders. Journals. 67/5/2/1 item 424
26 Post Office Directory of Devonshire 1866, 1277-1278; Exeter Flying Post 9 January 1867 p 7 col 5
27 Will. Richard Mortimore, late of Kingsmill, Cullompton. Tanner. Died 4 July 1868
28 Cullompton census 1871 – RG10 2167 f 76 p 9
29 Will of Richard Mortimore, late of Kingsmill, Cullompton. Tanner. Died 27 February 1875. Estate £6000.
30 Cullompton census 1881 – RG11 2233 f 57 p 30
31 Ordnance Survey map, Devonshire, 25" = 1 mile, sheet 46.14 of 1889

Court Tannery
32 Bridport census 1851 – HO 107 1861 f 180 p 2 West Street. John B Ewens, H M, 55, bleacher, dyer ..
33 Cullompton census 1851 – HO 107 1888 f 279 p 10
34 Cullompton census 1861 – RG9 1477 f 29 p 16
35 Cullompton census 1871 – RG10 2167 f 12 p 20; Post Office Directory of Devonshire 1866, 1277-1278 – Court tannery not listed; The Post Office Directory of Devonshire and Cornwall, Kelly, 1873 – listed
36 Ordnance Survey map, Devonshire, 25" = 1 mile, sheet 57.2 of 1889
37 Kelly's Directory, Devonshire, 1883, 784; 1902, 1136; not listed in 1906 edition.
38 Personal communication from Muriel Coxhead, January 2005.

Dalwood

Newton's	
Location	ST 2447 0015
Hutchins Barton	
Location	ST 248 005

Dalwood was an outlying parish of Dorset until 1842 when it was absorbed into Devon. There were tanners here in the 17th century – Richard Lugg and Barnard Tookes were recorded in 1648. [1]

The Hodges family appeared to be actively involved in tanning throughout the 18th century – Thomas Hodges was also concerned with land in Branscombe parish in 1705 and was again noted in 1711. [2] Thomas and Samuel Hodges were active in 1769 and Samuel was involved in property in Stockland, then another parish belonging to Dorset, in 1770. [3] Samuel Hodges was still producing leather in 1785. [4]

Hutchins Barton had ceased to be a tanyard by 1840 whereas Newton's Tan Yard, 11 acres in all, included lands identified at Tanyard Plot and Tanyard Orchard. These lay by the village reading room and primary school at Carter's Cross, south west of the village. In 1840 this property belonged to and was occupied by John Gould. [5] William Gould was the Dalwood tanner in 1850, [6] presumably using these premises, but aged 35 in 1851, he was farming 100 acres at Brimblecombe and tanning wasn't his primary source of income. Indeed tanning may well have ceased by this date. [7]

Dalwood from the tithe map of 1840. Hutchings Barton stands east of the church, across the Corry Brook. The second tannery – Newton's – at Carter's Cross was to the west of the Rising Sun, itself now a housing estate. Brimblecombe lies to the north of this tanyard at the cross roads. To the south, Dalwood Mill was powered by a leat taken from the Corry

Hutchins Barton in 2004. Now two or more private houses: the outbuildings have been converted

There is nothing to identify as a tanyard at Newton's today. A dry pond of about an acre with its dam, near Carter's Cross, was identified in the 1980s. [8] Hutchins Barton stands just beyond the Corry Brook and so had access to a good water supply. The barton has been rebuilt at some stage, as have its outbuildings.

Dalwood sources
1. G M Chapman, Dalwood, A Short History of an East Devon Village, 1983, 42
2. DRO 123M/L1305 of 1705, L1307 of 1710-11
3. DRO 1926 B/D/FS/2/1 of 1769, 1926 B/D/T/4/1 of 1770
4. DRO 281M/T1081 of 1774 and 281M/T1082 of 1785
5. DRO Dalwood tithe map and apportionment, 1840
6. White's Directory, 1850
7. Dalwood census 1851 – HO107 1862 f 494
8. Information from Derrick Warren, May 2005

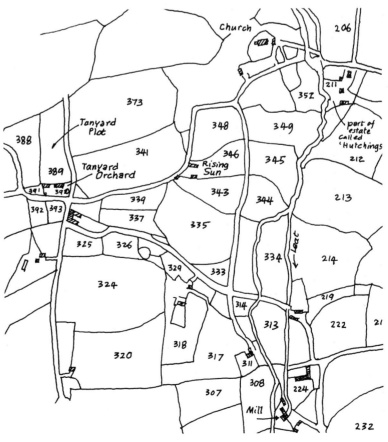

Dartmouth

Old Mill
Location	SX 8618 5192
Operational	until c 1850

Henry Sutcliffe was recorded as tanner at Old Mill in 1830. [1] The property was part of a 416 acre estate, which included Lower Norton Farm, owned by Sir John Seale and occupied by Richard Coombe and his subtenants in 1840. [2] The yard may have ceased work by that date; tanning had certainly ceased by 1851. If there was a bark mill here it would have been water powered.

Dartmouth sources
1　Pigot & Co's Directory, 1830, reprinted 1993, 63
2　DRO – Dartmouth tithe map and apportionment, 1840-1841, item 152, House, Garden and Tan pits
3　Dartmouth census 1851. No tanner recorded here

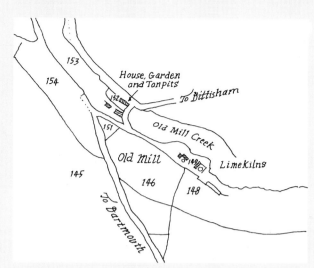

The tan yard at Old Mill in 1841. The nearby lime kilns would have been useful to a tanner here. Adapted from the Dartmouth tithe map.

Devonport

King Street and Chapel Street
Location	SX 454 546 – Chapel Street
Operational	to 1897 or later

John Blight was the Devonport tanner in 1841, aged about 40. [1] Jane Blight, his widow, aged 48, ran the tannery business based at 10a King Street, with 10 men in 1851; her eldest son Charles, aged 19, no doubt assisted. [2] From at least 1871 until at least 1883 the premises were at 8 King Street and the company was known as Blight & Son. Charles was the tanner, unmarried and now aged 38. [3] By 1881 Charles Henry Blight, still single, was employing 21 men. His mother had died and his unmarried sister, Mary Jane, 54, was his business partner. [4] As J Blight & Son in 1897 the firm was based at 1 Chapel Street. [5]

A tannery at Millbrook, in Cornwall, across the Plymouth Sound, was run by the same family in the 1850s, when it belonged variously to Blight and Edwards, J T Blight, and Blight and Sons. John Thomas Blight was the son of John and Jane Blight of Devonport and ran the Cornish tannery with three men in 1851 and two men in 1861. He married twice; his first wife may have died in childbirth. [6] Blight died in September 1888, leaving an estate valued at £3,507; His brother Charles, of Devonport, and his second wife, Jane Doidge Blight proved the will, together with his son John, a Callington solicitor. [7]

The firm Blight and Sons was still here in 1893 and Dodbrook House, Millbrook, was thought to be the family residence. The tannery buildings were still extant in 1973, used as a council store.

Devonport sources
1　Devonport/Stoke Damerel census 1841 – HO107 273/2 f 4 p 1
2　Devonport census 1851 – HO107 1882 f 88 p 51
3　Devonport census 1871 – RG10 2133 f 63 p 51; The Post Office Directory of Devonshire and Cornwall, Kelly, 1873; Kelly's Directory of Devonshire and Cornwall, Kelly, 1883, 784
4　Devonport census 1881 – RG11 2209 f 46 p 7
5　Kelly's Directory, Devonshire, 1897, 1111
6　Millbrook census, Maker parish, 1851 – HO107 1900 f 44 p 16 and for 1861 – RG9 1522 f 49 p 3
7　John Thomas Blight of Millbrook's will; he died 30 September 1888

East Budleigh

Tannery
Location	not known
Operational	to 1830 or later
Tan pits	52 at closure

A tannery was in operation here in 1711. In 1810, tanner Mr Carpenter of East Budleigh married. [1] Tanning had ceased by April 1840:

'East Budleigh. To Tanners and Others. To be Sold by Auction .. (in consequence of the Tan Yard, late the property of Mr H L Carpenter, being about to be broken up) .. consisting of 52 tan pits, drying and other sheds, with their covering of several thousands of tiles, a large quantity of thatch, glue press, tanning implements, &c. The above is a favourable opportunity, and worthy the attention of tanners and others enlarging their premises ..' [2]

East Budleigh sources
1　D&CRS transcription from parish records, Exeter Flying Post 26 July 1810 p 4 col 1
2　Woolmer's Gazette 13 June 1840 p 1 col 3 and p 3 col 7

Exeter

Heavitree
St Thomas
Lion's Holt
Westgate/Commercial Road

Exeter was a regional centre for the leather trade in the late-medieval centuries. Much of the meat eaten by its citizens was beef. Trade in hides developed from this consumption. Tanners from Tiverton, Okehampton, South Zeal and even Tavistock came to Exeter to buy hides, often returning to sell their leather in the city. Taunton and Milverton in Somerset were also involved in the Exeter trade. Hides were also exported across the Channel; 103 were shipped by merchant Richard Bozoun in 1376. Rouen was one destination at this time. [1]

In 2004 a Grade I listed chapel at 38 South Street underwent conversion to a Witherspoon pub and extensions were made on the south and east. Staff from Exeter Archaeology investigated the excavations and found structures dating from the medieval period including 20 pits. A large stone-lined pit featured joint slots for a boarded floor, indicating industrial use, and a possible interpretation is that it was used as a tanning pit. [2] The site was just within the city wall at Southgate.

By the 19th century there were four large tanneries operating within the city limits, but outside the walls – at Haven Banks, St Thomas; Westgate; at Lion's Holt, near the London-Exeter railway and at Heavitree on the ancient highway to Honiton.

All the Exeter tanneries have now been swept away. BT's Exbridge House stands on the site of the old Westgate tannery.

Sources

1   Maryanne Kowaleski, Local Markets and Regional Trade in Medieval Exeter, Cambridge University Press, 1995, 160; 303-306
2   Peter Weddell, Exeter Archaeology, c August 2004

Right: Exeter location map. The location of the four post-medieval tanneries in Exeter, and the nearby tannery at Alphington

Below: a romanticised view of Exeter in 1828. The partly-completed Colleton Crescent stands in front of the Cathedral with rack fields still evident, right. Image courtesy of Devon Library and Information Services

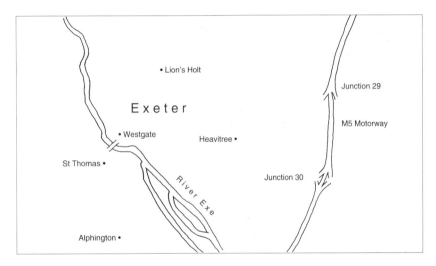

Heavitree tanyard

Location	SX 947 921
Operational	to circa 1882
Output	50 to 60 hides a week in 1853
Bark mill	steam powered by 1875
Tan pits	50 in 1851, 80 in 1857

Heavitree once had two breweries and is probably best known for this industry, rather than tanning. One of these survives today, at least in name. The Wonford, a small tributary of the Exe running south from Stoke Hill, through Polsloe, flowed past the tannery, located close to Heavitree Bridge [1] on the main road from Honiton and the east, later the A30 Trunk Road. There was a tanyard in the parish in 1686. [2] In 1800 Heavitree was still a country village, not yet swallowed up by Exeter.

James Rew was the Heavitree tanner in 1809: he was advertising for workers then. [3] In 1812 he served on the Devonshire committee chaired by George Barne of Tiverton responsible for compiling a memorandum to the Board of Trade on the burden the new leather tax would have on the industry. [4]

By the end of the Napoleonic wars the tannery came under the direction of William Underhay. He ran the yard for forty years and was regarded as the senior representative of the industry in 1842, when he chaired a meeting of the county's tanners at the George Inn, Exeter, to petition the government to reconsider its proposed reduction in the tariff of imported leather goods. By 1836 Underhay also occupied a warehouse in Coombe Street, where he was offering for sale 70 tons of imported Valonia, damaged in transit. [5]

Among others in 1851 he employed the journeyman tanners Hitchcock and Pitfield, next door neighbours.

[6] Underhay was then 66 and John Hitchcock, 63, was actually resident at the tanyard, three doors away, possibly his manager or warden. [7]

Two years later the business was auctioned: *'Freehold Tan Yard, Heavitree. For Sale, at Auction .. Two undivided third parts with the Dwelling-House, Garden and Orchards, containing 1a 1r 14p now in occupation of Mr Underhay who has carried out a successful business thereon for nearly 40 years .. capable of tanning from 50 to 60 hides per week .. only a mile and a half from the Exeter Quay ..'* [8]

The significance of the port facilities was the ready access to imported hides from Buenos Aires, which were favoured by 19th century tanners and leatherworkers, and valonia from the Mediterranean. Robert Aplin, a fellmonger, leather dresser and woolstapler of Okehampton Street, St Thomas's, took over the business and was established here in 1856. [9] Born at Silverton, he was living at East Wonford House with his wife Frances, three sons and infant daughter in 1861. [10]

Aplin had bought the tannery for £500 at Christmas 1855. In fact he bought two thirds of it: the other third belonged to the Heavitree Charities, associated with the Church of England. Leasing the additional third became a matter of dispute between Aplin and the trustees. Aplin thought the rent worth £10 a year at most; Pitman Jones, secretary to the Trustees required £16 a year, while admitting the premises were in *'a very ruinous condition notwithstanding they have been repaired from time to time, they will require a considerable sum to place them in proper repair'*.

Aplin offered to effect repairs provided the rent was reduced to £7 a year. The Trustees offered a lease for 21 years at £10 a year. Aplin was unable to accept, observing their surveyor had assumed the bark mill

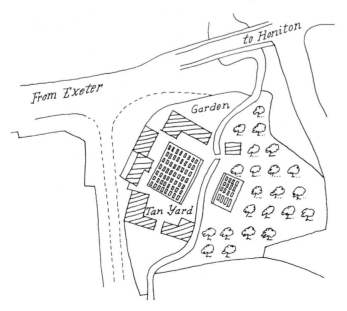

The tanyard at Heavitree Bridge in 1857. By the old Roman road from Honiton, it may well have been established in the medieval period. The layout of the yard, with the tanpits largely surrounded by the dwelling house and outbuildings, is not untypical. The river runs through the property.

From a survey by Dawson, 13 February 1857. The original plan was orientated south and has been redrawn with north to the top [DRO 3004A/PFA 341]

Heavitree Bridge circa 1920. The tanyard was on the left, out of shot, and demolished by 1890. But the tall building beyond was William Underhay's residence; he was the tanner in 1842. The city council has since extensively remodelled the area and all the old houses have gone as has the bridge. Photograph courtesy Peter Thomas

was part of the property. In fact it was wholly owned by him. Likewise he pointed out the dwelling house was no longer fit as a family residence. The tanyard, however, was in good order. It contained 80 pits, 30 of which had been added by Aplin and were his sole property.

The house was built largely of cob on stone footings. It contained five bedrooms and a brewhouse, cellars, a stable, a bark house and the bark mill were attached. A garden and orchard completed the estate of a little over an acre. Eventually, it appears, a lease was arranged at a reduced rent.

In 1864 matters came to a head when the trustees served notice on Aplin to quit. While he'd accepted a reduced rent, he'd failed to carry out the required repairs, excepting the rebuilding of the stables. In 1865 the premises were auctioned: *'Dwelling house, Tanyard, Garden and Orchard at Heavitree'*. But as Aplin wholly owned part of the tanyard, and as 30 pits and the bark mill were his, he remained on the premises. [11]

Aplin was still here in 1875 when a fire broke out: from this it is clear a steam engine was part of the installed machinery :

'A fire occurred on Monday afternoon at Mr Aplin's tannery. It appears that some tar which was being prepared boiled over and set fire to the engine house. A messenger was despatched to the city on horse back for the fire engines and in a short time the West of England was on the spot, followed closely by the Norwich Union and the Sun.
Meantime the workmen and neighbours had succeeded in checking the flames and with the help of two engines the fire was .. extinguished. A large shed filled with dry bark adjoins the engine house, and this had a very narrow escape. The damage done was relatively slight, and was, we hear, covered by insurance.' [12]

Aged 66 in 1882, Aplin chose to retire. His sons may have reached the conclusion that oak bark tanning was a declining business and sought careers elsewhere:

'Heavitree Tanyard, Heavitree Bridge .. Auction .. on the Premises, 500 Butts fully tanned, Tanyard machinery, Implements, Live stock, Vetches and Trifolium, the property of Mr R Aplin, declining business, comprising 500 green butts fully tanned, in lots to suit purchasers, bark mill by Huxham and Brown, hydraulic press 400 tons pressure by ditto, splitting machine, zinc bed and brass rollers, four hogshead copper furnace nearly new, glue press .. Live stock – 2 fat heifers, 4 two-year-old steers, 1 cow and calf, 1 cow in calf .. 1 cart horse 4-year-old .. a bay hackney, six year-old, 16 hands high, broken to saddle and harness and one waggon ..' [13]

There were no buyers, it appears, and the tannery was not indicated on the map published in 1890. The site had been cleared. [14]

Heavitree sources
1 DRO – Heavitree tithe map, 1844, and apportionment, 1842. Tanyard item 444, occupied William Underhay
2 DRO – 3004A/PFT 116 of 1814
3 Exeter Flying Post 24 August 1809 p 4 col 5
4 Exeter Flying Post 20 August 1812 p 4 col 5
5 Woolmer's Gazette 26 March 1842 p 3 col 6; Exeter Flying Post 3 March 1836 p 1 col 3
6 Heavitree census 1841 – HO107 263\14 f 15 p 24; Underhay was listed here in 1844 – Pigot's General Directory, Devonshire, 1844
7 Heavitree census 1851 – HO107 1866 f 391 p 38
8 Exeter Flying Post 1 September 1853 p 1 col 3
9 Exeter St Thomas census 1851 – HO107 1867 f 90 p 33; Post Office Directory, Devon and Cornwall, 1856
10 Heavitree census 1861 – RG9 1387 f 51 p 30
11 DRO – DRO 3004A/PFA 330, 331, 334, 335, 336, 341, 347, 350, 354
12 Exeter Flying Post 3 February 1875 p 5 col 4
13 The Western Times 12 May 1882 p 1 col 3
14 Heavitree: Ordnance Survey map 25" = 1 mile, sheet 80.7 of 1890

St Thomas

Location	SX 9168 9190
Operational	to 1896
Output	120 hides a week in 1832
Bark mills and pumps	
	steam powered by 1862

Tanning was a long-established trade in St Thomas's parish. George Crook was a tanner of Cowick Street in 1583. [1]

In the late 18th century the yard at Haven Banks was run by James King: he died in 1788 [2] and the tannery was subsequently for sale in 1789 and 1798. [3]

James Lee Sanders was tanner at the end of the Napoleonic wars. His status was such that he married the only daughter of John Langdon, esquire, of Tedburn St Mary [4] – James, it can be inferred, was a businessman rather than a tradesman. He and his wife Maria lived at Painter's Row, near the works. Three sons were born here in the period 1814-1819. [5] For some reason Exeter didn't appeal and the family moved to Bow, between Crediton and North Tawton, to run the yard at Halse. [6]

The next proprietor at St Thomas tannery was James Francis. He was probably established here in 1820 when he married Jane Rowe at Sampford Peverell. [7] Painter's Row continued as the residential address. But James never really settled and in 1832, aged 37, he chose to retire from tanning and the premises were offered to let. This was, by Devon standards, a large establishment as the following notice illustrates:

'Capital Tan Yard, Dwelling-House and Premises to be Let, for a Term of 14, 21 or 28 years. All that commodious Dwelling-House and Garden, with a Tan-Yard, and all requisite and convenient Buildings belonging thereto situate in St Thomas the Apostle, adjoining the City of Exeter, now and for several years past in the occupation of Mr James Francis, Tanner, the Proprietor, who is about to retire from business.
The Tan-yard is large and convenient and capable of being worked to the extent of 120 Hides a week. The Pits are for the most part under cover and there is a never failing supply of water.
The premises are situated near the Quay, and about the distance of half a furlong from the new Basin, into which vessels of large Tonnage enter and discharge their cargoes .. the taker will be expected to purchase the stock of Leather in store (which is considerable) and also the Machinery and Utensils.
There is also upwards of 120 Tons of English Oak Bark on the Premises .. Immediate Possession may be had. For further particulars and to treat for the same apply to Mr Francis on the Premises ..' [8]

In the intervening years the yard may have been let to another tanner: but by 1841 William Francis, James's younger brother, had taken on the yard. He'd married Charlotte Tremlett in 1830 [9] and they were living at Painter's Row with their four offspring and Charlotte's brother Elias, a journeyman tanner. [10]

James Francis hadn't completely retired: he lived next door and had become an agent or hide merchant. Across the river, a mere five minutes walk away was the Exeter cattle market, the site now landscaped parkland and river walks.

William, in contrast to his brother, ran the establishment for at least 38 years. The two brothers came from Cheriton Fitzpaine, the sons of John Dunning Francis and his wife Mary. [11] William operated the yard with 13 men throughout the period 1841-1861. By 1851 one of his sons, William, was in the team; in 1861 Charles Sweet, 19, an apprentice tanner, was living with the family. [12] From at least 1861 the family lived at Haven Road and by 1871, specifically at Sydney House, a large Victorian or late Georgian villa with garden, backing onto Alphington Street. A new house now stands on the site.

On 3 March 1858 William Francis took the train to Bristol and visited the leather fair, an important venue for tanners. While he was away, and again on a later occasion that month, William Thorn, one of his labourers, stole a quantity of leather from the yard which he disposed of to an Exeter shoemaker, Richard Mortimer. Other workers gave evidence that convicted Thorn and Mortimer and Thorn was imprisoned for four years; Mortimer was sentenced to eighteen months hard labour for knowingly receiving stolen goods. [13]

A steam engine had been installed at Haven Banks, possibly at quite an early date – the Exeter Quay was not far away and there was no water power on site. In 1862 Francis employed men from Bodley's foundry, also close at hand, to make repairs. The steam engine was used to pump the oozes or tannic acid around the tan pits and no doubt ground oak bark as well. [14]

The following year fire broke out in a shed used for drying skins. The alarm was raised by a passer by but Francis's men had it extinguished before the insurance company engines arrived. [15] It was some years before the city council assumed responsibility for fire engines. Francis had had the premises insured with the Norwich Union office.

He retired in 1879, aged 72. William, his son, aged 47, also gave up work. It would seem that the business had been profitable. The family remained living close to the yard in 1881 and Richard Searle, who was resident at Cowick Street, was now in charge, aged 27. Initially he ran the business in partnership with his brother Tom Hayden Searle. They came from Sidmouth and employed ten men and a boy: expansion was not attempted. [16]

Like Wippell and Rew of the nearby Alphington tannery, Searle obtained some of his bark from the Fulford Estate and in 1879 paid £14-17-0 for 3 tons 6 cwt; in 1881 he paid £14-8-6 for 3 tons 4 cwt 1 qr. On both occasions he was charged at £4-10s a ton, and this would have covered the cost of the bark, ripping it and delivery. [17]

William Francis died in 1883 leaving £23,268, a not inconsiderable estate for the period. [18] Searle's premises were damaged by a further fire in 1886 [19] and ten years later tanning ceased. [20] Chrome tanning – a much faster process – had been introduced by this date and oak bark tanning would become uncompetitive. Over a hundred years later, in 1998, a warehouse used as a bark store and for drying hides remained on site, but has since disappeared under redevelopment. [21]

St Thomas sources
1   Exeter St Thomas parish register transcribed by Devon and Cornwall Record Society: from A H Shorter, The Tanning Industry in Devon and Cornwall, 1550-1850. Devon & Cornwall Notes & Queries, Volume XXV, 1952, 10-16
2   Exeter Flying Post 31 July 1788 p 3 col 2
3   Exeter Flying Post 21 January 1789 p 3 col 4; Exeter Flying Post 14 June 1798 p 3 col 4
4   Exeter Flying Post 27 May 1813 p 4 col 2
5   Exeter St Thomas parish register transcribed by Devon and Cornwall Record Society
6   Exeter Flying Post 28 February 1828 p 2 col 5 and 13 March 1828 p 2 col 5 – references to a waggoner working for Sanders at Bow injured
7   Mormon IGI: James Francis married Jane Rowe at Sampford Peverell on 18 April 1820
8   Exeter Flying Post 25 October 1832 p 2 col 4
9   Mormon IGI: William Francis married Charlotte Tremlett on 19 October 1830
10   Exeter St Thomas census 1841 – HO107 265\9 f 6 p 5 and 6
11   Mormon IGI: James Francis, baptised 19 February 1795 and William Francis baptised 23 April 1807, were sons of John Dunning Francis and Mary his wife, of Cheriton Fitzpaine
12   Exeter St Thomas census for 1851 and 1861 – HO107 1867 f 78 p 9; RG9 1389 f 13 p 18
13   The Western Times 10 April 1858 p 4 cols 1-2
14   DRO – Bodley records 67/5/2/1 folio 187-188
15   Exeter Flying Post 21 January 1863 p 5 col 4
16   Exeter St Thomas census for 1881 – RG11 2144 f 11 p 15
17   DRO – 1926D/FU/F7/22
18   Will of William Francis, tanner, late of St Thomas, died 25 May 1883. Executor William Francis. Left £23,268 15s
19   Exeter Flying Post 9 June 1886 p 5 col 3
20   Mike Bone and Peter Stanier, A Guide to the Industrial Archaeology of Devon. AIA 1998, 12
21   Ibid

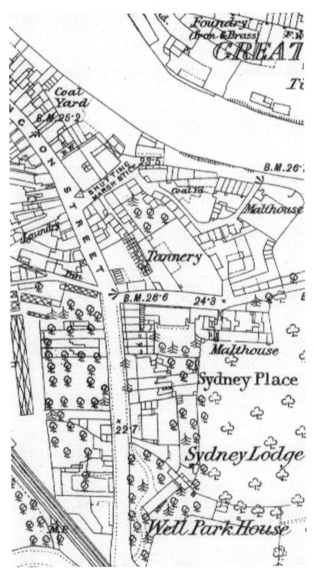

Exeter St Thomas Tannery, Alphington Street, in 1888 – also known as Haven Banks, with the river Exe to the north. The tan pits are visible. Sydney House, William Francis' home, stood by Sydney Place. From the 1: 2500 Ordnance Survey map, sheet 80.14, published in 1890

Inside an Exeter tannery: Westgate – the tannery across the river from St Thomas – with tanned hides stored out of the sunlight to avoid discolouration. Photograph courtesy Peter Thomas

Lion's Holt
Location   SX 927 934 or SX 9257 9401
Operational   to circa 1873
Staff   14 in 1851

When offered for sale in 1867 this tannery was described as '.. one of the oldest businesses in the county of Devon ..'. [1] Joseph Sparkes Dymond was the proprietor in the late 18th century and was one of the tanners who gathered at a meeting in Exeter in August 1790. [2] Business was brisk in the war years and Dymond was attempting to recruit staff in 1803:
'To Journeymen Tanners. Wanted immediately, a MAN who underftands DRYING of LEATHER, but who is capable of conducting the Yard work, in bufinefs to a moderate extent – Any man qualified to fill the above Station will, if approved, receive conftant Employment and good Wages, by applying to Jofeph S Dymond, tanner, Exeter.' [3]

He died in January 1810 and a notice was printed in the Exeter Flying Post assuring clients that:
'.. the Business of the late Joseph Sparkes Dymond, of the City of Exeter, hide merchant, leather factor, and tanner, will be carried on as heretofore. NB A Quantity of Buenos Ayres, and other foreign Hides now on sale ..' [4]

From 1810 to 1815, Harriet Dymond, his widow, managed the premises but in April of the latter year she sought a leaseholder:
'Tan Yard in Exeter to Let. To be Let for a Term, all that desirable Tan-Yard and Premises situate at Lyon's Holt, in the City of Exeter, for many years in the occupation of Joseph S Dymond, deceased, and since of his widow Harriet Dymond .. good dwelling-house, .. offices, a complete tan-yard well supplied with water .. two gardens and an orchard ..For viewing apply to Harriet Dymond at the house ..' [5]

It is not certain who the tenant was in the intervening years, but by 1830 James Rew was resident at Lions Holt. [6] James and his son William ran the business in 1841 and journeymen tanners lived in cottages nearby. [7] James' two other sons were also in the leather trades – his second son James was a master currier of 6 Castle Street, Exeter, in 1851, and his third son Robert was tanner at Alphington from at least 1841 until his premature death in 1857. [8]

The partnership was still active in 1851, although James by this time was 68 and his son 45. They employed 14 men in the yard, so it can be assumed that the establishment was similar in size to the tannery in St Thomas' parish. [9] By 1861 James Rew was still listed as tanner: but much of the work was no doubt managed by James Ball, a journeyman tanner of 42, who lived next door. [10]

The tanyard was put up for sale in 1867:
'.. Lyon's Holt Tan Yard and Works, Exeter. Comprising a Dwelling-House, Tanyard, Limepits, Drying-Lofts, new Bark Barns, Mill House, Store Houses, Stables, six Cottages, Gardens and Meadow, containing altogether two acres and a quarter and close to the South Western Railway. This valuable freehold property now in full working order and one of the oldest businesses in the County of Devon will be offered for Sale, by Auction, in April next, unless previously disposed of by private contract ..' [11]

James Rew died in April 1868. [12] It seems there were no buyers for the yard and it does not appear on large scale Ordnance Survey maps of the city published in 1890. Tanning had probably ceased by 1875. Lions Holt was a district of Exeter in 1890, [13] but like the tannery the name has gone and this part of the city is now known as St James Park. If the tannery was here its site lies on what is now the Exeter City Football Ground. In 1842 James Rew owned an acre and more here, but also had a house and garden on the city outskirts by Pennsylvania Road at SX 9257 9401, next to six cottages, an alternative location. [14]

Tan yards need water – from sale notices above it is evident that Lions Holt was 'well supplied with water' and 'close to the South Western Railway'. Exeter's water supply, first constructed in circa 1200, tapped a spring at the city end of the Mount Pleasant railway tunnel at Lions Holt, and was piped and then run in underground passages to Cathedral Yard. In constructing the railway, the supply was interrupted and subsequently lost. The Salisbury-Exeter railway was opened in July 1860: it may be that the construction work that affected the spring also affected the source of water to the tannery, although this is not apparent in the 1867 sale details. [15]

Lion's Holt sources
1 Exeter Flying Post 18 December 1867 p 1 col 3
2 Bristol Mercury 30 August 1790
3 Exeter Flying Post 21 July 1803 p 4 col 5
4 Exeter Flying Post 15 February 1810 p 4
5 Exeter Flying Post 13 April 1815 p 1 col 3
6 Pigot's General Directory, Devonshire, 1830
7 Exeter St Sidwell's census 1841 – HO107 268/7 f 10 p 14
8 Exeter St Lawrence census 1851; Alphington census 1841 – HO107 262\2 f 6 p 6; Alphington census 1851 – HO107 1867 f 235 p 17; Robert Rew died 6 August 1857
9 Exeter St Sidwell's census 1851 – HO107 1868 f 215 p 5
10 Exeter St Sidwell's census 1861 – RG9 1394 f 36 p 13
11 Exeter Flying Post 18 December 1867 p 1 col 3
12 Exeter Flying Post 15 April 1868 p 5 col 2
13 Ordnance Survey map of Exeter. 25" = 1 mile, sheet 80.6
14 DRO Exeter St Sidwell Tithe Map and Apportionment, 1842, items 24, 25 – by Pennsylvania Road, 86 and 124
15 Exeter's water supply – W G Hoskins, Two Thousand Years in Exeter, Phillimore 1963, 37; David St John Thomas. A Regional History of the Railways of Great Britain. Volume 1. The West Country. Phoenix House, 1960, 33

Commercial Road / Westgate
with a note on site at Great Shilhay
Location   SX 918 921 ~
Operational   to 1896
Output   120 hides a week in 1832
Bark mills and pumps
                steam powered by 1862

The 19th century history of this site is not yet entirely transparent. Complexities arise through the activities of the Tanner family. James Newman Tanner (1766-1848) was the leading Plymouth tanner of his day; he was a leather merchant and industrialist, with contacts in banking and a part-owner of collieries in the Forest of Dean, not to mention a glove manufactory and a glue works. [1] His four sons were all involved in the leather industry, three of them with businesses in Exeter. Frederick Tanner (1799-1843) ran a tanyard on the Shilhay in 1830. [2] The Shilhay was an island in the Exe, separated from the city by the Coney Gut, an artificial watercourse. For centuries it had been used by fullers for their rack fields, where cloths were stretched to dry on tenterhooks. [3] By the nineteenth century other industries were encroaching. Frederick also had a tanyard at Commercial Road; in 1844 this site was in the hands of his executors, and may well have been the Westgate Tannnery. The yard was sited just to the north of Commercial Road and the Lower Leat, on Exe Island, and separated from the city by the Higher Leat. [4] Tanneries had existed on Exe Island from medieval times. And the four-times mayor of Exeter, William Crugge, who was the city's richest merchant on his death in 1520, began his career here as a tanner. [5]

Returning to the Shilhay site, James Jones Tanner (1790-1850), James Newman Tanner's eldest son, leased the segment of Great Shilhay nearest the Exe from the city for 31 years from 1835. A leather dresser and glovemaker, [6] rather than a tanner, he was also a successful businessman. In 1836 he was narrowly elected Sheriff of Exeter. [7] The premises on Shilhay included lime pits, frizing, grounding, fleshing and pulling shops, glue spread racks and press-house, store and drying lofts, together with a cart shed, stables and coach house. [8] James Tanner was also occupying a glove manufactory sublet from his father in the parish of St Mary Steps and a water-powered shammy leather mill at Upton Pyne. [9] He died at his home in Southernhay on 27 August 1850. An obituary cited his: *'.. great mercantile ability .. was well known and highly esteemed by his fellow citizens, to whom he was endeared by his great worth and his high character .. he was a liberal benefactor ..'* [10] The Shilhay lease passed to his younger brother William Tanner (1809-1872). William was listed as leather dresser and glue manufacturer, Westgate and Well Court, Queen Street, London, in 1852. [11] He had an Exeter residence at 39 Southernhay and later lived at 2 Colleton Crescent, overlooking the Exe. [12] He bought the Shilhay estate from the city council in 1866 for £3056. His nephew Edmund F Tanner inherited the property in 1872. [13]

It is not entirely clear if the premises off the Commercial Road occupied by the Tanners then became the Westgate Tannery, which, it appears, was in the hands of James Wilson in 1856, [14] or whether they were a separate establishment. By 1875 the Westgate business was known as Wilson and Tremlett, when a fire was reported:
'The first fire of the series [two other destructive fires in Exeter followed] broke out in the top loft of a building occupied by Messrs Wilson and Tremlett, tanners, in the West Quarter. About eleven o'clock on Thursday morning, while the men were engaged in their usual work, smoke was seen from the street to be issuing from the loft, which is used as a drying shed, and alarm was at once raised. The seat of the fire was soon discovered, and a plentiful supply of water being easily obtained, the workmen had no difficulty in subduing the flames before the arrival of the engines, which were speedily on the spot. The fire was supposed to have been caused by sparks from one of the chimneys on the works ..' [15]
The indications are that these premises were steam powered. The Westgate works adjoined the lower leat, which may have been useful as a water source for boilers, although probably not for tanning. [16]

Alfred Wilson was the senior partner in 1881. Aged 42, he came from Camberwell in south London, and lived some way from the factory, at Compass Cottage, Stoke Hill, with a large family and a governess and four servants. His partner, Charles Henry Tremlett, a native of Exeter, lived at 25 St David's Hill, and, aged 28, was a *'master tanner'*. His wife Emma came from London and this fact may explain the link with Wilson. [17] Charles was the youngest son of William Tremlett, an Exeter paper manufacturer and his elder brothers were involved in the paper business rather than tanning. [18]

Wilson and Tremlett employed 40 men in their tannery, in 1881 – then the largest leather processing concern in Exeter. [19] In the 20th century the company was known as Tremlett Brothers Limited. It specialised in *'high class sole and insole leathers'*. There were workshops and premises at Commercial Road and at Westgate, nearby. [20]

Tremlett Brothers pursued an expansionist policy according to one source. They bought up the redundant Queen's Head Hotel and turned it into laboratories. From this it can be deduced that Tremletts had abandoned oak bark tanning and adapted their operations to the more efficient chrome tanning, invented in the 1890s in Germany. Business was conducted from offices in Edmund Street, fronting the Westgate tanyard.

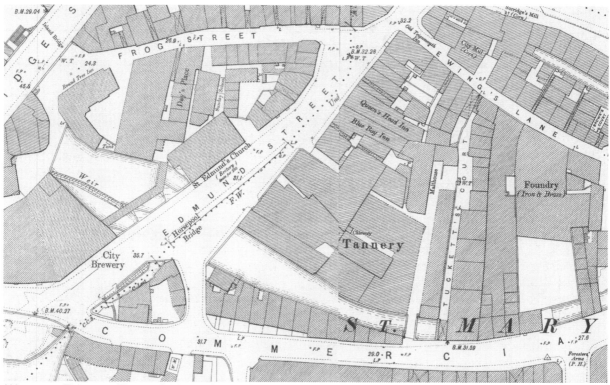

Westgate Tannery, Exeter, in 1876. It stood north of the Lower Leat and Commercial Road and east of Edmund Street, the medieval way into the city from the west, by way of the old Exe Bridge. New Bridge Street replaced this thoroughfare as the main route in the 19th century. This area, part of Exe Island, was the industrial heartland of Exeter, much affected by Second World War Baedeker raids, and since extensively remodelled. From the Ordnance Survey 1:500 maps, sheets 80:6.21 and 80:6.22

2 Colleton Crescent, the home of William Tanner in 1866

The main works survived the bombing in the Second World War but quite a serious fire got a hold here in July 1949. [21] The factory was rebuilt but a later unit was established out at Marsh Barton. Further expansion took place when the company bought Sellwood's tannery at Cullompton. Another fire at Marsh Barton pursuaded the directors to concentrate activities at Cullompton; [22] this tannery closed in 1969 and the remaining leather business was sold to a company in Beverley, Yorkshire, then reputedly the largest tannery concern in Europe. [23]

As W G Hoskins has observed, tanning was very probably Exeter's oldest industry, extant two thousand years ago with cattle and hides making

the short sea crossing from Rouen in Normandy. [24] Tremletts was the last of a long line of tanners.

Exeter sources – Commercial Road tanyard

1. James Newman Tanner's will. PROB 11/2088 f 385-390
2. Pigot's General Directory, Devonshire, 1830
3. City of Exeter in 1792. Plan by Charles Tozer. See W G Hoskins, Two Thousand Years in Exeter
4. Pigot's General Directory, Devonshire, 1844
5. W G Hoskins, Two Thousand Years in Exeter. Phillimore, Chichester, 1963, 53
6. DRO – D7/1080/1
7. Exeter Flying Post 7 January 1836 p 4 col 4-5
8. The Western Times 26 April 1851 p 1 col 2
9. James Newman Tanner's will; The Western Times 26 April 1851 p 1 col 2
10. Woolmer's Gazette 31 August 1850 p 5 col 6
11. Slater's Directory 1852
12. Southernhay: Exeter census, 1851 – HO107 1869 f 22 p 10; Colleton Crescent in 1866 – DRO D7/1080/3
13. DRO D7/1080/5. William Tanner's will, 1872
14. Post Office Directory, Devon and Cornwall, 1856
15. Exeter Flying Post 15 September 1875 p 5 col 4 ; Wilson and Tremlett, tanners, Commercial-road. Harrod's Devonshire Directory, 1878
16. See Ordnance Survey sheets 80:6.21 and 80:6.22 of 1876
17. Heavitree St Thomas census 1881 [Wilson] – RG11 2143 f 28 p 26; Exeter St David's census 1881 [Tremlett] – RG11 2153 f 108 p 10
18. Mormon IGIs, Exeter census index, 1881
19. Heavitree census 1881 – RG11 2143 f 28 p 26
20. Kelly's Directory of Devonshire and Cornwall, 1919, 1116
21. Jean Maun. Exploring Exeter. The West Quarter. Obelisk Publications, 1999, 27
22. Express and Echo 18 August 1964
23. Western Morning News 28 October 1969
24. W G Hoskins, op cit, 1963, 2

Great Torrington

High Street and Caddywell
Mill Street
New Street / Stonemans Lane
South Street

Glovemaking and the woollen industry were leading Torrington trades. There were tanners but the fell-mongers, glovers and curriers tended to outnumber them, not to mention the shoemakers. Torrington's leather industries were already well developed by the 17th century, with a Company of Cordwainers and a Leather Hall. Regulations controlled the quality of leather with fines imposed on those who sought to avoid meeting established standards. But the 'Body of Master Cordwainers or Shoemakers' had become overbearing by 1722 that local justices sought, in the town's interests, to have it dissolved. [1]

The town was a thriving and 'spirited' place in 1801. [2] A typical fellmonger's yard was that owned by Benjamin Sheppard, which came on the market in 1819, having been run by Sweet and Bagehot:

'To Tanners and Fellmongers. To be Sold by Auction .. for the remainder of a term of 99 years, determinable on the deaths of three young healthy lives, held under the Rev. John Phillipps, all those very desirable Premises, known by the name of the YARD, situate in Great Torrington .. now in the occupation of Mr Benjamin Sheppard, the Proprietor. The Premises are most advantageously situated and consist of two good Dwelling Houses, nearly finished with substantial materials, extensive Yard and Lofts, Lime Pits, Courtlage and a large Garden or Bleaching Ground, directly facing the South and every way calculated for the business of a Tanner or Fell-monger, on an extensive scale and situate on the bank of a fine stream of Water ..' [3]

In the 18th century members of the Walter family were producing leather here. Two tanners were listed in 1824 – John Kingdon at Mill Street and George Stoneman at New Street. Leading curriers were John Adams and James Rude, both of South Street. [4] Representatives of these four families were responsible for the tanning industry in Torrington for much of the 19th century. John Slee, another tanner, died in 1828. [5]

Torrington tanners worked exclusively with English hides; imported hides sold by Plymouth and Exeter dealers were disregarded. When the tanneries were in production the local oak woods were extensively coppiced and maintained, supplying the young bark vital for the ancient industry. [6]

Mill Street
Location   SX 489 189
Operational   to circa 1875

Mill Street is a long and in part steep way, lined with cottages and terraced houses, running up from the ancient Torridge Inn in the valley to the town at the top of the hill. Tanning here must have been less than ideal – the back yards are steep and water may only have been available from wells. Access to the yard was from The Warren.

This tannery was run by John Kingdon until about 1847 when his wife died. [7] In 1851 he, it appears, was a retired farmer, aged 75: [8] he died in 1853. [9] John Bound Kingdon then managed the business from circa 1850 until closure by 1875, although the business was still listed at 100 Mill Street in 1890. It appears Kingdon was the town's mayor in 1872. [10]

A view of Mill Street: steeper and narrower higher up. Not an ideal site for a tannery

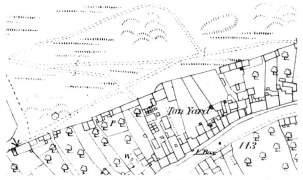

The Mill Street tanyard was still indicated on the 1887 Ordnance Survey map, sheet 29.8

New Street / Stonemans Lane
Location   SX 492 192
Operational   to c 1875

George Stoneman, a Torrington tanner, married Susan, the daughter of the mayor, George Greek, in 1794.[11] In 1820 he appears to have held property in Barnstaple. [12] He occupied the New Street premises until about 1828 when George Stoneman junior took control. The family had also owned the tannery at Petrockstowe and father or son, it is not clear who, put it up for sale in 1830. [13]

The younger Stoneman was a committed Baptist who attended chapel three times on the day before he was found drowned near Rothery Bridge in September 1846. Suicide was suspected, although the jury at an inquest returned a verdict of 'found drowned'. The New Street yard appears to have been unoccupied in 1843; it was then owned by Agnes Stoneman. [14] Richard Adams, son of John, the currier and leather cutter of South Street, was listed at New Street, aged 39 in 1851 and employing three men; he may have taken over the Stoneman tanyard. [15]

A yard, probably the New Street premises, was offered to let by C W Stoneman, a glove manu-facturer, in 1853:

'Extensive Tan Yard, Great Torrington. To be Let. Forty Pits, Good Drying Lofts, Mill House, Bark Store and Warehouses .. is well supplied with Water ..' [16]

By 1856 the firm Richard Adams & Son was established at South Street, probably moving there after the retirement of John Adams. [17]

The tanyard was sited on the east side of Stone-man's Lane, running north from New Street. It had closed by 1875 and material from the redundant buildings was used to construct a cottage, extant in 1947. [18]

Tanners Row, Church Lane. A 2005 conversion of a building which may have served the High Street yard

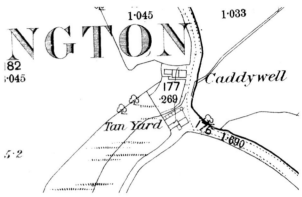
The small tanyard at Caddywell in 1887. Only one cottage survives here; the rest is a builder's yard

High Street and Caddywell		
Locations	SX 4948 1915	High Street
	SX 5012 1908	Caddywell
Operational	to 1883	
Bark mill	steam powered	
Tan pits	7 latches, 13 layers, 24 handlers at High Street; 2 grainers, 5 lime pits, 2 soak pits at Caddywell	

James Rude was tanner here in 1850; a currier of the same name had operated from an address in Well Street in 1830. [19] It is doubtful if there was a tannery here much before that date – it may originally have had a horse-powered bark mill, but was later steam powered. In 1851, James, aged 55 and employing nine men and two boys had probably the largest combined tannery and currier's shop in the town at the time. His son John, 28, had followed him into the trade. [20]

The business was titled 'J Rude & Son' in 1856. [21] In 1858 John Rude married Ann, fourth daughter of John Adams, the Torrington currier, demonstrating once again the close-knit fraternity in the Devon leather business. [23] His firm was still going strong in 1883. [22] But in 1888 it was for sale. The following notice gives quite an insight into the facilities of a late 19th century steam-powered yard and also shows that the lime pits, for instance, were at Caddywell, on the edge of town, where there was probably a better water supply:

'Great Torrington .. To be Sold by .. Auction .. Freehold and Leasehold Properties .. Lot 1. – a capital Freehold Dwelling House, with shops and outhouses in rear, situated in the High-street, together with extensive tannery, warehouses, drying sheds and other buildings, and yards, now and for many years in the occupation of Mr John Rude, tanner.
The Dwelling House is very substantially built .. and a conservatory heated with hot water pipes from waste steam from engine in tan-yard, stocked with excellent full bearing vines and a fine collection of ferns.
The Tan-yard is fitted with steam engine working up to 6 horse power, large boiler, and fireplace made to consume spent tan, with stocks, bark mill, and cutters, and double action steam pump, all worked by steam. The pits consist of 7 large latches, 8 large layers, 5 smaller layers, 24 handlers, with steam pipes fixed and laid from boiler, over which are large drying lofts, with steam drying stove, a large bark loft, capable of holding 150 tons, two-stall stable and coach-house, large currier's shop and loft over same, large store room and sale shop below. Lot 2.
– Two Leasehold Cottages and Garden .. situated at Caddywell and a substantial Building adjoining, with loft over, storehouses and workshop, 2 grainer pits, 5 lime pits, 2 large soak pits, and a plentiful supply of running water. This lot is held under a lease granted by the Trustees of the will of the late Lord Rolle, for the residue of a term of 99 years .. yearly rent 7s 6d and subject to a heriot of 15s ..' [24]

74

John Rude was now 65 and may well have retired. At the High Street premises the bark house was later converted into a cinema, other buildings became gas company offices and private housing. [25] At Caddywell only the cottage survives in 2005.

South Street

Location	SX 4941 1907
Operational	to circa 1925
Staff	4 in 1851

Members of the Adams family in Torrington were related to Edward Adams, a successful Crediton tanner. John Adams, Edward's brother, was a currier here in the years 1824 -1843. [26] Aged 63 in 1851, he employed four men at South Street. [27]
Richard Adams, previously at New Street, was listed as tanner and currier at South Street in 1866, 1870 and 1873 [28] but his wife Mary Ann was widowed by 1881 [29] and her son George Doe Adams came to direct operations. [30] The premises at 41 South Street were too cramped to run a profitable tanning business and a tannery at Petrockstowe [qv], five miles away, with a water-powered bark mill and large bark barns, tan pits and covered working areas was purchased and a manager given control of day-to-day running there. [31]

The business thrived and Adams were the last tanners listed in Torrington, there in 1919 and the Petrockstowe yard was still at work in 1924. [32]
The tanner's house survives in 2005; in 1947 the tanyard was occupied by a market gardener. [33]

41 South Street. The frontage of the house and tannery belonging to the Adams family in the 19th century

John Adams
bp 7-4-1786 Crediton
= Mary
Tanner *and currier of South Street,*
Great Torrington
fl 1841-1851, employing 4 men in1851

Richard
1811-
Tanner and currier, South *Street, Torrington, 1866-1873, employing 3 men; Owned Petrockstow tannery 1866 - 1873*
= Mary Ann

John
c 1821
Grocer
his daughter
Alice
= Charles
Doe, wine merchant

Mary *c 1825*

Margaret

Fanny *c 1831*

Ann
c 18xx
=
John Rude, tanner, Torrington m 16-06-1858

George Doe
1852 -
Tanner *+ currier Torrington 1881*

Edward Charles
1857 -
George and Charles Adams, **tanners,** *Quarry Hill Petrockstow, 1919*

Agnes Allen
1860 -

The Adams family of Great Torrington and Petrockstowe, a branch of the Crediton family. Ann Adams married John Rude, tanner at High Street and Caddywell, Torrington

Great Torrington sources
1. J J Alexander and W R Hooper, The History of Great Torrington in the County of Devon, Advance Studio, Sutton, Surrey, 1948, 174-175
2. W G Hoskins, Devon. Devon Books, 1992, 504
3. Woolmer's Gazette 27 February 1819 p 1 col 4
4. Pigot's General Directory, Devonshire, 1824
5. Exeter Flying Post 1 May 1828 p 2 col 4
6. Alexander and Hooper, op cit, 174-175
7. Exeter Flying Post 28 January 1847 p 2 col 7; DRO tithe apportionment, 1842 - item 780, House and Tan Yard
8. Great Torrington census, 1851 – HO 107 1894 f 537 p 61
9. Exeter Flying Post 1 August 1853 p 8 col 6
10. Post Office Directory, Devon and Cornwall, 1856, 1866, 1873; Devon Directory, 1870; Alexander and Hooper, op cit, 174-175; Kellys Directory, 1883, 1890
11. Sherborne Mercury 23 June 1794
12. NDRO 1534M/T15
13. Sherborne Mercury 27 August 1832
14. Exeter Flying Post 10 September 1846 p 3 col 5; DRO tithe apportionment, 1842
15. Great Torrington census, 1851 – HO 107 1894 f 512 p 11
16. Exeter Flying Post 1 September 1853 p 1 col 1
17. Adams R & Son, South Street, Great Torrington Post Office Directory, Devon and Cornwall, 1856
18. Alexander and Hooper, op cit, 174-175; DRO tithe apportionment, 1842 - item 1095, House, Yard ..
19. James Rude, tanner, High Street, Great Torrington Harrod's Devonshire Directory, 1850, 754; Pigot's General Directory, Devonshire, 1830, 138
20. Great Torrington census, 1851 – HO 107 1894 f 553 p 1; DRO tithe apportionment, 1842 - item 1068
21. Post Office Directory, Devon and Cornwall, 1856
22. The Western Times 19 June 1858 p 6 col 3
23. Kellys Directory, 1883
24. The Western Times 7 February 1888 p 1 col 1
25. Alexander and Hooper, op cit, 174-175
26. Pigot's General Directory, Devonshire, 1824 and 1830; DRO tithe apportionment, 1843 - item 1063
27. Great Torrington census, 1851 – HO107 1894 f 545 p 76
28. Post Office Directory of Devonshire 1866, 1873; Devon Directory, 1870
29. Great Torrington census, 1881
30. George D Adams, tanner and currier, South Street. Kellys Directory, 1883
31. Richard Adams was listed as Petrockstowe tanner by 1866. Post Office Directory of Devonshire 1866
32. Kelly's Directory of Devonshire and Cornwall, 1919, 1116; Information from owner Alan Anthony, April 2004
33. Alexander and Hooper, op cit, 174-175

Hartland

Hartland Town

Location	SS 2582 2452
Operational	until c 1850

Hartland is still a remote parish, but two hundred years ago it was much more isolated: *'The roads were so bad that carriages and carts were rare and nearly everything was carried on horseback ..'*[1] This was a community that was of necessity self-reliant and a tannery probably existed here from early times.

Thomas Cholwill was tanner in 1613. He was, it appears unmarried, though the parish was full of widows at that time.[2] But by 1625 he had wed, as his wife Anne was buried in February.[3] The churchwarden, William Galsworthy, ran the tannery in 1660 and near the end of the century the tanner Richard Juell was buried. One family of longstanding in the parish was Prust: there were twelve Prusts recorded in 1566, and earlier, a Prust had been abbot of Hartland. Joseph Prust, 'tannower', was buried in September 1713. John Wilcock was tanning here in the mid eighteenth century.[4]

By 1805 a Prust was again making Hartland leather: *'In the early part of the present century there was a scarcity of silver money and, to meet this, tokens of a somewhat different character were issued at Hartland by Thomas Prust, who being a tanner, was thoroughly convinced that there was 'Nothing like leather'. His tokens, instead of being metal, were small rectangular pieces of leather, about the size and shape of an ordinary visiting card; they were of the values of sixpence and a shilling and, no doubt, had an inscription stamped on them.'*[5]

The family had become non-conformists and two William Prusts, one the tanner and the second a yeoman, were involved in the establishment of an independent chapel in the parish in 1821.[6] William Prust continued as tanner until about 1850, when it is thought the tannery closed.[7] He also owned and occupied two farms and was majority owner of Tucking Mill.[8]

Buildings behind Hartland Manor in North Street may have served as drying lofts and survived until a house was built on the site in 2004.[9] The bark mill was possibly horse powered but the source of the water supply to the tan pits is a mystery.

Hartland sources
1. R Pearse Chope, Notes of the Past. One Hundred Years Ago. Hartland Chronicle, February 1901, 53, 8
2. R Pearse Chope, op cit, Church Sittings in 1613, Hartland Chronicle 244, 12 March 1917
3. D&CRS, transcription, Hartland parish register, 381
4. ibid, 496, 418; R Pearse Chope. An Elizabethan Directory. Hartland Chronicle April 1906, 115, 7; transcribed parish register, 426, 256
5. R Pearse Chope, Notes from the Past. Hartland Chronicle 30, March 1899
6. R Pearse Chope, Nonconformity in the Parish. The Hartland Independents. Hartland Chronicle 219
7. Pigot & Co's Directory, 1830, reprinted 1993, 80; White's Directory, 1850
8. DRO – Hartland tithe apportionment, 1846
9. Correspondence from Stephen Hobbs, 19 May 2005

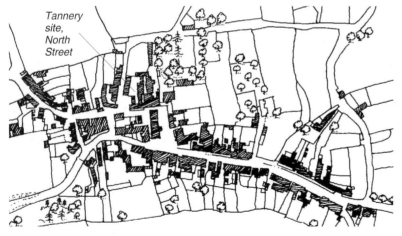

Tannery site, North Street

Edge runner, possibly for grinding bark, near North Street in 2005

Left: Hartland town in 1886. From the OS map, sheet 17.10

Hatherleigh

Location	SS 541 042 or nearby
Operational	until 1800 or so

This was an 18th century tannery that survived into the 19th century. Leonard Facy was tanner in 1777.[1] In 1791 the tenant was John Darke:
' .. To be Lett and entered upon at Lady-day next .. a very good Dwelling-House, Outhouses, and a pretty compact and convenient Tan-Yard, fituate in the town of Hatherleigh .. together with or without all or any part of 50 acres of Land called Moretowns, capable of great improvement .. now in the occupation of Mr John Darke, of Hatherleigh, who will .. accommodate the Taker with all or a part of his prefent ftock of Bark .. being about to decline the bufinefs .. apply to Mr William Hole, in Barnftaple, Devon.'[2]

Operations continued through the Napoleonic Wars into the 19th century. This 1835 notice appears to have followed the yard's demise:

'To be Sold .. that Dwelling-House, Drying-lofts, Workshops, and Premises attached, and which were formerly used as a Tan Yard, situate on the bank of the River Looe [sic, Lew], in the town of Hatherleigh .. All which said Premises are now in the occupation of Mr George Pearse, the Proprietor ..'

Hatherleigh sources
1   NDRO 2378/6/6
2   Exeter Flying Post 3 February 1791 p 2 col 3
3   The Western Times 17 January 1835 p 1 col 3

Hemyock
Prings & Scaddings
Tanhouse

At Hemyock, tanning was an industry which, on present evidence, failed to benefit from the boom years at the beginning of the 19th century. Thomas Clode was a Hemyock tanner in 1694 [1] and John Marks was possibly tanning in 1756. [2]

There are two known sites in the parish – Tanhouse to the north and Prings and Scaddings, at Madford, to the south.

Prings & Scaddings
Location	ST 145 111
Operational	until c 1792

Scaddings, a house at Madford, and the location for an 18th century tannery

Prings and Scaddings, then about 25 acres, was offered to let in 1796 and was described as:
'.. all that Meffuage and Tenement called by the name of Prings and Scaddings, lately in the possession of Mr Clement Waldron, fituate at Madford .. well fituated for a Tannery, that Bufinefs having recently been carried on there; and diftant about Eight Miles from the Market Towns of Honiton, Cullompton and Wellington ..' [3]

Clement Waldron may well have been running a tannery here in the 1840s, but there is no indication of the industry as such: when the property was owned by the Reverend Nicholas Lightfoot, the acreage was largely unchanged. [4]

Today a thatched house of some vintage survives here and the stream, once forded at Madford, would have supplied the water for tanpits. The evidence, if any existed – for water power – has long gone.

Tanhouse
Location	ST 148 147
Operational	18th century

A farmhouse sign – practically the last remaining evidence for a tannery at the second Hemyock site

Tanhouse was a 60-acre estate, offered for sale in 1810. By then it was solely a farm:
'To be Sold by Auction, at the Squirrel Inn, in Wellington, county of Somerfet .. The Freehold and Inheritance of all that very desirable and compact Farm and Eftate, called TANHOUSE .. Sixty Acres ..' [5]

'Tan Plot Mead' is recorded on the Tithe Apportionment and adjoined the house, outbuildings and garden then surviving. [6] This appears to be where the tannery once stood and may have been used by John Marks in 1756. It stands above the stream, however.

Hemyock sources
1   A H Shorter, D&CNQ, 1952, from Devon and Conwall Record Society transcriptions of Hemyock parish registers: Clode's marriage
2   DRO 3137A/PO 48/12. Job Morgan apprenticed to John Marks of Tan house by consent, 1756
3   Exeter Flying Post 2 June 1796 p 2 col 3
4   DRO – Hemyock tithe map of 1843 and apportionment of 1841. Prings and Scaddings, Madford. Owned by Reverend Nicholas Lightfoot; occupied by Richard Benedictus. 1825 = Buildings, Courtlage and Mow plot 1825a = Garden, 1826 = Front Orchard, 1824 = Linhay and courtlage
5   Exeter Flying Post 31 May 1810 p 2 col 2
6   DRO – Hemyock tithe map of 1843 and apportionment of 1841. Tanhouse then owned by William Rowcliffe, occupied by James Twose. 62a 1r 25p total 867 = Tan Plot Mead, Meadow, 2-1-26

Holcombe Rogus

Ford Place

Location	ST 0507 1817
Operational	until circa 1840
Bark mill	water powered
Output	45 hides in 1826,
	60 hides a week in 1836

Leather was being made here early in the late 17th century: Ed Garnsey was tanner in 1667. [1] In 1710 Richard Garnsey, tanner, nominated a bondsman as a surety in a contract. [2] Richard Johns was a Holcombe tanner in 1731. [3]

The tanyard, at Ford Place, recently rebuilt by Elias Jarman, was offered for sale by auction in 1826. Jarman, like several other west country tanners, looked to expand his business after the wars with France. But trade slumped and he was forced into bankruptcy that year, [4] shortly after putting the tanyard on the market:

'To Tanners and Capitalists. TO be SOLD in FEE .. Lot 1. – An Excellent DWELLING-HOUSE, with a good Garden adjoining; together with a capital TAN-YARD, Capable of tanning from 40 to 50 hides per week, with a Bark Mill driven by water, with the necessary sheds and other requisite buildings, stable, cow-houses &c, and .. 18 Acres .. the Tan-Yard has lately been fitted up in a superior style, is now in full work .. 2,– A good MEADOW .. For viewing the Premises apply to Mr. ELIAS JARMAN (the owner) Holcombe Rogus, near Wellington ..' [5]

Jarman may have been related to the tanners of that name who ran a somewhat larger establishment at Bickleigh.

The premises were still for auction early in 1827. [6]

Business continued as the yard was offered to lease in 1836, and besides a further reference to the use of water power for grinding bark, the capacity had apparently increased to 60 hides per week:
'To Tanners. To be Let, for a Term of Years, with immediate possession, an excellent Dwelling-House, Offices and Tan-Yard, now in work by the owner, capable of tanning 60 Hides per week; with a Water Mill for grinding Bark, and every convenience attached; – situated well for purchasing Bark, there being no other yard within 6 miles. The taker may be accommodated with .. Land not exceeding 18 acres, and four cottages for Labourers. Sixty tons of bark may be had at a valuation ..' [7]

Closure came before mid century. By 1850 the tannery had been taken over by James Scott, a wood turner. [8] He and his family established a successful business manufacturing chairs, which are well known in the neighbourhood to this day. Waterpower continued to be used and an overshot waterwheel survived below the pond at Ford until the 1960s. [9]

Holcombe Rogus sources
1. DRO 1936M/L24
2. A H Shorter, The Tanning Industry in Devon and Cornwall, 1550-1850. Devon & Cornwall Notes & Queries, Volume XXV, 1952, 10-16, from Devon and Cornwall Record Society transcriptions of Holcombe Rogus parish registers
3. DRO 1936M/L150
4. Exeter Flying Post 17 August 1826 p 3 col 1
5. Exeter Flying Post 13 July 1826 p 3 col 3
6. The Alfred 26 December 1826 p 1 col 1, Woolmer's Gazette 6 Janary 1827 p 1 col 3
7. Woolmer's Gazette 30 January 1836 p 3 col 6
8. White's Directory, 1850, 327, Billings Directory of Devon, 1857, 222
9. Personal communication – Mr and Mr Tristram of Marjery's, and West End Farm, Holcombe Rogus, 2003
10. DRO Holcombe Rogus tithe map and apportionment, 1838, 16-acre Ford estate owned and occupied by William Webber including buildings by pond, item 552

The millpond at Ford Place in 2004. It has been considerably remodelled since the mid nineteenth century and partly occupies the site of tannery buildings [10]

Holsworthy

East Stanburys (part of yard)
Location   SS 3449 0348
Operational   to 1883

Part of the 19th century tannery stood on the bank of a tributary of the river Deer, opposite Cole's Mill. Local information suggests a second component was closer to the centre of town. But this may not have been the only yard in the parish: by the next stream further south three fields belonging to South Chasty farm in 1843 were known as Higher Tan-yard, Lower Tan-yard and East Tan-yard Marsh – at SS 341 021. This second site had by 1843 already reverted to arable and coarse pasture. [1]

Holsworthy individuals were tanning leather in the 17th and 18th centuries: William Bennett and John Kingford junior both held property in the town in the decade 1660-1670. [2] Leonard Fary was recorded as tanner here in 1731. [3]

The East Stanburys site was leased to members of the Hoskin family: John Hoskin in 1830, [4] and Richard Hoskin in 1841-1843 when it was owned by Elizabeth Heard. John Hoskin was a local man, baptised in Holsworthy in May 1785. His family lived in Chapel Street and suffered the early deaths sometimes familiar to our ancestors. His eldest son John died in July 1831, aged 21 and his daughter Mary died after a long illness, aged 24 in January 1840. [5] There was a demand for leather – in 1844 the town supported two curriers, a saddler and a harness maker. [6]

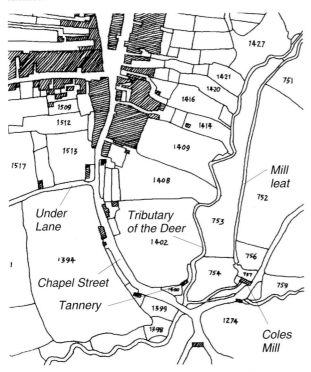

Part of the yard stood by a tributary of the river Deer. Part was in the town. From the 1843 tithe map

The tanyard suffered a disaster in April 1841:
'.. *On Monday last, a tremendous fire broke out at about 9 o'clock, in the Yard of Mr Richard Hoskin, tanner, of Holsworthy, which raged with increasing fury for several hours, and at one time (the adjoining houses being covered with thatch and the wind blowing strong from the SSE) threatened destruction to the whole town .. A large part of the tan-yard premises was burnt down, and the dwelling houses adjoining belonging to Mr Pearse, surgeon, Mr Bennett, butcher, and Mr Sleeman, carpenter and builder, were burnt to the ground ..*' [7]
This fire must have started in premises to the east of Fore Street or the north end of Chapel Street, to have affected so many neighbouring properties.

William Cole, previously a currier in the town, ran the tannery, aged 48 in 1851, with ten men. He was succeeded by William S Cole, probably his son, 33 in 1871, who then employed six men and a boy. Business had declined by 1881 when only two men worked here. The Coles lived at Myrtle Cottage in Chapel Street.[8] The tannery was still active in 1883 and Cole was the last tanner in the parish. [9]

Holsworthy was lacking in coppice land – oak bark wasn't available in any quantity locally in 1843 and was probably sourced from surrounding parishes. From 1825 Holsworthy had access to freight via the Bude Canal, with wharfs north east of the town. The canal was closed from 1891, the railway having reached the town in 1879: it may have hastened the closure of the tan yard, bringing leather goods from Crediton and possibly Northampton. [10]
What survives today? A housing development, Coles Mill Close, has been built on the site which may have housed a water-powered bark mill. Other buildings behind the Old Market Inn, thought to have been the drying sheds and working areas have gone too.

Holsworthy sources
1   DRO Holsworthy tithe map and apportionment: tanyard at East Stanburys item 1401, with garden 1400. Fields at South Chasty, items 1109, 1113, 1114.
2   NDRO 2239B-8/33, 2378/9/1
3   Transcript from parish records: D&CRS
4   Pigot & Co's Directory, Devonshire, 1830, reprinted 1993, 82
5   DRO – Holsworthy tithe map and apportionment 1843; Holsworthy census 1841 – Chapel Street, Richard Hoskin, 25, tanner, with wife and three sons. HO107 257\11 f 13 p 19; John Hoskin's baptism from Mormon IGIs. Woolmer's Gazette 6 August 1831 p 2 col 5 Woolmer's Gazette 25 January 1840 p 2 col 7
6   Pigot & Co's General Directory, Devonshire, 1844
7   Woolmer's Gazette 1 May 1841 p 3 col 5
8   Holsworthy census 1851 – Myrtle Cottage, William Cole, 48, tanner and currier employing 10 men. HO107 1896 f 127 p 2; 1871 census, Myrtle Cottage – RG10 2210; 1881 census, Myrtle Cottage – RG11 2265 f 47 p 28
9   The Post Office Directory of Devonshire and Cornwall, Kelly, 1873; Kelly's Directory 1883, 784
10   Bill Young and Bryan Dudley Stamp. Bude Canal. Past & Present. Privately published 1997.

Honiton

High Street/King Street
High Street/Silver Street

Honiton is a town on an old-established route to Exeter, a place serving travellers for centuries, with a long street once full of inns and stabling and with gig harness manufacturers and saddlers offering their services. [1] The town possessed two tanneries and unsurprisingly their public addresses were on the High Street, where most of the town's trade was conducted. One of the yards was away from the highway, roughly to the north of Silver Street, behind St Paul's church. [2] The other tannery was located behind the High Street and in King Street, running parallel to the south.

In 2004 an edge-runner stone, reputedly dating from c1780-1790, and from a Honiton tanyard, stood at the entrance to Tracey Mill, saved from a planned export to Japan.

Philipp Levermore, a Honiton tanner, was buried in 1655 [3] and John Colesworthy, tanner, died in 1790. [4] The Colesworthy family offered two tanyards to let in 1818:
'Tan Yards to Let, Honiton .. drying and bark houses .. well-established and extensive trade has there been conducted by the owner and his ancestors for a long series of years ..'
They were reputedly the only tanyards in Honiton at that time. [5]

Robert Adams was a Honiton tanner in 1830, but at which yard is not known. [6] In 1868 tanning was still a leading industry here, with the local historian Farquharson stating: *'There are also two breweries, two tanneries, and an iron foundry in the town ..'* [7]

Below: edge runner stone, reputedly used in a Honiton tannery in the late eighteenth century. It would have been used to grind oak bark. The rescued stone now stands at Tracey Mill

King Street/High Street

Location	ST 1595 0043
Operational	until circa 1886

Beed and Darke were at King Street in 1842-1844 [8] and this concern was then taken up by Richard Patch Harrison, here in 1851 and possibly earlier. He was a tanner and a currier, born in Topsham about 1823. The census gives his address as High Street [9] but the 1856 trade directory lists the location as 'King Street Tan Yard'. [10]

At King Street steam power may have been used to operate the liquor pumps and grind oak bark: new liquor valves and pipes to a cistern and a boiler were provided by Bodley's Foundry, Exeter, at some time between 1861 and 1865. [11] The yard stood by the Gissage, a tributary of the Otter, and this stream no doubt provided the water for the tan pits.

Richard Harrison, tanner, fellmonger and currier, continued business here in 1874 when he formed a partnership with William George Wheaton. The partnership ceased on 11 May 1875 with Harrison continuing alone. [12] In 1881, Harrison was aged 58; his son Richard J I Harrison, 23, as tanner and currier, contributed to the trade. [13] In 1883 the firm was trading from the High Street as Harrison & Pearce: Richard Harrison senior may have retired and his son appears to have gone into partnership. [14] Richard Harrison junior was not in Honiton on census night 1891 and the firm was not listed in 1897. [15]

High Street/Silver Street

Location	ST 163 008
Operational	until about 1900

The tannery behind Silver Street has, by a process of elimination, to relate to the second Honiton firm making leather.

In 1851 Martin and Edward Ashley were listed as curriers in Honiton; their housekeeper was their unmarried sister Elizabeth. The family came from Modbury, probably in 1849. [16] Edward and John Ashley were tanners in the High Street in 1856, 1873, 1878 and were still listed in 1902, although by then they would have been aged 80 and 78 respectively. [17] No details of their business have yet come to light – the numbers they employed, the facilities installed at the yard remain unknown.

Honiton sources
1 Sherborne Mercury 3 June 1805, p 4
2 A tannery at Honiton shown on OS 25" map of c 1890, sheet 70.4. Sited off Silver Street, and to NNE of St Paul's church
3 A H Shorter, D&CNQ, 1952, transcribed from D&CRS records

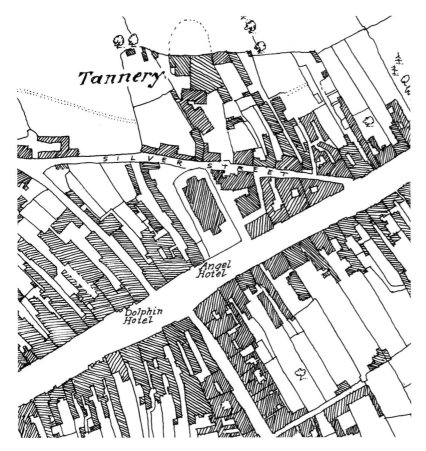

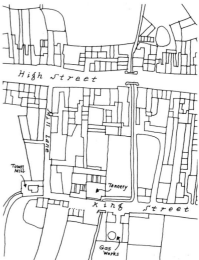

Left: one of the two Honiton tanneries stood to the north of Silver Street. From the 25" = 1 mile Ordnance Survey map of circa 1889, sheet 70.4

The other tanyard was in King Street, by the Gissage stream. From the Honiton Tithe Map and Apportionment, 1842

4 Exeter Flying Post 4 February 1790 p 3 col 1
5 Sherborne Mercury 30 March 1818 p 4, Exeter Flying Post 2 April 1818 p 1 col 3
6 Pigot's General Directory, Devonshire, 1830
7 A Farquharson, The History of Honiton, 1868, 63
8 DRO: Honiton tithe map and apportionment 1842, Thomas Beed owned house, buildings and tanyard, item 324; Pigot & Co's Directory, Devonshire, 1844, 69
9 Honiton census 1851 – High Street – HO 107 1863 f 192 p 2, also Mormon IGIs
10 Post Office Directory, Devon and Cornwall, 1856
11 DRO Bodley journals 67/5/2/1 folio 169-170
12 DRO 282M/Title H10. Harrison was due to pay Wheaton £1905-15-7 for his share of the partnership.
13 Honiton census 1881 – High Street – RG11 2132 f 65 p 14

14 Kelly's Directory, Devonshire, 1883, 784
15 Kelly's Directory of Devonshire and Cornwall, 1897, 1111
16 Honiton census 1851 – HO107 1863 f 129 p 17; Promissory note for £200 for Martin and Edward Ashley of Honiton to their father Martin Ashley of Modbury, P&WDRO 899/9 of 1849
17 Post Office Directory, Devon and Cornwall, 1856, The Post Office Directory of Devonshire and Cornwall, Kelly, 1873, Harrod's Devonshire Directory, 1878, 330, Kelly's Directory of Devonshire and Cornwall, 1897, 1111; Kelly's Directory of Devonshire and Cornwall, 1902, 1136; in the 1891 census Edward Ashley was aged 69 and John Ashley was 67; their sister Elizabeth was 65. They still lived in High Street. Honiton 1891 census – RG12 1670 f 115 p 13

Ilsington

Knighton

Location	not known
Operational	possibly to 1805 or later

This was an 18th century establishment, barely surviving, it seems, into the 19th century. John Motton was an Ilsington tanner in 1738. [1] The tanyard was offered for auction in 1805:

'TO TANNERS .. To be SOLD by AUCTION, at the Bell Inn, in Newton Abbot .. The Fee fimple of a TAN-YARD TENEMENT confifting of a dwelling-

houfe, with convenient out-houfes, a tan-yard, and two gardens, fituate in Knighton village, in the parifh of Ilfington, about midway between Newton Abbot and Afhburton.
For a view apply to Mr Penny in Knighton, aforefaid and for particulars application to be made to Mr Harris, Land-surveyor, Barnftaple ..' [2]
There is no evidence for the yard at Knighton today.

Ilsington sources
1 A H Shorter, D&CNQ, 1952, from D &CRS transcriptions from parish sources: John Motton, tanner, married in 1738-9
2 Sherborne Mercury 24 June 1805

Ipplepen

Combe Fishacre

Location	SX 8440 6474
Operational	until perhaps 1845
Bark mill	water powered
Output	15 hides per week in 1814

As in many Devon parishes, tanning was an established trade here in the 18th century: William Savery, an Ipplepen tanner, married in 1739. [1]

The tanyard on the Combe Fishacre estate was in existence in 1794. [2] The estate included a mansion, a lime kiln and a smithy, among other properties. In 1814 the tannery was offered to let, equipped with *'One of Bodley's Patent Bark Mills .. driven by water'*. George Bodley, an Exeter ironfounder, together with a Cullompton tanner and a teacher, had developed and patented the bark mill in 1801. [3] The property was then owned by T B Studdy, Esq: the throughput of the yard was small – only 15 hides per week. [4] Studdy probably lived at the nearby Combe House, rather than Combefishacre House which dates from 1830. Combe carries a stone plaque above a doorway with the inscription *'This house was built by T B Studdy in the year 1793'*. [5]

In 1834 the whole estate came onto the market, including a grist mill and thrashing machine: [6] *'For Sale, a Residence for a Respectable Family, Coombe House and Estate in the parish of Ipplepen, in the County of Devon; a large-size, substantially built Dwelling-House. Also a good Dwelling-House with a Tan Yard in full work, now out to rent, and to each of the Houses are Walled and other Gardens, Shrubberies and every necessary office for the Gentleman, Agriculturist, and Tanner with a Farm-House, Labourer's Cottage and Smith's Shop .. with 153 Acres of very rich Orchard, Watered Meadow, Pasture and Arable Land, in the South Hams, near the fashionable watering places and sea ports of Torquay and Teignmouth .. For a view and particulars, apply to Mr Studdy, on the Premises ..'* [7]

W Philpe was tanner here in 1842 when the High Sheriff of Devon ordered the sale of his stock – which would indicate he'd defaulted with the rent: *'Auction, on the Premises of Mr W Philpe .. Tanner .. comprising about 150 prime light Butts, 80 English Hides, 340 East India Kip Hides, 50 Calf Skins, 50 Salter Spanish Horse Hides, 150 Light Shoulders, 100 Light Bellies, a few Tons of English Bark, Bark Mill, Leather Roller, 2 Light Carts, 2 good Horses fit for all work .. there will be no reserve ..'* [8]

In 1844 the tanyard was in the hands of John Harris. Robert Petherbridge occupied premises which included the lime kiln and millpond. The kiln would have been useful, so close to the tannery; its lime used to remove the epidermis from the animal skins. The tanyard was then occupied by William Willcocks, with dwelling house, buildings, garden and orchards. He also leased a cottage and smithy nearby. [9]

Tanning ceased quite early here. It is not clear if Willcocks was making leather or using the premises for other purposes. At any rate no tanners were recorded at Combe or Combe Fishacre in 1851. [10] By the mid twentieth century the millpond had silted up and was marsh [11] and in June 2004 it appeared that the tannery buildings had been demolished.

Ipplepen sources
1. A H Shorter, from D&CRS transcriptions from parish sources
2. Sherborne Mercury 24 April 1794
3. Patent 2537 of 30 September 1801. Specification by Whitby, Bodley and Davis. The latter was a 'Dissenting Teacher' of Cullompton. The bark grinding mill was designed for wind, water or horse power.
4. Exeter Flying Post 10 March 1814, 31 March 1814 p 2 col 2
5. DOE Listing of Buildings of Special Architectural or Historic Interest, District of Teignbridge, parishes including Ipplepen, 1987, 78
6. Sherborne Mercury 23 June 1834 p 1
7. Woolmer's Gazette 5 April 1834 p 1 col 1
8. Woolmer's Gazette 11 June 1842 p 2 col 4
9. DRO – Ipplepen tithe apportionment 1844
   1510 = Lime Kiln and Quarry 0a 1r 7p
   1684 = Tan Yard Meadow. Pasture 3a 1r 34p
   1699 = Mill Pond 0a 2r 13p
   1682 = Tan Yard and Buildings. 0a 0r 24p
   1703 = Cottage & Smith's shop
10. Ipplepen census, 1851 – HO107 1871 f 432
11. Ordnance Survey map, Pathfinder 1351, Torbay, 1970

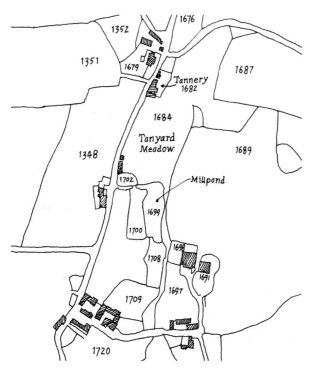

Left: the tannery at Combe Fishacre was extant in 1844 – from the parish tithe map and apportionment. The water-powered bark mill was driven using the millpond lying to the south

Ivybridge

Fore Street

Location	SX 636 561
Operational	until at least 1910
Bark mill	water powered
Output	70 - 80 hides per week, 1832-1850

The tanyard stood at the southern end of the town by the banks of the River Erme and on the tail race from the Union Corn Mills

A tanyard had recently been constructed here when offered for sale by the proprietor, Richard Westlake in 1808. Its capacity was '150 market hides'. [1] Ivybridge was then a village within the parish of Ermington. In 1814 George Tatershall leased the tannery from Sir John Leman Rogers. [2] The tanner here, John Sanders, was bankrupt in 1821, [3] but must have recovered sufficiently to have been listed in business in 1830. [4] The premises were for sale in 1832 with this notice made by James Lee Sanders, tanner of Bow [qv], very probably a relative of John:
'A DWELLING HOUSE and TANYARD at Ivybridge .. tanning 70 to 80 hides per week ..The pits and a 30 hogshead furnace are under cover, and there are extensive Drying Lofts, Bark Stores attached to the yard with a large never failing stream of water through it, which drives a well-constructed Wheel and Mills for grinding bark .. There is at all times a good supply of bark .. His Majesty's Victualling Office at Plymouth and the markets near produce a great many hides; and at Plymouth foreign ones, with Valonia and Bark, are imported.' [5]

There were no local buyers: in 1841 George Tatershall was in occupation. [6] The Tatersalls came from a family of landowners in Exbourne, on the other side of Dartmoor, and were related to the Dunnings, tanners of Winkleigh. [7] In 1847 the tannery was again for sale and was purchased by

John Tatershall: John and his relatives had borrowed £500 in 1842 and a further £1000 on bond in 1845. [8] The Ivybridge yard had been let by 1850 when once more on the market; William Wellington was the tanner at that time:
'JOHN TATTERSALL, Esq. the owner .. premises comprise a most comfortable residence and two productive Gardens, a Tan Yard, which is capable of tanning about 80 hides per week. with extensive Drying Lofts, and Bark Barns, Stabling and Wagon sheds. The Yard with the exception of the Lime Pits is under cover, and the Bark Mill and Pumps are worked by Water Power only, of which there is an unlimited supply. To view the premises apply to Wm. Wellington, the person having charge of the same, and for all further particulars to the Owner at Exbourne, Devon ..' [9] There were no buyers in 1850 and the yard was put up for auction in 1851. [10]

By 1855 Head & Sons ran the business here: Head's youngest son met with a fatal accident that year:
'On Thursday afternoon last, while the youngest son of Mr Head, tanner, at Ivybridge, a promising youth of 19 years of age, was occupied in feeding the bark mill, the machinery of which was driven by water – about 20 horse power – one of his feet by some unaccountable means was caught in the machinery .. he was drawn in and most dreadfully crushed .. such was the nature of the injuries received that human aid was of no avail.' [11]

In 1866 the firm took delivery of a new bark mill and drive gear from Bodley's Old Quay Foundry, Exeter. [12] Samuel Head had charge of affairs throughout the 1870s and into the 1880s. [13] The company was known as S Head & Son in 1910. [14] Sited by the leat from Union Mills, the Erme provided the motive power for the bark mill and water for the tan pits. [15]

Ivybridge sources
1 Sherborne Mercury 1 February 1808
2 DRO 1909B/T63 of 1835
3 Exeter Flying Post 18 January 1821 p 4 col 1
   From London Gazette 16-1-1821
4 Pigot's General Directory, Devonshire, 1830
5 Sherborne Mercury 26 November 1832
6 Ermington tithe map and apportionment, 1841, item 242 = House and Tan Yard; Pigots General Directory, Devonshire, 1844: John and George Tatershall, tanners
7 Exbourne census 1841, HO107 257/2 p 1: Agnes Tatershall living in John Tatersall's household, aged c50. Agnes Tatershall, born Exbourne, sister in law to Richard Dunning, tanner, Woodterrill, Winkleigh and resident there in 1851: Winkleigh census 1851. HO107 1894 f 229 p 12
8 DRO 1909B/E49
9 Sherborne Mercury 2 July 1850 p1
10 The Western Times 11 September 1847 p 1 col 3, Exeter Flying Post 25 September 1851 p 1 col 2
11 The Western Times 11 August 1855 p 7 col 3; Post Office Directory, Devon and Cornwall, 1856
12 DRO Bodley journals 67/5/2/1 folio 1309
13 The Post Office Directory of Devonshire and Cornwall, Kelly, 1873; Kelly's Directory 1883
14 Kelly's Directory of Devonshire and Cornwall, 1910, 1143
15 OS 25" map Devonshire sheet 125.2 of 1887

Kingsbridge and Dodbrooke

Fore Street, Kingsbridge
Church Street, Dodbrooke
Market Place, Dodbrooke
Wallingford, Dodbrooke

Kingsbridge was a leather producing town by the 16th century: John Knight was tanner here in the decade 1526-1536. [1] Hercules Lock and James Barry were both Dodbrooke tanners in the 17th century. [2] And Nicholas Bligh, tanner, married at Dodbrooke in 1703. [3]

William Hele ran a Dodbrooke yard – probably the premises at Church Street – from at least 1768 until his death in circa 1803:
'To Tanners. To be Lett for a Term of 21 years, a Tan-Yard, in Dodbrooke, near Kingsbridge, in which for a number of years the Tanning and Feltmonger- ing Bufinefs has been carried on with succefs by Mr Wm. Hele deceafed, confifting of ftore rooms, drying- places, wool lofts, a large Bark-barn, a Mill on a new construction, lately erected, which answers well. The Yard has a conftant fupply of excellent water for Tanning and will contain with Eafe 600 Hides. The taker to begin taking in new goods at Midsummer next .. Also to be Lett .. Malt-House, adjoining the Tan Yard ..' [4]

In the early 19th century Robert Pinhay was tanning at Kingsbridge as were J Gillard [5] and William Branscombe. Branscombe's yard was for auction in 1814. It may have been Hele's Dodbrooke premises – a fellmongering yard and a malthouse are referred to in both notices – or it may have been the Kingsbridge concern in Fore Street:
'To Tanners, Fellmongers .. To be Sold by Public Auction .. now in the possession of the proprietor, William Branscombe .. A Roomy Tan-Yard, with Coffee and Stone Mills for grinding Bark; a large Bark Barn, and Drying Lofts; a Fellmonger's Yard adjoining, with large Wool-Lofts; Working and Store-Rooms; a Tenement for a labourer; House for washing Wool and Skins, with a Drying Loft over, the whole most complete for carrying on these trades on a large scale. Also about 1 acre of Prime Orchard .. Farm-Yard, Malt-House, Pound-House .. barn called Kingston's Tenement or New Parks with a threshing machine ...'
This yard was still for sale in 1818. [6]

So in the Napoleonic era there were three tanneries in the town and this remained the case in 1824 when Kingsbridge could claim operations run by William Beer, by Branscombe & Cridland, and thirdly by John Miller. [7]

By 1884 the town was reduced to one tanyard: [8] the railway was yet to arrive but steamers were trading regularly with Plymouth.

The Beer family operated from Market Place, Dodbrooke in 1873 and was established in Kingsbridge for over fifty years: as noted, a William Beer was tanner in Fore Street in 1824. [9]
From at least 1830 to 1844 or sometime later Samuel Beer was listed as tanner of Dodbrooke. He was a merchant according to the 1841 census and was owner of the 70-ton schooner *Lady Buller*, launched at Salcombe in 1842. [10]

By 1871 this was William R Beer's concern; a landowner living at Quay House, he was Samuel's son. [11] The day-to-day running of the yard was then in the hands of Henry Brown, 34, who came from Newton Abbot and may have learnt his trade in that town. [12] The business ran as a partnership in 1878 – as Beer & Balkwill. Balkwill was probably Charles Balkwill, son of banker Benjamin Balkwill. [13] Dodbrooke Market was held where Church Street and Bridge Street meet, by the King of Prussia inn; Market Place tannery was nearby.

Quay House, Kingsbridge, the residence of William R Beer, in 1871. Now the offices of Kingsbridge Town Council

The Church Street tanyard was run by Henry and Robert Grant in 1830 and is shown on an 1841 map of Kingsbridge. [14] From 1850 or earlier this yard was run by James Pritchard & Co. [15] Pritchard had been a journeyman tanner at Market Place in 1841. [16] He was in partnership with Joseph Wyatt in 1851 and in 1856 the firm was known as Wyatt, Cowling & Pritchard, renamed Cowling, Pritchard & Gay by 1866. [17]
The yard was a little to the south of Duncombe Street and west of Bellevue Road which was known as Batts Lane in 1841.

Wallingford, Dodbrooke

Location	SX 736444
Operational	until circa 1907

One Dodbrooke yard was still functioning in the period 1897-1906 when James Wellington was listed at Wallingford, Dodbrooke.[18] Wallingford is out at the north end of the town, but the tanyard was sited near Bellevue Road,[19] and so 'Wallingford', listed in the directories of the time, may be just another name for the Church Street tannery. Wellington was born at Ivybridge and is very possibly the son of William Wellington, the manager of that town's tannery in 1850. This, the last Kingsbridge tannery, appears to have closed before 1910.[20]

Kingsbridge sources

1. 1526 – P&WDRO 69/M/2/406, 1535-6 – P&WDRO 69/M/2/89
2. Hercules Lock, 1641 – DRO 5721A/PF16, James Barry, 1651 – DRO 5721A/PF19-20 [and PF21-22 for 1655; PF 23-24 for 1656-7]
3. A H Shorter D&CNQ: transcribed from D&CRS Dodbrooke parish registers
4. Exeter Flying Post 23 February 1804 p 2 col 4
5. 1809 – Mary Wyatt, aged 9, apprenticed to Robert Pinhay, tanner of Kingsbridge. DRO 5721A/PO364, and Robert Penhay [Pinhay?], tanner of Kingsbridge, P&WDRO 567/84/2; Exeter Flying Post 23 June 1814 p 2 col 4
6. Sherborne Mercury 7 February 1814, 11 May 1818 p 2
7. Pigot's General Directory, Devonshire, 1824
8. James Fairweather. Salcombe and Neighbourhood. A Descriptive and Historical Guide. 1884
9. Tanners: 1830 – Samuel Beer, Dodbrooke – Pigot's General Directory, Devonshire, 1830; 1844 – Samuel Beer, Dodbrooke – Pigot's General Directory, Devonshire,

Leat from sluice below pond at Dodd Meadow

Stream – the Dod Brook

Approximate site of Lavers' woollen mill with an undershot waterwheel at Duncombe Street. Extant c 1810-1880

Church Street tannery. The one tannery shown on the map. It may have used the leat serving Lavers woollen mill. It may also have been the site of the Wallingford Tannery, which was near Bellevue Road, known as Batts Lane when this map was drawn

Lidstone's iron foundry, served, it seems by the Eastern Backway leat running on from Lavers woollen mill

Possible site of the Market Place tannery, close to the King of Prussia Inn

Town Mill, Kingsbridge, fed by a second leat running down Western Backway

The 19th century tanneries. An attempt to define the sites, using the 1841 map of Kingsbridge as a base. Map courtesy the Town Clerk's Office and the Cookworthy Museum

Kingsbridge sources, continued

1844, 74; 1850 – William Beer – White's Directory; 1866 – W R Beer, tanner, Dodbrooke – Post Office Directory of Devonshire 1866, 1277-1278; 1873 – W R Beer, Market Place, Dodbrooke – The Post Office Directory of Devonshire and Cornwall, Kelly, 1873

10 Pigot's General Directory, Devonshire, 1830 and 1844; Kingsbridge census 1841 – living next to Bridge Street and Boxhill; Woolmer's Gazette 14 May 1842 p 3 col 3

11 Kingsbridge census 1871 – RG10 2103 f 63 p 8 and 1881 – RG11 2183 f 59 p 6

12 Kingsbridge census 1871 – RG10 2103 f 46 p 6

13 White's Directory, Devonshire, 1878, 1090; Kingsbridge census 1881 – RG11 2183 f 28 p 10

14 Pigot's General Directory, Devonshire, 1830

15 White's Directory, 1850

16 Kingsbridge census 1841

17 Kingsbridge census 1851 – HO 107 1876 f 91, Post Office Directory, Devon and Cornwall, 1856

18 Kelly's Directory of Devonshire and Cornwall, 1897, 1111

19 Kingsbridge census 1881 – RG11 2183 f 65 p 18 – 22

20 Kelly's Directory of Devonshire and Cornwall, 1902 and 1906 editions

Kingskerswell

Broadgate
Location   not yet identified*
Operational   until c 1821

William Mengery Hole owned the tannery here. In 1808 he was then advertising for staff. [1]

By 1811 he may have been struggling to make the business successful as the tannery was for lease or sale:

'.. All that Capital TAN-YARD, with the Patent Bark Mill and Copper Pumps, and Eleven Acres of Ground, more or less, about three acres of which orchard, a new-built Dwelling-House, a barn, bark-house, stable, &c, situate in the parish of Kingscarswell, near Newton Bushell, in the county of Devon. The bark mill is worked by water; the same wheel also works the pumps.
For which purpose a Survey will be held at the Public-house in Kingscarswell .. For viewing the premises apply to Mr. W. M. Hole, the proprietor.' [2]

Hole attempted to sell again in 1813 and 1818 but by the latter year the market was heading for a slump and in 1822 he was forced into bankruptcy, to re-appear later at Ottery St Mary. [3]

Kingskerswell sources
1 Exeter Flying Post 2 June 1808 p 4 col 3
2 Sherborne Mercury 15 April 1811
3 Exeter Flying Post 18 March 1813 p 2 col 3, 30 April 1818 p 4 col 4, 28 February 1822 p 1 col 3; 11 April 1822 p 1 col 2 [* sale of house and tan-yard: Broadgate and tanyard with 2.25 acres of orchard and 7.25 acres of land. Right of common on Milber Down. Adjoined new road [to Torquay]. Possible location in Haccombe parish. Not evident on Kingskerswell TA].

Kingston

Kingston Town
Location   SX 637 478
Operational until 1789 or a little later
Tan pits   capacity for 70 kieves of leather

Kingston's tannery lasted only until the late 18th century, it seems. It was advertised to let for 14 years by Mrs Joan Froude in 1784. [1] Mrs Froude advertised again in 1789:

'A TAN-YARD, &c. To be LETT, A good FARM-HOUSE, Pound-Houfe, Engine-Pound and Prefs, with convenient Out-Houfes, an Orchard, three Herb-Gardens and a little Field; together with a large and commodious Tan-Yard, capable of holding 70 kieves of leather .. The premifes are fituate in Kingfton Town, three miles from Modbury, feven from Kingfbridge, and twelve from Plymouth and within a mile of a navigable river.
A furvey will be held at the aforefaid .. for letting the above premifes .. And if there be no bidders inclined to take the premifes for the tanning bufinefs, the furvey will be continued for letting the fame without the tan-pits, which in that cafe are to be taken up, and the yard will be capable of being made a very good walled garden ..' [2]

It may be that there was no one wishing to run a tannery at Kingston in 1789; the parish is relatively remote and the yard was probably small, and a tenant would have had to compete with Plymouth, Plympton and Modbury tanners, not to mention those at Kingsbridge. There was a stream in the village, but possibly not powerful enough to operate a bark mill.

A car park behind the fire station in Kingston village is believed to be the tanyard site. [3]

Kingston sources
1 Sherborne Mercury 9 August 1784
2 Sherborne Mercury 27 May 1789
3 Personal communication from Mrs Trumble of Kingston, March 2005

Kingston Fire Station is said to be close to the 18th century tannery site which lies between it and the Dolphin Inn, in Yellands Park. A stream runs in culvert under the road here

Loxbeare

Chopland	
Location	SS 9135 1485
Operational	to 1887 or later
Bark mill	possibly water-powered – leat from Pantacridge
Staff	8 in 1851, 9 in 1871

The tanyard at Loxbeare was known as Chopland in 1787 when the tanner was Henry Besley. [1] He'd been leasing the yard since at least 1774. [2] Chopland has been renamed Leigh Farm and is now a private residence: the old name is thought to be a corruption of 'Chapel land' as a medieval chapel stood nearby at Leigh Barton.

A successor to Besley was Thomas Moon, who in 1804 was seeking a journeyman tanner – at the height of the Napoleonic wars. [3]

Moon was a family associated with tanning in Bristol and North Somerset, rather than Devon. By 1812 and possibly earlier but certainly in 1817 the tannery was occupied by Peter Sharland. His daughter Elizabeth married John Ashford of Woodbury in April that year in the parish church. [4] [See the section on the Sharland family]. Peter Sharland died in 1829 and his son William ran the family's other tannery at Lower Waterhouse, Cheriton Fitzpaine, retiring to Exeter in 1851. Ashford either inherited, bought or leased the Loxbeare tannery He was tanner here in 1841 and ten years later, aged 63, he employed eight labourers. By then he was a widower. His unmarried niece, Catherine Sharland, born in Hampshire, appears to have kept house. His unmarried son John Henry Ashford, 28, farmed the 198 acre Leigh Barton, adjoining, also employing eight labourers. His sister Jane kept house at the Barton. [5] Her sister

Elizabeth married Plymouth merchant Alfred Jefferd at Loxbeare in 1852. [6]

Then John Henry Ashford married Elizabeth Wills of Tiverton in August 1857. [7] In 1870 his father had retired to Leigh Barton and John Henry Ashford, now 48, was running the tannery with nine men and farming 191 acres with a further eight. [8] He was still running both the tannery and the farm in 1883, aged 70. [9] He may have retired thereafter and while his wife Elizabeth bore six children, none appears to have taken on the business and it seems the tannery closed before the 19th century was out, although it was still in use in 1887. [10]

Today the leat which ran from Pantacridge can still be traced as it approaches the tannery. The tan pits at Leigh Farm now form a sunken garden given over to lawn; the leat ran in at high level above them, so providing water as it was required, without the need to pump. There is now no evidence of a water-powered bark mill, although it would have been feasible to have had such an installation here.

Loxbeare sources
1 Exeter Flying Post 10 May 1787 p 3
2 DRO 1148Madd/2/L25/4
3 Exeter Flying Post 16 August 1804 p 1 col 5
4 Exeter Flying Post 20 August 1812 p 4 col 5
  [1812: Peter and William Sharland, tanners, serving on a committee at Exeter under George Barne's chairmanship]
  Exeter Flying Post 1May 1817 p 4 col 2
  [Peter's daughter's marriage to John Ashford]
5 Loxbeare census for 1841, HO 107 255\3 f 7 p 6
  Loxbeare and Calverleigh census, 1851
  HO 107 1889 f 381 p 5
6 The Western Times 18 September 1852 p 4 col 5
7 The Western Times 15 August 1857 p 5 col 2
8 Trade directory for 1870;
  Loxbeare census 1871. RG10 2174 f 62 p 7
9 Kelly's Directory 1883
10 Ordnance Survey Devonshire, 25"= 1 mile, sheet 34.13 of 1889, surveyed c 1887

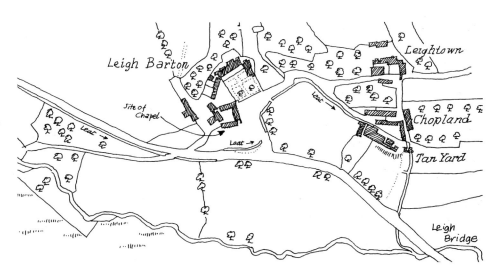

Loxbeare tannery in 1889 from the 25" to 1 mile Ordnance Survey map. The leat, which came from Pantacridge, runs in alongside the Witheridge road on the left of the map. Chopland may well be a corruption of chapel land

Milton Abbot

Park, Chillaton
Location   SS 4334 8195
Operational   until circa 1879
Bark mill   water powered

Thomas Courtice was a tanner of Milton Abbot in 1781 [1] and Isaac Mason was tanner in 1795.[2] The Courtice family continued to run a yard here for the following century: Richard Courtice was producing leather in the period 1816-1822 [3] and a second Thomas Courtice had control in 1833. [4] He was listed as Thomas Curtis in the 1839 tithe apportionment, which identified the site at Park, in Chillaton village. The property, then owned by the Rev. J P Carpenter, was a little over 7 acres. [5]

In 1841 Courtice's household included his wife Mary, two infant sons, Thomas and Richard and three tanners – journeymen Charles Symons and Thomas Node, both aged 20, and apprentice George Blake, 18. In addition he employed two servants. [6]
From the 1851 census we also learn that Thomas Courtice was farming 50 acres and employing two labourers, that he was 43 and born in Marhamchurch in Cornwall. His wife Mary was born in Landrake. [7]

Thomas Courtice died on 13 February 1859, aged about 51. He left an estate worth nearly £1,000. The 1861 census return records his widow Mary Courtice running the tannery with her two sons Thomas and Richard now aged 21 and 20 respectively. The servants had gone: presumably her four daughters helped in the house. The farm was now 97 acres. [8]

In 1871 Mary was still at Park, aged 58. She'd reduced the farmland to 42 acres. Her sons were still resident, but possibly not involved in the tannery: her daughter Elizabeth had married Charles Marshall, 29, from Stoke Damerel, and he was listed as the tanner here, living in the same household as the Courtice family. [9]

Ten years later the farm was reduced to 20 acres and Mary lived alone with her eldest son. Her second son Richard had an 80 acre farm elsewhere in the parish. His sister Catherine was housekeeper. [10] Mary was still recorded as tanner at Park in 1883, [11] but in practice tanning had possibly ceased by 1879, as there was no one listed as tanner at Park in 1881.

The bark mill here was water-powered, with a leat, partly in culvert, running from the stream that once powered Chillaton Mill. The bark mill is now a garage; the tanner's house remains, as do outbuildings, possibly once serving as working areas and drying lofts, but now converted to residential use.

Milton Abbot sources
1   P&WDRO 460/57
2   P&WDRO 460/59
3   NDRO 1142B/T61/11, P&WDRO 460/66, 68 and 69
4   P&WDRO 460/70
5   DRO – Milton Abbot tithe map and apportionment, 1839: item 617 = House, Tan Yard &c
6   Milton Abbot census 1841 – HO107 249\3 f 11 p 15-16
7   Milton Abbot census 1851 – HO107 1884 f 151 p 7
8   Milton Abbot census 1861 – RG9 1463 f 94 p 7
9   Milton Abbot census 1871 – RG10 2148 f 91 p 12
10 Milton Abbot census 1881 – RG11 2220 f 84 p 11, RG11 2221 f 20 p 5
11 Post Office Directory of Devonshire 1866, 1873 and 1883

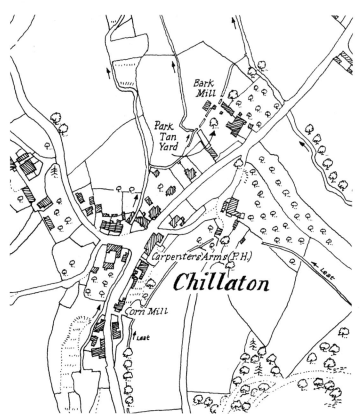

Left: Chillaton in the 1880s, from the Ordnance Survey sheets 97.2 and 97.6. Information on Park tanyard added from the tithe map, after a site visit. The water-powered bark mill was powered by a partially culverted leat. The Carpenter's Arms is now the Chichester Arms

Park Farm, Chillaton. Once the tanner's house; converted bark mill below

Modbury

New Road / Poundwell Street

Location	SX 658 515
Operational	closed before 1887
Tan pits	50 in 1819
Staff	5 in 1851

An 18th century tannery very probably existed in the town but there is no historical record for it at present.

R Horsewell, the Modbury tanner, married in 1813. [1] In 1819 his tanyard was for sale. Like a number of other Devonians, Horsewell seems to have expanded operations during the wars with France only to be undone by the postwar slump:

'To be Sold .. in Fee, An excellent TAN-YARD, in Modbury, late in possession of Mr Horsewell, comprising 50 pits, a large newly erected Drying-Loft with Store House .. [contact] Messrs Andrew & Sons, solicitors, Modbury ..' [2]

By 1830 Francis Cridland was at the New Road yard, then known as New Street: he may be the Cridland who partnered Mr Branscombe at Fore Street, Kingsbridge, in 1824. [3] His address was Poundwell Street in 1844 and 1850: the tannery probably stood between New Street and Poundwell Street. In 1850 woolstapling was a second trade for Cridland [4] and he may have died in 1850 as his will dates from that year. [5]

John Lightfoot, a Modbury tanner, died in 1844, but his premises are not presently known. [6]

Henry Choake or Coake was running the New Road yard by 1851. Aged 35, he employed five labourers here, having moved from Ivybridge some time after

Owner of the Brownston Street tannery, Richard Ashley. Photograph courtesy Modbury Local History Society

1847. [7] Choake was listed as tanner, fellmonger and currier in 1870 and eight years later his tannery was still at work. [8] It is not indicated on the Ordnance Survey map of 1887 and there is no clear evidence on the ground today. [9]

Brownston Street

Location	SX 6587 5168
Operational	from 1861 to 1890 or later

A second tannery was at Bermondsey Place, Brownston Street. Martin Ashley, born circa 1786, at Callington in Cornwall, had established a currier's business at Brownston Street by 1841. He and his wife Grace raised a large family which included five sons all of whom became curriers. [10]

Two elder sons, Martin and Edward Ashley, had left Modbury and set up their own business in Honiton at some time between 1841 and 1851: curriering initially, but later tanning as well. [11] Edward was later joined by his younger brother John. [12]
Martin Ashley senior died in May 1861, leaving an estate valued at a little under £600. His will was proved by two sons who had remained in Modbury, Richard and Charles. [13] Following the death of their father they too ventured into tanning – tanners and curriers were permitted to operate on the same premises from 1850; previously the two trades had been required to function on separate sites.
Their father's home had been 9 Brownston Street; the new business was established where this street met Back Lane and was otherwise known as Bermondsey Place. In 1891 Charles, aged 60, lived with his wife and daughters at 18 Brownston Street, and Richard, aged 69, was next door at number 19, with his wife and daughters. [14]

Bermondsey Place recalls the centre of tanning in London; the country's leading leather-producing district. Possibly an Ashley served an apprenticeship there. The facade of this building survives on the corner of Brownston Street and Back Lane. The old

The Brownston Street tannery in 2005

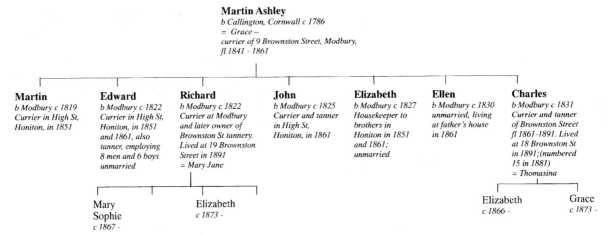

Martin Ashley
b Callington, Cornwall c 1786
= Grace –
currier of 9 Brownston Street, Modbury,
fl 1841 - 1861

Martin
b Modbury c 1819
Currier in High St,
Honiton, in 1851

Edward
b Modbury c 1822
Currier in High St,
Honiton, in 1851
and 1861, also
tanner, employing
8 men and 6 boys
unmarried

Richard
b Modbury c 1822
Currier at Modbury
and later owner of
Brownston St tannery.
Lived at 19 Brownston
Street in 1891
= Mary Jane

John
b Modbury c 1825
Currier and tanner
in High St,
Honiton, in 1861

Elizabeth
b Modbury c 1827
Housekeeper to
brothers in
Honiton in 1851
and 1861;
unmarried

Ellen
b Modbury c 1830
unmarried, living
at father's house
in 1861

Charles
b Modbury c 1831
Currier and tanner
of Brownston Street
fl 1861-1891. Lived
at 18 Brownston St
in 1891;(numbered
15 in 1881)
= Thomasina

**Mary
Sophie**
c 1867 -

Elizabeth
c 1873 -

Elizabeth
c 1866 -

Grace
c 1873 -

The Ashley family, curriers and tanners of Modbury and Honiton. Source: census returns

Modbury in 1886: the Brownston Street tannery is indicated at the junction of Back Street – now Back Lane – and Brownston Street. The second tannery was not indicated but probably stood just north of Poundwell House and west of New Road. The stream running in from the north east, above Broad Street, may well have supplied its tan pits. From the Ordnance Survey map, 25" = 1 mile, sheet 125.15, published in 1887

south wall also survives, but the rest of the structure has been gutted and rebuilt as a block of flats. The stream rising at Silver Well, to the north, may have supplied the yard's tanpits with water.

Modbury sources

1 Exeter Flying Post 18 November 1813 p 4 col 2
2 Exeter Flying Post 28 January 1819 p 4 col 5
3 Pigot's Directory, 1830, 88; Pigot's General Directory, Devonshire, 1824
4 Pigot's General Directory, Devonshire, 1844, 75; White's Directory, 1850
5 Will of Francis Cridland of Modbury DRO – 1078/IRW/C/1402 of 1850
6 Exeter Flying Post 13 January 1842 p 2 col 7
7 Modbury census 1851 – HO 107 1876 f 296 p 19
8 Post Office Directory, Devon and Cornwall, 1856, Post Office Directory of Devonshire 1866, 1278, Devon Directory, 1870, Harrod's Devonshire Directory, 1878, 390
9 New Road, Modbury, shown on OS 25" sheet 125.15 of 1887
10 Modbury census 1841 – HO107 216/8 f 10 p 13
11 Honiton census 1851 – HO107 1863 f 129 p 17
12 Honiton census 1861 – RG9 1375 f 103 p 15
13 Will of Martin Ashley, senior, died 10 May 1861
14 Modbury census 1891 – RG12 1719 f 49 p 6; also Post Office Directory of Devonshire 1866, 1278; White's Directory, Devonshire, 1878, 1090; White's Directory 1890 and Modbury, Our Inheritance. Modbury Local History Society, 1980

Moretonhampstead

Lime Street/Millbrook
Steward
Leign, Doccombe

In the late 18th century leather manufacture provided a living for a number of Moreton tradesmen – for tanners, tawers, curriers, saddlers, a heelmaker and a dozen shoemakers. [1] Tanning was still noted as 'rather extensive' in the town in 1844, [2] but after 1850 the business appears to have dwindled. Until the arrival of the turnpike road from Exeter in 1815, Moreton was relatively isolated from the outside world, and of necessity, a self-reliant place. Even as late as 1850 the Exeter road was described as no better than a ploughed field in places.

Hornhills, Lime Street	
Location	SX 7550 8621
Bark mill	Possibly horse powered
Tan pits	80 in 1852
Operational	until 1852 or later
Staff	5 in 1851

As in other Devon parishes, farming and tanning were often combined. Thomas White, listed as a tawer – a maker of white leather – in 1793, was also a farmer and tanner with a tanyard and houses at the end of Lime Street, where it becomes Shute Lane. [3] In 1851 the family residence was in Forder Street, later Ford Street. Here too in the mid nineteenth century lived James Neck, James Aggett and Samuel Pasmore, all curriers. Neighbours included tawers, saddlers, harness-makers and shoemakers.

Thomas White, who had married Susanna Dunsford in 1802, [4] was listed as a tanner of Market Place in 1824. [5] He was in business until at least 1847, when there was a fire at his house:
'Moretonhampstead. A destructive fire occurred here on Monday afternoon. It commenced in the back part of the extensive premises of Mr Thomas White, tanner &c, near the Shambles, and notwithstanding the prompt and persevering efforts of the inhabitants, aided by two engines, the whole of Mr White's premises, including his dwelling-house, and the houses of Mr Loveys, ironmonger, and Miss Cole, dressmaker, were destroyed. Several houses in the vicinity are also much injured. It is not known how the fire originated but it is believed to have been accidental.' [6]

In 1850 his sons Thomas and Edward ran the tanyard, employing four men and a boy. Their father was farming 50 acres, aged 70, in 1851. [7] His eldest daughter married the magistrate John Hill of Exeter and lived at the Georgian Pitt House at 48 Forder Street. William White (1816-1853), a younger brother to Thomas and Edward, became a lawyer. Thomas (1806-1881) and Edward (1811-1886) lived in The Square in a building now known as Moreton

House. Members of the family were staunchly Unitarian; their tomb stands in the chapel graveyard.

George Bragg of Forder House was a successful tanner in the decade 1820-1830. His offspring didn't venture into the trade; like William White they entered the legal profession. [8] White offered the yard to let in 1852: *'.. consisting of 80 pits, with Bark Mill, Drying Lofts, Barns, &c ..'* [9]

Forder House, 50 Ford Street, dating from 1800. George Bragg's residence

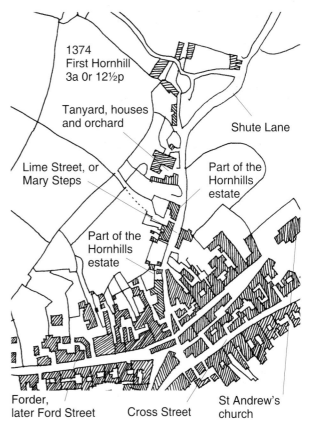

From the Moretonhampstead tithe map and apportionment of 1839: the Lime Street tanyard and some other properties owned by Thomas White. The tanyard site had been redeveloped by 1902

Steward
Location	SX 765 852
Operational	converted to flour mill by 1860
Bark mill	water powered
Tan pits	59 in 1826

The overshot waterwheel at Steward is probably a second-hand 20th century import. It was cast by Bartle of Carn Brea, near Redruth, in Cornwall

A second tannery was at Steward, south of the town and hard by the road to Bovey. John Nosworthy was tanner here in the early nineteenth century. [10] Bankrupted in 1826, in the decade of decline following the Napoleonic Wars, the tannery was put on the market, the sale notice providing a rare insight into the features of one of the Moreton concerns:
'*TO be SOLD, (by Order of the Assignees of JOHN NOSWORTHY, a Bankrupt,) by Public Auction .. Lot 1.– All that TAN-YARD, 61 feet 6 Inches, by 45 feet, inclosed by a Wall; containing 59 Tan-Pits, with a Copper Furnace, .. Courtlage, and .. Stream of Water, with which a Bark-Mill is worked; a commodious Drying Shed over the said Tan Yard, 60 feet 6 inches by 22 feet 6 inches; two Store-Rooms, one 28 feet by 14, and the other 18 feet by 14, Bark-house, Work-house, &c — The Buildings are all in excellent repair .. at Steward, within a mile of .. Moretonhampstead .. a neighbourhood where plenty of Bark may be obtained at a small expense of carriage .. Lot 2,— All that WOOD or COPPICE ..*' [11]
The bark mill was powered by a waterwheel utilising the waters of the Wray Brook, a tributary of the River Bovey.

In 1839 a mill and the tanyard here were owned by John Saunders and occupied by William Coombes. [12] Sometime before 1860 the premises reverted solely to milling grain, an activity here prior to 1811:
'*Moretonhampstead. To be LET, for a Term, from Christmas-day next, all those FLOUR and GRIST MILLS, called "STEWARD MILLS", the property of Mr William Snow, now in the occupation of Mr Arscott, situate about one mile from Moreton .. ..*

with about one acre of land. The mills are in good repair ..' [13]
Today the mill buildings have been converted. The overshot waterwheel seen turning by the road was cast by Bartle of Carn Brea, near Redruth, probably towards the end of the 19th century.

Leign, Doccombe
Location	SX 783 875
Operational	until circa 1845
Output	12 hides a week in 1845

The third known tannery in the parish was near the turnpike road, on the Exeter side of the village. The 166-acre estate was owned by the Dean and Chapter of Canterbury. [14] John Germon, the tanner here in 1802, suffered the loss of leather from his drying loft, valued at £20. [15] Richard Medland Germon, a relative no doubt, was recorded as a tanner on his marriage in August 1814. [16] He died in 1845 and this tanyard, three miles away from the town, was offered for sale. It was small scale, with an output limited to only 12 hides a week. [17] Tanning at Leign then appears to have ceased.

Entrance to Leign Farm in 2005: the tannery stood out of shot some way to the right of the vehicle

Moretonhampstead sources
1 Universal Directory 1793
2 Pigots General Directory, Devonshire, 1844, 79
3 DRO Moretonhampstead tithe map and apportionment, 1839. Hornhills estate; item 1523 - tan yard, houses
4 Moretonhampstead History Society web site, 2004. Section on 'The Leather Trade'
5 Pigot's General Directory, Devonshire, 1824
6 The Western Times 11 September 1847 p 5 col 3; for a full report see: Exeter Flying Post 9 September 1847 p 3 col 1
7 White's Directory, Devonshire, 1850; Moretonhampstead census 1851 – HO 107 1871 f 59 p 8-9
8 Moretonhampstead History Society, op cit; George Friend, Memories of Moretonhampstead, Devon Books, c 1987, 31-32; Pigot's General Directory, Devonshire, 1830
9 Exeter Flying Post 15 April 1852 p 1 col 1
10 Pigot's General Directory, Devonshire, 1824
11 Exeter Flying Post 29 June 1826 p 1 col 4
12 Tithe map and apportionment: items 1610/1 - tanyard, mill
13 Exeter Flying Post 19 December 1860 p 1 col 1
14 Tithe map and apportionment: item 551 - tanyard, offices
15 Moretonhampstead History Society, op cit
16 Exeter Flying Post 18 August 1814 p 4 col 2
17 Exeter Flying Post circa 4 September 1845

Musbury

Fore Street
Location   SY 272 946
Operational   until circa 1875

Malvern House. Owned with the tannery by Francis Gillett in 1841

The tanyard at Musbury was in Fore Street, now known as 'The Street'. A stream provided water for the yard's tan pits. There was a tannery in the parish in 1712, possibly here. [1] Thomas Roper was the tanner in 1831. [2] In 1841 the tannery was owned by Francis Gillett and consisted of a house, buildings and yard, a garden and a tanyard – in all occupying a space of 2 rods 21 perches. [3] Following the death of Thomas Farwell Roper his stock in trade and the lease of the tanyard were offered at auction in 1842. The stock included: *'2402 Butts, 3006 Kips, 2988 Shoulders and Bellies, about 200 Horse Hides, 448 Hides in the Hair'*, and *'about 50 tons of Bark'*. Prior to 1830 Roper had been tanning at Colyton. [4]

Francis and Mary Gillett also owned and ran the nearby 128 acre Knights Farm at Maidenhayne. Compton, one of their sons, was 15 in 1841; a tanner's apprentice. [5] In 1850 he was recorded as the Musbury tanner. [6] The following year he was aged 27, employing six men; his wife Elizabeth was a domestic economist. [7] In 1856 he was here but died in 1860, aged 36, cause unknown, and in 1861 his widow Elizabeth, aged 34, was operating the tannery with six men and a boy. She may have had assistance from John W Gillett, a relative it appears, who was present on census night. Her neighbour Samuel Collins, aged 48, was also a tanner. [8]

Elizabeth Gillett continued to run the yard into the 1870s, but now with only two men. [9] By 1881 she had given up the business and was living in Musbury with one unmarried daughter. [10] The concern was probably too small to remain competitive with Baker's tannery at nearby Colyton.

The road from Axmouth to Axminster, bypassing the village, did not exist in 1841. The entrance to Malborough Close and the Musbury garage overlie the site; Malvern House was the tanner's residence.

Musbury sources
1. From D&CRS transcripts of parish records
2. Woolmer's Gazette 25 June 1831 p 3 col 3
3. DRO – Musbury tithe map and apportionment, 1841: tanyard items 687, 688 and 689. Knight's Farm – house, stables, barn and cottage, item 505
4. Woolmer's Gazette 26 March 1842 p 1 col 1; Pigot's Directory, 1830
5. Musbury census 1841 – HO 107 201\8 f 5 p 4
6. White's Directory 1850
7. Musbury census 1851 – HO 107 1862 f 611 p 3
8. Post Office Directory, Devon and Cornwall 1856; George Pullman, Book of the Axe, London 1875, 748; Musbury census 1861 – RG9 1373 f 96 p 9
9. Musbury census 1871 – RG10 2036 f 19 p 11, The Post Office Directory of Devonshire and Cornwall, Kelly, 1873
10. Musbury census 1881

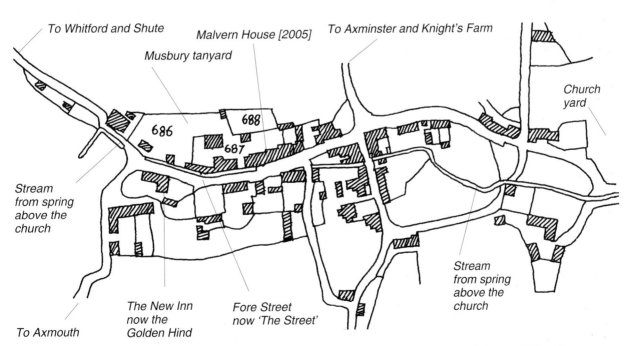

Musbury in 1841. From the tithe map, but re-orientated to the north. The tanyard, items 687 – House buildings and yard, 688 – Garden and 686 – Tan Yard, stood on the north side of Fore Street. The street lost it status when the village was bypassed by a new road from Axmouth to Axminster

Newton Abbot

Bradley Lane
Vicary's tannery
Location	SX 856 713
Operational	until circa 1940
Staff	250 in 1881

Branscombe's tannery
Location	SX 856 713
Operational	absorbed into Vicary's, it seems
Staff	10 in 1851
Tan pits	over 100 in 1837

Vicary's bark mill
Kingsteignton Road
Location	SX 8632 7166

a water-powered mill

Newton Abbot is a 19th century creation, formed from Newton Abbot in Wolborough parish – once held by Torre Abbey – on the south bank of the Lemon and Newton Bushel in Highweek parish on the north bank. These communities grew to form the present town, near the head of the Teign estuary. [1]

In the Victorian era tanning was to become one of the town's leading industries, together with heavy engineering and malting. Following the extension of Brunel's broad gauge here in 1846, the South Devon Railway established its locomotive and carriage works by the station [2] and there were also three independent iron foundries run by Beare, Polyblank and Webber.

Two tanneries were operational in 1844, both sited along Bradley Lane and water was supplied by leats from the Lemon. Downstream, the last mill powered by the river before its confluence with the Teign was a bark mill serving the tanneries. It ground oak bark brought from woods in the vicinity of Ashburton. [3] Vicary and Branscombe were the two families associated with the tanning industry in the town. Moses Vicary owned the tannery to the west, covering quite an area and his competitor Samuel Branscombe held a more compact yard, immediately to the east, but west of Highweek Street. Both Vicary and Branscombe then effectively lived 'over the shop' with houses in this street. [4]

Robert Vicary was the first of the family involved in the trade in Newton Bushel. He arrived from Crediton in 1747. [5] A Moses Vicary was trading in wool in 1788; [6] he was possibly the father of Moses Vicary who married Rebecca Doke on 29 August 1802 at Wolborough. [7] Moses was a Newton Bushel tanner in 1824, as was Samuel Branscombe junior. Samuel Branscombe senior was listed as a fellmonger. [8] There was very possibly a third tannery in the town at that date as Samuel Pope was advertising a yard for sale or lease in the following year. [9]

In 1825, too, Branscombe suffered a major setback when his premises were destroyed by fire:
'On Saturday morning last, a fire broke out in the stables of Mr Vicary, tanner of Newton Bushel, in which a horse was burnt and two others much injured, a bark-mill and leather loft, with its contents were also destroyed; the flames blown with a strong west wind next caught the premises of Mr Samuel Branscombe, tanner and fellmonger, adjoining, and we regret to say, the whole of the buildings in his yard (with the exception of an empty loft) with a heavy stock of leather and wool was consumed: – poor Branscombe's loss is very severe, all his future prospects being apparently destroyed, no part of his property having been insured since Michaelmas last, but such is the estimation in which he is held that a subscription has been entered into by his fellow townsmen, a list of which has been handed to us, and as we find he is also well known and much respected in this city [Exeter], we trust the exertions his friends are making for him will be crowned with success .. The present ascertained loss amounts to £1000.' [10]

Branscombe latterly worked in partnership with Goodenough and their tannery was offered for sale by auction in 1837. It was advertised as:
'.. having more than 100 pits and latches, and a proportionate number of lime-pits, with a good supply of water; Bark mills, with machinery for raising water from the pits attached; large Lofts for drying and preparing the leather; a large and newly-erected Bark Barn, Stable, Cart Linhays, ranges of Turf Racks; &c and a plot of Orchard Ground behind. These Premises .. are about an acre and a half of ground ..' [11]

Branscombe continued to run his tannery until about 1852. He was 59 in 1851 and employed ten men in his yard. [12] His wife Mary had died in 1847, aged 45, leaving Branscombe a widower with nine children. [13]

Moses Vicary, the owner of the larger tannery to the west, had a somewhat diverse family. His eldest son Gilbert Doke Vicary was running a woollen factory in North Tawton on the other side of Dartmoor. [14] Moses Vicary junior was uninvolved in either woolcombing or tanning and lived with his parents. [15] John Vicary, who in 1844 lived in a house adjoining the bark mill off Kingsteignton Road, leased from the Duke of Somerset, [16] became the driving force in Newton's tanning industry. His energy brought him enemies and in 1846 his counting house was destroyed in a fire probably started by an arsonist. [17]

John Vicary was listed as one of the two tanners in the town in 1850: Branscombe, soon to retire, was still his rival. [18] Moses' fourth son, William Vicary, was also a tanner, but had moved to join his brother

Gilbert in North Tawton. [19] His fifth son Robert was a magistrate.

1852 was a difficult year for the Vicary family. Heavy and almost incessant rains in November swelled the Lemon and the Teign and one Sunday morning the waters of the Lemon swept through the tannery in Bradley Lane, causing damage to the premises and stock worth £1000 or so. [20]

But the decade was otherwise benign. The railway greatly facilitated communications and employed no less than 600 of the town's inhabitants. The tannery and other mills employed 300. [21] Nearby Teignmouth developed as a harbour and provided valonia and hides for the yards. Valonia was a type of acorn which hastened the tanning process from 9-18 months to 4-8 months. [22] 150 tons of this material came through the port in 1854 and had increased to 529 tons a decade later. In 1864, 390 tons of foreign hides were shipped to Teignmouth. [23] Teignmouth shipowners and others invested in a tug to bring vessels into and out from the port: John Vicary was one of the owners of the *Industry*, a paddle-wheeled sloop, holding 4-64th shares. [24]

Samuel Branscombe retired and John Vicary, now of Highweek Street, was sole tanner in the town in 1856. [25] His father Moses died in 1859 leaving an estate of £7000. [26]

By 1866 the Bradley Lane tannery was employing steam as well as water power: Bodley's Old Quay Foundry at Exeter supplied boiler fittings and a feed pump for the engine, together with driving gear for a crushing mill. [27] John Vicary was now not only involved in tanning but was engaged, like his brother in North Tawton, in the woollen trade, through the sale of English and foreign wools. As a tanner and woolstapler he employed 166 staff in 1871 (145 men, 14 women and 7 boys). Vicary farmed 360 acres with a further 11 labourers. At his house, The Knoll, in Highweek, four servants waited on the family: Vicary was a respected Victorian businessman and an establishment figure in south Devon. His son John joined him in partnership. [28] John and his brothers William and Robert then formed J Vicary and Brothers, running the business from at least 1873. [29]

In 1874 John and William purchased the Dartmouth-built ketch *Fiona*, 66 tons, and traded to Liverpool, London and Antwerp. The vessel brought raw materials such as sheepskins, coal, bark, valonia, gambia and myrobolan. Valonia has been mentioned; gambia was a plant extract used in the tanning process and myrobolan was a fruit similarly employed. With a downturn in trade the *Fiona* was sold in 1883. She had been registered at Teignmouth and operated with a local crew. [30]

The bark mill used by the Vicary family stood some way downstream from the town centre and was derelict for many years in the 20th century. In 2004 it was restored and converted into office space for an accountancy practice. The wheelpit was on the left, the wheel supplied by a long leat from the River Lemon. This was probably the largest bark mill in Devon

John Vicary senior died in January 1880, leaving an estate valued at £100,000, a relative fortune for the time. [31] His son John now developed the woollen business as tanning had reached its zenith. Robert and William concentrated their efforts on the latter trade. John was also a magistrate and the family, well-to-do and no doubt well-travelled compared with previous generations, were not content to confine themselves to Devon. Their wives were cosmopolitan – John's wife was born in Gibraltar; Harriett Vicary, Robert's wife, was born in Blackheath and Rose Vicary, William's wife, also came from London. [32]

It is probable that the brothers utilised Branscombe's tannery in addition to the yards their grandfather had owned in 1844. William Vicary employed 250 staff in the tanneries in 1881. [33] By 1891 he had also become a wool merchant. [34] John's youngest brother, Charles G Vicary, continued as a tanner and fellmonger. [35]
Ten years later William Vicary was a magistrate and a member of Devon County Council. [36] The company continued as John Vicary & Sons with a tanning operation and a woolcombing business.

The tannery closed in the 1940s [37] and the site has been adopted by other industries. Wool combing ceased in 1971, the company already a subsidiary of Sanderson Murray and Elder of Bradford. This business had employed 300 in 1941 but had shrunk to no more than 55 staff thirty years later. [38] The family contributed significantly to the growth and prosperity of this south Devon town. Today the bark mill, once ruinous, has been rebuilt to form part of a complex of offices for Channon & Co, chartered accountants, known as 'The Mill'. Remnants of leats exist, visible from Murrays Volkswagen dealership, beyond the fire station.

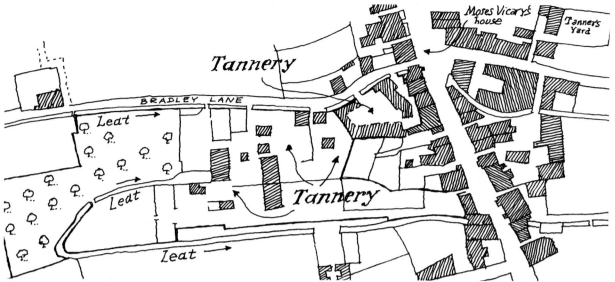

The Newton Abbot tanneries in 1847. The larger of the two, lying to the south of Bradley Lane was run by the Vicary family in 1844 (Highweek tithe apportionment). The enclosed tanyard to the right of it was occupied by Samuel Branscombe. He also had storage or stabling facilities to the east of the present day Highweek Street – the road running roughly north-south on the plan. Leats from the River Lemon served the tanneries. Moses Vicary's House was by the junction of Bradley Lane and Highweek Street. Forty-two years later, by 1889, Vicary's tanyard had been significantly developed with ranges of large workshops

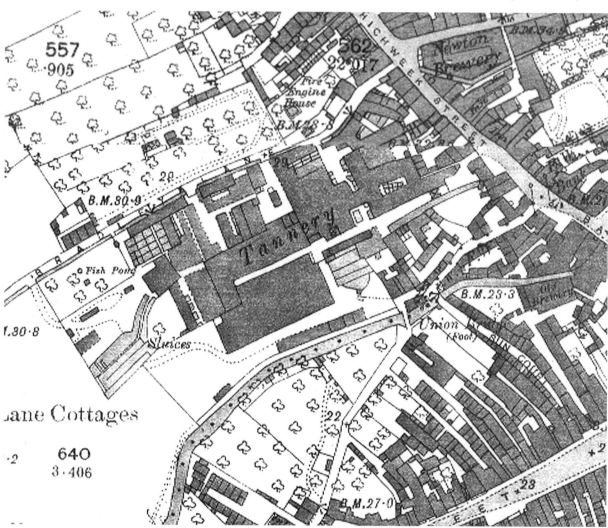

Vicary's tannery in 1887: the largest leather factory west of Bristol. The massive expansion since 1847 is evident. Some of the tan pits, not under cover, are indicated and the River Lemon runs diagonally left to right, below the yard. The bark mill referred to was some way downstream. From Ordnance Survey 1:2500 sheets 109:2 and 109:15, published in 1890 but surveyed by 1887

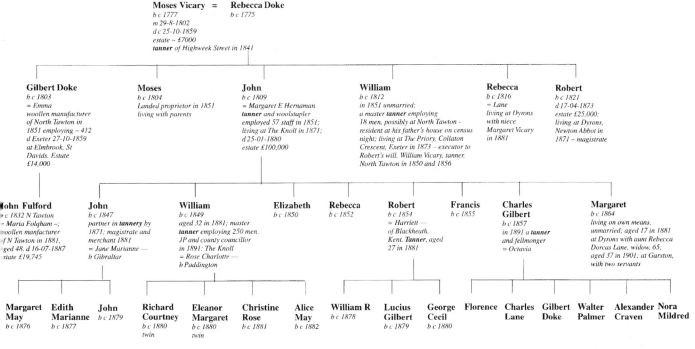

The Vicary family of Newton Abbot and North Tawton, tanners and woolstaplers. There are three generations of tanners in this tree, compiled largely from census returns for the two towns, from 1841-1901

Newton Abbot sources

1 W G Hoskins. Devon. Devon Books, 1992, 441-442
2 Mike Bone and Peter Stanier. A Guide to the Industrial Archaeology of Devon. Association for Industrial Archaeology, 1998, 34
3 Derek Beavis. Newton Abbot. The Story of the Town's Past. Barracuda Books, Buckingham 1985
4 DRO – Highweek and Newton Bushel tithe map and apportionment, of 1847 and 1844 respectively. The Vicary tannery, item 957 = Tan Yard and Buildings. Samuel Branscombe owned and occupied: 961 = Dwelling house, 962 = Tan Yard &c. He also owned and occupied 1074 = Buildings and Yard, 1075 = Garden – these located towards Kingsteignton Road. And north from Newton Bushel, along Highweek Street he occupied: 735 = Barn and stables, 736 = Browning Meadow and 737 = Waste
5 'The original tanning branch here [of the Vicary family] was established by Robert Vicary of Crediton'. (Information from John Vicary and Sons Ltd). A H Shorter, The Tanning Industry in Devon and Cornwall, 1550-1850. Devon and Cornwall Notes & Queries, XXV, 1952
6 Exeter Flying Post 18 December 1788 p 2 col 4
7 Mormon IGI
8 Pigot's General Directory, Devonshire, 1824
9 Exeter Flying Post 17 March 1825 p 1 col 2
10 Exeter Flying Post 22 December 1825 p 4 col 2
11 Woolmer's Gazette 1 July 1837 p 2 col 1
12 Newton Abbot census 1851 – HO 107 1871 f 602 p 10
13 The Western Times 13 November 1847 p 4 col 4
14 North Tawton census 1851 – HO107 1885 f 650 p 33
15 Newton Abbot census 1851 – HO 107 1871 f 602 p 10
16 Newton Abbot tithe apportionment 1844 – item 1145 = Barn Park, pasture, 1-0-21. Then the mill: item 1141 = Dwelling house, Bark Mill, 0-0-32; 1142 = Shrubbery 0-1-6; 1143 = Lower East Park, pasture, 0-3-12; 1144 = Land, pasture 0-0-38. Estate total 1-2-8
17 Woolmer's Gazette 14 February 1846 p 3 col 2
18 White's Directory, Devonshire, 1850
19 North Tawton census 1841 – HO107 252/2 f 12 p 18; White's Directory, Devonshire, 1850
20 Exeter Flying Post 11 November 1852 p 4 col 2
21 Beavis, op cit
22 Victoria County History, Gloucestershire, vol 2, 1972, 210
23 H J Trump, Port of Teignmouth and Teignmouth Harbour Commissioners 1836-1932. Appendix II Foreign and Coastal Imports. Maritime History, 4, 1, 65
24 H J Trump, Westcountry Harbour. The Port of Teignmouth 1690-1975. Brunswick Press, 1976, 110-111
25 Post Office Directory, Devon and Cornwall, 1856
26 Moses Vicary's will; he died circa 23 October 1859. Executors: John Vicary of Newton Bushel, William Vicary of St David's, Exeter, sons
27 DRO – Bodley foundry journals – 67/5/2/1 - folios 917-918, 927-928
28 Newton Abbot census 1871 – RG10 2082 f 96 p 21
29 The Post Office Directory of Devonshire and Cornwall, Kelly, 1873
30 H J Trump, Westcountry Harbour. The Port of Teignmouth 1690-1975. Brunswick Press, 1976, 87-88, citing records at DRO
31 Will of John Vicary. Died 25-01-1880 at Knoll, Highweek. Executors: John Vicary, William Vicary and Robert Vicary, all of Highweek, gentlemen and sons
32 Newton Abbot census 1881 – Robert Vicary at Churchills. RG11 2163 f 61 p 22; John Vicary at Broadlands, Ashburton Road. RG11 2163 f 69; William Vicary at The Knole. RG11 2163 f 101
33 Newton Abbot census 1881 – RG11 2163 f 101
34 Newton Abbot census 1891 – RG12 1699 f 83 p 36 schedule 218
35 Newton Abbot census 1891 – Elmhurst, Knowles Hill. RG12 1699 f 83 p 36 schedule 221
36 Newton Abbot census 1901 – RG13 2056 f 62 p 11
37 Bone and Stanier, op cit, 1998, 38
38 Western Morning News 9 February 1971

North Tawton

Off Fore Street

Location	SS 660 017
Operational	to circa 1855
Bark mill	possibly water-powered
Staff	18 tanners listed in 1851 census

Tanning at North Tawton was closely linked with the woollen trade in the 19th century: tanners and woollen cloth manufacturers came from the same families. There were tanners here in the 18th century, but the 19th century yard was established by Charles Sweet, a sergemaker, in 1806. [1]

Charles Sweet was one of 16 tanners appointed to an Exeter committee led by George Barne of Tiverton, to lobby the Board of Trade on the damage caused by the government's new leather tax, in 1814. [2] Sweet was one of the committee who found himself in financial difficulties following the end of the Napoleonic Wars and was declared bankrupt in 1825. His 'recently-planned' tanyard was advertised to let. [3]

The Vicary family then became influential in the town. Gilbert Doke Vicary, eldest son of Moses Vicary, a Newton Abbot tanner, married Emma Fulford at Crediton in May 1829 [4] and subsequently settled in North Tawton. The Fulford family had been leading serge makers in the town in the 18th century and the Vicarys were also engaged in woolcombing activities here by 1800. [5]

Gilbert Vicary took over the woollen factory on the Taw, which had been established by John Fulford on the site of the Town or Manor Mills in 1808. This site was rented from the Hon Newton Fellowes, who was to become the Earl of Portsmouth. The trade was continued by Robert Fulford until his death, aged 36, in 1821. John Fulford succeeded as head of the concern until 1837. Gilbert Vicary then inherited the woollen mill, as his wife Emma was John Fulford's daughter. [6]

By 1841 Gilbert and Emma and their son John and mother-in-law Sibella Fulford were living at Park House, near the tannery. The woollen factory, which still stands in 2004, was erected by Gilbert at about this time; [7] by 1844 it is clear that he owned the site. [8] Also resident at Park House in 1841 was William Vicary, Gilbert's younger brother, and he was listed as tanner. [9]

In 1844 Gilbert Vicary and others owned the tannery and William leased it. [10] He employed upwards of 100 men; [11] 18 were listed as tanners in the parish in 1851. The tanyard closed at some time in the 1850s – it was not listed in trade directories for the 1860s and no tanners were present in the town's 1871 census [12] – and William retired to Priory House, Exeter. He never married but with independent means could afford to live in comfort, employing two servants. [13]

Gilbert Vicary retired from managing the woollen mill in the 1850s. His workforce had been 412 in 1851, of whom perhaps 250 worked directly in the factory. He and his brother William must have made a considerable impact on the economy of this town in the mid nineteenth century. Scarlet serge was exported from the woollen mill to China and blue serge was manufactured for Her Majesty's Navy. [14]

John Fulford Vicary, Gilbert's only son, took up the reins. Maria Folgham Church of Bedford Row, London, was his bride in July 1857. [15] They lived at Park House in 1861 but then moved to Nichols Nymett House. Here in 1871, Vicary was recorded as employing 600 workers, not all of them in North Tawton. This number had eased to 503 ten years later, when he was resident at Burton Hall, a new house he had built overlooking the town in 1872. [16] Vicary was a solicitor as well as a woollen manufacturer; [17] as a magistrate he sometimes chaired the petty sessions at South Molton. In 1882 he personally summonsed Joshua Wilson, an employee who had arrived from Rochdale and had quit without notice after only three days work. [18]

He also leased two further water-powered mills known as the Higher and Lower Factories, at Chagford, on Dartmoor, from 1867 to 1882, when they were offered for sale or to let. [19] 1882 was a demanding year for Vicary. His Tawton woollen mill may well have suffered and probably stopped work when the Taw flooded its banks in October. At much the same time the thatched Waterloo Cottages, close to his factory, burnt down. [20] John Fulford Vicary died in July 1887, aged about 55, leaving an estate of nearly £20,000. [21] With his death the woollen mill closed. His widow sold it to the Shaw family from Halifax, West Yorkshire, for £6,000. And so the industry was saved and with it, the lifeblood of the town for many of its inhabitants. [22]

While the woollen factory clings on, now and for some decades disused, the tannery has disappeared under a new housing development. All oak-bark tanneries need water and this one was fed by a vigorous tributary of the Taw that runs down from the town along Fore Street, now largely in open culvert. Because it appears never to have come onto the open market in the 19th century, the number of tan pits are unknown; water-powered bark mills were probably employed but this cannot be assumed at present. It was clearly a large establishment, although not as large as John Vicary's tannery in Newton Abbot. The tannery closed before John Elston and Samuel Gimblett revolutionised and expanded boot manufacture in Crediton in the 1850s, but possibly some Tawton leather found its way to George Elston's earlier manufactory there.

Park House, the original Vicary residence, has survived, now converted into several homes.

North Tawton sources
1   Alison Baker, David Hoare and Jean Shields, The Book of North Tawton. Halsgrove, 2002, 89
2   Exeter Flying Post 20 August 1812 p 4 col 5
3   Exeter Flying Post 21 April 1825 p 1 col 2; The Alfred, West of England Journal and General Advertiser. 1 March 1825 p 1 col 4
4   IGI: Marriage 27 May 1829; Emma was the daughter of John Fulford and Sebella, bapt Bower Hill Presbyterian church, Crediton 26 January 1807
5   Baker, Hoare and Shields, op cit, 48 – the Fulfords, like the Vicarys, originally came from Crediton; Vicary family here in 1800 – DRO – 2914/A/P 259
6   Baker, Hoare and Shields, op cit, 48
7   North Tawton census of 1841 – HO107 252/2 f 12 p 18; Baker, Hoare and Shields, op cit, 48
8   DRO – North Tawton tithe map and apportionment, 1844
9   North Tawton census of 1841 – HO107 252/2 f 12 p 18
10 DRO – North Tawton tithe map and apportionment, 1844
11 Baker, Hoare and Shields, op cit, 89
12 Peter Walker, Decline or Change in Some West Devon Market Town Parishes 1841-1891. Thesis, University of Exeter, 2001, 130
13 Exeter census 1881 – RG11 2152 f 60 p 10
14 North Tawton census 1851 – HO107 1885 f 650 p 33; Baker, Hoare and Shields, op cit, 49
15 The Western Times 18 July 1857 p 5 col 2
16 Baker, Hoare and Shields, op cit, 49
17 Ibid
18 The Western Times 15 December 1882 p 7 col 3
19 The Western Times 23 June 1882 p 1 col 2
20 The Western Times 27 October 1882 p 5 col 7
21 John Fulford Vicary's will; he died 16 July 1887
22 Baker, Hoare and Shields, op cit, 49

Park House, North Tawton, the Vicary family residence in 1841, and since converted into a number of smaller homes

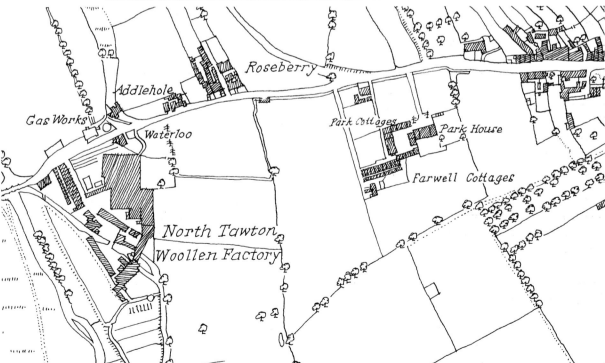

North Tawton in 1887. The woollen factory, powered by a leat from the river Taw, to the left, and Park House, to the right of centre. The edge of North Tawton village can be seen to the right. The tan yard is not indicated but was near Park House; buildings just to the north of Park Cottages may represent remnants, by the stream. Adapted from the Ordnance Survey map, Devonshire, sheet 65.3 of 1887

Okehampton

Westbridge

Location	SX 586 951
Operational	to 1906 or later
Bark mill	possibly water-powered – by the West Okement

Okehampton tanners enjoyed a certain status in the medieval period: they were witnesses to deeds and were involved in land transactions. John Stondon, one of their number, was provost of the borough in the late 14th century – the leading official. He and his competitors bought hides and skins in Exeter markets in the period 1370-1390 and these same markets were also used by 'country' tanners to sell their leather. Other Okehampton tanners at this time included Henry and John Breghe, and Henry and John Sampson [1]

The town's leather heyday was perhaps in the last decade of the 17th century when no less than three tanners were taking on apprentices: Thomas Burd, John Nosworthy and John Perin were all tanning in the period 1690-1701. Two, maybe three, of their apprentices were sons of Richard Vugler or Vogler. [2] The record for the 18th century is thin: John Stanbury was tanner in 1718; [3] in 1797 John Webber died and his house and tanyard were to let.[4] William Braddick, Okehampton tanner, transferred a £700 mortgage to an Exeter saddler and a Dawlish yeoman in 1798. [5]

The town, unsurprisingly, was endowed with oak woods and papers dated 1811 refer to estimates of building work including a bark house at Okehampton Park. [6] By the 19th century tanning was carried on in a yard at Westbridge. William Pike was a second Okehampton tanner, active in the decade 1830-1840, but a second yard has yet to be identified. [7]

Westbridge was by the new road leading out of Okehampton to Tavistock, and a crossing of the West Okement. The river would have supplied water for the tanpits and possibly powered a waterwheel to grind oak bark, although there is no evidence for this at present. John Newcombe ran this concern from at least 1830 until 1856 or so. He was born in Sampford Courtenay and was aged 58 in 1851. His next door neighbour, another Newcombe, was a leather seller. In 1844 there were several other local outlets for leather – seven boot and shoe makers were listed in Okehampton, as well as William Ashley, a currier and leather seller. [8] John Newcombe died in 1863, having retired, [9] and Thomas Newcombe, clearly a relative, and also a tanner, died the previous year [10]

Samuel Landick junior then ran the Westbridge yard from at least 1866 until 1873 or so. [11] It appears that

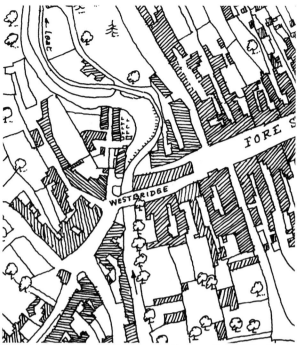

The tannery site in 1886 – to the north of West-bridge, in the bend of the river. OS sheet 76.4

he had farmed Court Farm, Exbourne, owned by the Tatershall family, from 1852. The Landick family also owned land adjoining the Okehampton tanyard in 1841. [12] His unrecorded and apparently premature death resulted in the tanyard being managed by his widow, Laura Landick, from 1873 until 1906 or later – well over a quarter of a century, if the 20th century trade directory is accurate. [13] Aged 50 in 1881, she was helped in the day to day operations by her son Frank, 20, one of four offspring resident at West Street on census night. [14]

The town was still a centre for oak in 1886: *'Okehampton. The bark trade is now in full swing, about twenty wagon loads waiting to pass over the public weighbridge ..'* [15]

The area around Westbridge has been redeveloped with new housing in recent years and all vestiges of a tannery have gone.

Okehampton sources

1 Maryanne Kowaleski, Local Markets and Regional Trade in Medieval Exeter, Cambridge University Press, 1995, 160, 303-306
2 John Parker, son of John Parker, apprenticed as tanner to Thomas Burd of Okehampton, tanner DRO 3210A/PO 10/69 of 1690; John Vugler, son of Richard Vugler, apprenticed to John Nosworthy of Okehampton, tanner. DRO 3210A/PO 10/69 of 1692; Abraham Vugler, son of Richard Vugler, apprenticed to John Perin of Okehampton, tanner. DRO 3210A/PO 10/74 of 1694 and Ezekell Vogler apprenticed to John Nosworthy of Okehampton, tanner. DRO 3210A/PO 10/84 of 1701
3 A H Shorter, D&C N&Q, from D&CRS
4 Exeter Flying Post 11 May 1797 p 2 col 3
5 Knightshayes Estate Office records, Tiverton, Chest 49
6 NDRO – 2239B - 3/1/3/1/1-15 of 1811
7 Okehampton baptisms 1634-1843, transcripts by Devon and Cornwall Record Society

8   Pigot's General Directory, Devonshire, 1830, Pigot's General Directory, Devonshire, 1844, 82, White's Directory, 1850, Post Office Directory, Devon and Cornwall, 1856; Okehampton tithe map and apportionment 1841 – item 351, House, Office and Tanyard, owned and occupied by John Newcombe; Okehampton census 1851 – West Bridge. HO 107 1885 f 385 p 36 items 116 and 117

9   Exeter Flying Post 18 February 1863 p 1 col 5

10 Exeter Flying Post 16 July 1862 p 8 col 6

11 Post Office Directory of Devonshire 1866, 1277-1278, The Post Office Directory of Devonshire and Cornwall, Kelly, 1873

12 DRO 1909 B/T/14 of 1852; Okehampton tithe map and apportionment 1841

13 Harrod's Directory, Devonshire, 1878, 432, Kelly's Directory, 1883, 784; 1897, 1111, and 1902 and 1906 editions. Tanner Samuel Landick the younger of Okehampton, died 14 January 1873. Will proved by Laura Landick, widow, estate worth £600

14 Okehampton census 1881 – RG11 2224 f 36 p 28

15 Exeter Flying Post 9 June 1886 p 7 col 5

Offwell

Offwell Woods

Location	SY 190 991
Operational	prior to 1789
Bark mill	water-powered

The wheelpit and leats serving a now vanished bark mill survived in Offwell Woods in 1952. It is thought the mill was abandoned before 1789.

Offwell source

J V Ramsden. Mill for Bark Grinding in Offwell Woods. Devon and Cornwall Notes and Queries 25, 1952-53, 52-53, quoted in Devon CC Sites and Monuments Register 15/12/82.

Ottery St Mary

Mill Street

Location	SY 0949 9532
Operational	from circa 1750 to 1866
Bark mill	probably water-powered
Tan pits	water pit, 3 lime pits, 9 latches, soaking pit, 2 grainers, 46 handlers and 33 troughs in 1851
Staff	3 in 1851

Ottery had a tanyard in 1712 – when tanner Bartholomew Palmer married – but it may not have been the one by the leat. An 18th century tannery also existed at Alfington, in the north of the parish. [1] The Mill Street tanyard which survived into the 19th century appears to have been constructed in about 1750 and was close to the silk factory, built in 1788.[2]

Richard Salter was tanner here in 1788, when he employed Sarah Richards, aged 12, as an apprentice.

[3] In 1798 Salter sought staff. [4] His family must have been a source of deep grief to him: his son was drowned in 1810 and in 1813 his wife died. [5] In 1823 he offered the premises on lease:
'DEVON. TO TANNERS. TO be LET, with Immediate Possession, for a term of 7 or 14 years, from Lady-day last, AN EXCELLENT DWELLING-HOUSE & TAN-YARD, with every requisite that may be required to Tan 30 Hides per week, situate in the market town of Ottery St. Mary .. The situation is considered equal to any in the county for procuring Raw Hides, Skins and Bark. – There is on it an excellent Bark-Mill, by Bodley, with all the Utensils of the Yard, which the Taker will be expected to purchase ..' [6]

The bark mill was probably water-powered, utilising the water from the town leat. At this time leather mills at West Hill, Ottery were also for lease. These were very similar to fulling mills, but used sheepskins to produce shammy leather. Owned by Sir John Kennaway, they were leased to leather dresser George Phillips in 1823. [7]

Richard Salter didn't survive long, dying in October 1823, although the trade directory of the time lists him as tanner when published in the following year. [8] The tanyard was for sale in 1825:
'Ottery St Mary .. Sale by Auction, in Fee .. A most eligible Tan-Yard with Dwelling-House and offices, Cottage, Back-Houses [sic – Bark Houses], Lofts, Barn, Stables, Cow-Houses and Orchard; situate adjoining the Mill Leat, constantly supplied with two sorts of water, and in a good bark country, now tenanted by Mr W M Hole, for an optional term, determinable at Lady-day 1831 or 1834 .. And also with the above, or separately, Three Dwelling-Houses, Gardens, Meadow and Coppice contiguous thereto, called Late Beards or Tucking Mills .. about two Acres ..' [9]

William Mengery Hole had owned a tanyard at Kingskerswell and advertised for workmen there in 1808. Between 1811 and 1818 he attempted to lease or sell the yard but was declared bankrupt in 1822. [10]

At some time after 1825 George Taylor took over the ownership and running of the yard: together with Peter Sharland, one of the Woodbury tanners, he was involved in property relating to the Metcombe estate in 1837. [11] Ten years later Taylor put the Ottery yard on the market, but presumably the asking price was not met at auction, and he continued as tanner. [12]

He was aged 39 in 1851 and employed three men here; his sister Mary kept house. [13] The tanyard and related premises were put up for auction in the same year. It would seem, judging by the pits listed, that some expansion had taken place since 1823:
'Auction .. Lot 1. All that Convenient Brick-built Dwelling-House with suitable Offices, Garden

and Tan Yard, consisting of large Water Pit with a constant stream, Three Lime Pits, Nine Latches, Soaking Pit, Two Grainers, Forty-six Handlers and Thirty-three Troughs, with extensive .. Drying Lofts and Bark Sheds containing 0A 1R 10P .. now in the possession of Mr Geo. Taylor.
Lot 2 .. Premises opposite Lot 1, consist of a Dwelling-House, Courtlage, Barn, Pound-House, Cellar, Stable, large and lofty Shed, productive Orchard and Garden, containing 1A 0R 27P .. also in the possession of Mr Geo. Taylor .. The Business of a Tanner has been carried on on the aforesaid Premises for the last century. For viewing apply to the said Mr George Taylor, the Owner, on the Premises.' [14]
Richard Taylor remained in charge of leather production here in 1856. [15] George Taylor died in middle age in June 1865, leaving an estate valued at £600. [16]

Ottery suffered a disastrous fire in May 1866, in which the premises in Mill Street were burnt out:
'It was about five o'clock when the fire had nearly reached the factory walls at the bottom of Mill Street. About this time the wind veered, and carried the destroyer over the road to Mr Huxtable's shoemaker, whose premises were completely burned down. Mr Taylor's extensive tanning premises were also consumed ..' [17]

In 1869 all the utensils of the yard were auctioned:
'Tan Yard, Ottery St Mary. To be Sold by Auction .. A very superior improved Patent Bark Mill by 'Huxham' nearly new, Brass Leather Roller, Bark

beam and scales, iron and wood horse for beating leather .. a quantity of ox and cow horns. Cast iron cog wheel and gear .. two waggons and lades .. Richard Taylor, Esq, the owner ..' [18]
There is no further record of the trade in Ottery after this date.

Ottery St Mary sources

1 Transcribed from D&CRS records; Woolmer's Gazette 13 November 1820 p 3 col 5
2 Exeter Flying Post 9 January 1851 p 1 col 1; DRO Ottery tithe map and apportionment, c1840, item 516 House and Tanyard, part of properties owned by George Taylor
3 DRO 3327A/PO69/110 of 1788
4 Exeter Flying Post 3 May 1798 p 1 col 2
5 Exeter Flying Post 28 June 1810 p 4 col 2, Exeter Flying Post 21 January 1813 p 4 col 1
6 Exeter Flying Post 10 April 1823 p 1 col 4
7 DRO 337B/2/151(97/9) of 1823, also 337 Add 5 of 1834
8 Exeter Flying Post 23 October 1823 p 4 col 2
9 Exeter Flying Post 5 May 1825 p 1 col 5
10 Exeter Flying Post 2 June 1808 p 4 col 3, Sherborne Mercury 15 April 1811, Exeter Flying Post 18 March 1813 p 2 col 3, Exeter Flying Post 30 April 1818 p 4 col 4, Exeter Flying Post 28 February 1822 p 1 col 3
11 DRO 1926/B/CO/T/2/9-10 of 1837
12 The Western Times 15 May 1847 p 1 col 3
13 Ottery St Mary census 1851 – HO 107 1864 f 199 p 47
14 Exeter Flying Post 9 January 1851 p 1 col 1
15 Post Office Directory, Devon and Cornwall, 1856
16 Exeter Flying Post 9 August 1865 p 5 col 3; George Taylor's will proved by John Read Taylor, gentleman of Ottery St Mary and Richard Taylor of Clist Honiton, executors, brothers. Resworn in 1877
17 Frances Rose-Troup, The Great Fire at Ottery St Mary, 1866. Exeter 1936, 14, citing The Western Times 1 June 1866
18 The Western Times 19 March 1869 p 1 col 3

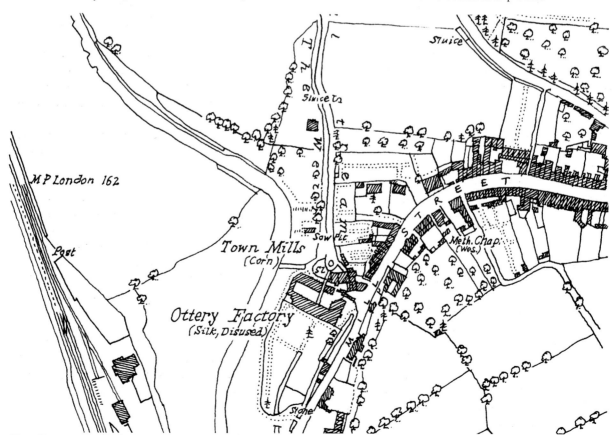

The Ottery tannery is not shown on the Ordnance Survey map of 1889, but adjoined the Town Mills by Mill Street. Note the river, leat and a second watercourse, top right. From sheet 70.13, 25" = 1 mile

Petrockstowe

Quarry Hills	
Location	SS 5049 1138
Operational	to 1925
Bark mills	one water-powered and one horse-powered
Tan pits	34 in 1817; 28 handlers, 9 layers, 7 latches, 3 limes, 1 watering pit, and 1 grainer in 1847

The tannery: conifers stand on the site of the pits. A wing extended towards the camera on the left

The Petrockstowe tannery lies some way to the north of the village.

'On June 29th, 1811, John, the Son of George Moase, Tanner, of the parifh of Petrockftow, near Hatherleigh, Devon, went from his father's houfe, in a ftate of infanity, the caufe of it is fuppofed to be an intenfe application to the ftudy of mechanifm. He is 19 years of age, about five feet eight inches high, dark hair, thin features, and of a pale complexion. He wore off a light nankeen jacket, calf-fkin waiftcoat, an old hat, a red filk hankerchief, dark corduroy breeches, worfted stockings, nailed fhoes, and a canvas apron, dyed tan-colour. He is perfectly inoffenfive to every one, and during the intervals of reafon, remarkably pious and confcientious. It is therefore hoped, that all perfons who fhall meet with him, will treat him with kindnefs and compaffion; and whoever will conduct him back to his father, or give information where he may be found, fhall be handfomely rewarded.' [1]

In 1817, with a decline in trade following the Napoleonic wars, Quarry Hills was offered for sale. George Moase was still the tanner then and the yard operated on a relatively small scale with 34 pits. [2]

The tannery was again for sale in 1832 when George Stoneman was resident. [3] He was tanner of New Street, Torrington in 1824 and a George Stoneman junior was also listed at this address in 1830. [4] In 1846 he was found drowned near Rothery Bridge, Torrington. It is thought he had committed suicide after attending a service at the Baptist chapel. [5]

William Powlesland was tanner here for some years – from before 1838 – offering the yard on lease in 1847:
'To be Let, by Private Contract, for a term of 14 years, from Michaelmas next, all those premises called Quarry Hills, consisting of a genteel residence, calculated for a respectable family; a commodious Tan-Yard, in full work, consisting of 28 handlers, 9 layers, 7 latches, 3 limes, 1 watering pit, and 1 grainer, all in excellent repair, and capable of doing a good trade. The currying business might be conveniently added; a bark house containing a mill worked by water, nearly new; a superior brass leather roller by Northam [an Exeter ironfounder], a barn, 3 stall stable, 2 labourer's cottages, piggery .. and about 20 acres of orchard, meadow and arable land. The whole having been in the occupation of the owner for many years, no expense has been spared in improvements. The premises adjoin the turnpike road between Torrington and Hatherleigh, in a good bark neighbourhood .. For further information and to treat for the same apply to Mr W Powlesland, the Owner, at Berry Farm, Petrockstow.' [6]

By 1866 Richard Adams was listed as tanner. [7] He was a nephew of Edward Adams, the Crediton tanner and son of his elder brother John, who was tanner and currier of South Street, Great Torrington, in the period 1841-1851. [8] Richard Adams was also tanning at Torrington – at New Street in 1851, with three men. [9] The tanneries in the town were very small and may not have had the space for a full range of pits or the water power necessary to run a bark mill; they may have been little more than currier's shops. It is thought that the Adams family acquired Quarry Hills, about five miles from Torrington, to provide these facilities. They would have employed a journeyman tanner as local manager. There is some evidence for this in census returns: Alexander Pyke, a journeyman tanner, was resident here for some years and recorded at Quarry Hills in 1841 and 1851. [10]

Richard Adams was still running the business in 1873 [11] but by 1919 George and Charles Adams, his sons, were owners of Quarry Hills. [12] Living here were Samuel Hutchins in 1901 and Mr Lucas, who is thought to have succeeded him. Lucas was the last tanner at Quarry Hills in the years following the First World War. Tanning continued until 1925. The premises were then offered to let. [13]

Substantial remains of the buildings survive. The tannery was L-shaped, of two stories and stone-built. At some time in the 1870s rebuilding took place and buff Marland bricks were bonded into the earlier stonework.

These buildings had drying lofts in the upper story, with louvred windows. The east range survives,

The old tannery building at Quarry Hills. The upper floor was used for drying leather and still retains working louvred windows. The complex was originally L-shaped in plan, with a longer block running off on the right

William Lucas working on a hide at Quarry Hills in the 1920s

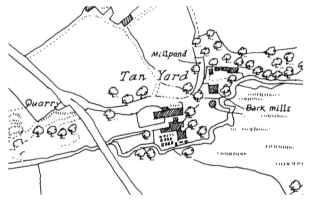

Owner Alan Anthony stands by the site of the wheel-pit at the bark mill. This mill, once two-storied, has been rebuilt as a barn. The water-powered mill was served by a small spring-fed pond and there was also a second, horse-powered, mill site

The tan yard in 1886, from the Ordnance Survey 25" map, sheet 40.12. It lies by the old turnpike road from Hatherleigh to Torrington. The horse-powered bark mill appears to have stood immediately south of the water-powered mill

its roof and floorboards renewed by Mr Anthony, the owner in 2004, but the north range has been demolished by a previous owner. Within the courtyard created by the buildings lay the tan pits. These were served by a leat fed from a small weir hard by a major stone embankment which carries the Petrockstowe – Torrington road over the stream.

To the east are the remains of a spring-fed pond. Surprisingly this, rather than the leat, worked an overshot waterwheel attached to a bark mill. This mill barn has been repaired by the present owners and is now partly open to the elements, its pillars rebuilt. Its upper floor has been removed and the ground floor raised. The wheelpit has silted up and the waterwheel, which had survived until the 1970s, was removed by the then owner, a poultry farmer. The pond allowed a running time in the mill of only two hours before it drained and had to refill. [14] This may not always have been adequate as nearby there was also a roundhouse for a horse mill, which was extant when the 25" OS map was made circa 1889.

Petrockstowe sources
1   Exeter Flying Post 4 July 1811 p 1 col 3
    (brought to my attention by the owner of Quarry Hills, Alan Anthony)
2   Exeter Flying Post 28 August 1817 p 2 col 3
3   Sherborne Mercury 27 August 1832
4   Pigots General Directory, Devonshire, 1824
    and Pigots General Directory, Devonshire, 1830
5   Exeter Flying Post 10 September 1846 p 3 col 5
6   DRO Petrockstowe tithe map and apportionment, July 1838, with homestead item 766, tanyard 767. Estate in all 17a 0r 30p; Petrockstowe census 1841 – William Powlesland, 30, tanner – HO107 244\5; The Western Times 7 August 1847 p 1 col 2
7   Post Office Directory of Devonshire 1866
8   Great Torrington census, 1851. HO107 1894 f 545 p 76
9   Great Torrington census, 1851. HO 107 1894 f 512 p 11
10 Petrockstow census 1841 – HO107 244\5; and 1851 – HO107 1894 f 348 p 26; personal communication from owner Alan Anthony, April 2004
11 The Post Office Directory of Devonshire and Cornwall, Kelly, 1873
12 Kelly's Directory of Devonshire and Cornwall, 1919, 1116
13 Information from owner Alan Anthony, April 2004
14 Ibid

Pilton
Bradiford

Pilton stands on a low hill between two river valleys, both tributaries of the Taw – the Yeo and the Bradiford Water. Barnstaple lies on the Taw, bordered on one side by the Yeo. The Taw, tidal at this point, was not a practicable proposition for water mills, so Pilton was better placed for water-power than its neighbour.

Several mills stood on the Bradiford Water and Pilton was also served by Raleigh or Rawleigh Mills, fed by a leat from the Yeo. Tanning was one of several leather industries in the town – now part of the borough of Barnstaple – others were fellmongering, glovemaking and shammy leather manufacture.

Bradiford

Location	SS 0504 3439
Operational	to circa 1857
Staff	7 in 1851

Lewis Cawsey insured the machinery and other elements of a mill above Bradiford Bridge in 1786:
'Lewis Cawsey of Bradiford in the parish of Pilton, near Barnstaple, in the Co. of Devon, Tanner. On his Millhouse including the machinery and going gears, Barkhouse and Drying House, £300. Situate in Bradiford aforesaid.' [1]

It is reasonable to assume that the bark at Bradiford was ground in a water-powered mill, although the insurance policy doesn't explicitly state this.

This mill site had been purchased by Sir Henry Rolle in 1613; [2] in 1800 mills at Bradiford were leased by John King, a tanner, from the Rolle family. There was a complex of sites here and one of the mills was at that time sublet to a corn miller. [3] King's partnership with William Trix of Pilton was dissolved in 1811 [4] and King is recorded as a Pilton tanner in 1816. [5] By 1820 he was in financial difficulties. [6] One of the establishments at Bradiford was known as Round Mill, a bark mill. Its name implies it was a horse-powered operation. Maybe it replaced the water-powered bark mill as nearby was a newly-built factory which may have utilised all the potential of the Bradiford Water in 1823. [7]

Another name for part of the Bradiford concern was Hope Mills, on the market in 1830:
'To be Sold, by Private Contract, all that excellent Range of Buildings, called HOPE MILLS WOOLLEN MANUFACTORY, Situate in Pilton, near Barnstaple, consisting of Factory, Dye House, Wash Houses, Fulling Mill, Comb Shop, with Wool Lofts, Kiln, Dwelling House & Gardens, with Ware Rooms and Shops adjoining; another Dwelling House occupied by John Passmore, two Stables; Grist Mill and Bark Mill adjoining; Coal House, Oil House and Linhay, the Rackfield, containing about three acres .. Also all the Machinery, Furnaces, Vats .. These Premises are remarkably well supplied with a copious and never-failing Leat of fifteen feet fall .. only one mile from the sea-port town of Barnstaple .. Mr Wm Rennels, the Proprietor ..'

This notice seems to suggest the Rolle family had relinquished its 200-year-ownership of the site and it was now owned by William Rennels. [8]

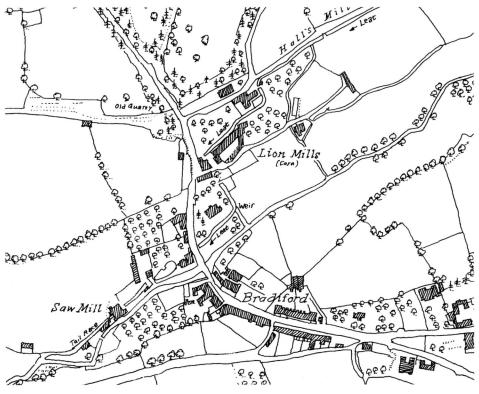

Bradiford, Pilton. The Bradiford Water runs diagonally from right to left and leats served Lion Mills, also known as Bradiford Mills, and the Saw Mill, also known as Bradiford Turning Mill. It is thought the tannery was at Lion Mills, along with a flour mill. A third mill site is indicated between Lion Mills and the Saw Mill on this plan, based on the Ordnance Survey 25" = 1 mile, sheet 13.2 of 1889

Lion Mills, Pilton, 2005. Left: the leat still runs from Anchor Mills. Right: part of the mill complex here, which was rebuilt as a flour mill in 1876 by George Davey and has since been converted to housing

John King & Son was listed here in 1844 and 1850. [9] Tanning continued: by 1851 John King was 78 and his son Thomas, 46, ran the business on ground known as Besley's Tenement while the toy manufacturer John Lee occupied Round Mill. King lived in a residence by the yard. Here he employed seven men, six of them Dimonds, a family from Winkleigh, who had moved to Pilton in the 1830s. [10]

Thomas King, by now a town councillor, died in 1857, aged 57, and his father John died a year later. [11] Thomas's son was aged 15, too young to take on the running of the tanyard and Thomas's wife offered the business for sale in 1858. [12] Leather making, however, almost certainly ceased at Bradiford with Thomas's death.

Raleigh

Raleigh was, by the 19th century, another complex of water-powered industries. In 1807 Samuel Bemridge the younger, who ran a tanyard and fellmongery at Pilton Bridge, also held a water-powered leather mill at Raleigh:

'.. To Tanners, Leather-Dreffers, Fellmongers .. Dwelling House, with offices, yards and drying grounds fituated at Pilton Bridge .. now in the occupation of Mr Samuel BEMRIDGE the younger, the proprietor .. furnifhed with ware-rooms, lofts, kiln, pits, furnaces .. .. Alfo will be fold, at the fame time, for the remainder of a term of 99 years, determinable on the deaths of three perfons, the oldeft of which is not 42. A LEATHER MILL, in complete repair, fituate at Rawleigh, in the parifh of Pilton, about half a mile from the above premifes, now in the occupation of the faid Samuel Bemridge, the proprietor, and worked by a never-failing stream of water ..' [13]

Such mills were used by fellmongers to full chamois leather using sheepskins and were not part of the traditional leather manufacturing process.

Bull House

The Sanders family had interests in a tannery at Boutport Street in Barnstaple but looked to expand their operations and John Sanders, a tanner and woolstapler, lived here in 1851. In 1854 part of this property was developed as a factory producing agricultural gloves and gaiters. Journeymen tanners, leather dressers and bark grinders lived in nearby streets – at Ladywell and Shute Court, close to the church. John Sanders later took up farming at East Down and by 1866 Joseph Bayliss, from one of the country's leading glove making companies, was heading the concern, refocusing the Pilton business on glovemaking. In 1869 Samuel Sanders took over the tannery at Pilton Causeway, [14] also known as the Rackfield Tannery, but run by the Smyth Brothers of Swimbridge from as early as 1873. [15]

Another Pilton tannery may have existed in the boom years: A Mr Mortimer, Pilton tanner, married in 1794, and a Joseph Oldfield, of the same trade, was bankrupt in 1824. [16]

Pilton sources
1 Royal Exchange Fire Insurance Policy 96799, 14 March 1786
2 Margaret Reed, Pilton – Its past and its people. Vineyard, Barnstaple, 1985
3 Ibid
4 Exeter Flying Post 10 January 1811 p 2 col 3
5 NDRO 1142 B/T43/16 of 1816
6 Reed, op cit
7 NDRO 1142B/T43/12 and 13 and 14; Reed, op cit, 117
8 Woolmer's Gazette 6 February 1830 p 1 col 2; Reed, op cit
9 Pigots General Directory, Devonshire, 1844, White's Directory, 1850
10 Margaret Reed, op cit, 118-119
11 Exeter Flying Post 19 March 1857 p 5 col 3; Reed, op cit
12 The Western Times 1 May 1858 p 1 col 2
13 Sherborne Mercury 27 July 1807
14 Margaret Reed, op cit, 101-102
15 The Post Office Directory of Devonshire and Cornwall, Kelly, 1873
16 Exeter Flying Post 27 March 1794 p 2 col 2, Exeter Flying Post 11 November 1824 p 1 col 1

Plymouth

Exeter Street
Frankfort Street/92 Cambridge Street
Mill Lane/Mill Street
Old Town Gate/Old Town Street
Tavistock Road and Tavistock Street
Stonehouse Lane/Fore Street/ High Street,
  East Stonehouse
Sutton Road, Coxside

Plymouth possessed the largest group of tanneries in Devon, including a site at Stonehouse. Devonport is covered separately in this gazetteer. Not all these premises were at work concurrently, but five yards were recorded as operational in 1815 [1] and typically there were four yards for much of the century, reduced to just two by 1890. [2]

Oak bark tanneries needed water for processing hides and ideally for grinding the bark, to provide tannic acid. It is reasonable to assume that the early tanyards were located near the Plymouth or Drake's Leat, which was completed in 1591. The leat brought water from Dartmoor and ran for 17.5 miles. [3]

Right: Plymouth in the 19th century: Henry Wallis' 'The Barbican, Pool ..' of 1832. Courtesy of Devon Library and Information Services

Below: Plymouth, Devonport and Millbrook and the locations of tanneries. For Devonport and Millbrook see page 64. Plymouth has gown rapidly from 1800 to the present day. The city's economy was established through the port's activities: trade, shipbuilding, ropemaking, sailmaking, and other maritime industries. Plymouth tanners made use of hides imported from Buenos Aires and elsewhere

The city expanded considerably in the 19th century, with shipbuilding yards, rope walks and other maritime activities. The conurbation was a leading supply base for Wellington's army fighting the Peninsular War in Spain and Portugal at the beginning of the century, and leather would have been essential for soldiers' and sailors' boots and for saddles for officers' horses, the cavalry and artillery. [4]

In the 19th century some Devon tanners were using imported hides from Buenos Aires and elsewhere: Plymouth yards were well placed to make use of this raw material.

The tanneries on or near the leat closed during the 19th century but new yards were established at Coxside and at Exeter Street, near Sutton Pool, and their proprietors installed steam engines to power their pumps and grind the bark.

Plymouth suffered heavily in the blitz during the Second World War. Thoroughfares with tanneries such as Cambridge Street, Frankfort Place and Mill Street have disappeared under postwar redevelopment following the bombing of the city centre.

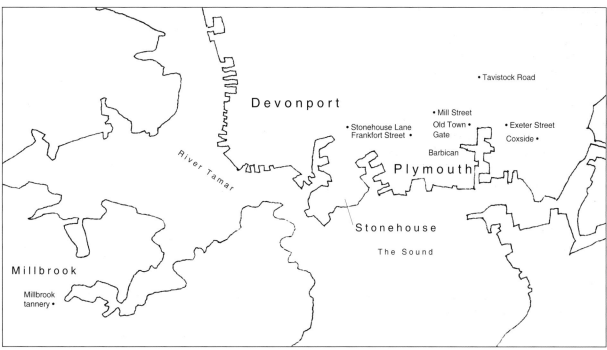

Old Town Gate / Old Town Street

Location	SX 479545
Operational	to 1873 and later
Bark mill	water-powered
Tan pits	30 vats, 21 troughs in 1784

Today Old Town Street can be found between Drake Circus and St Andrews Circus.

In 1784 the yard at Old Town Gate was for sale:
'.. all that new planted TAN-YARD .. fituated near Old Town Gate, in the town of Plymouth, in the county of Devon .. consisting of a very large yard, containing 30 vats under cover, with room for 10 more under the fame cover, 21 troughs, and room for three times as many moor [sic]; a large drying loft, a bark-houfe large enough to hold 140 tons of bark, a good pound-houfe and dry-houfe .. water from conduit in the yard .. the whole almoft new .. apply to William Steer, who is now in poffeffion .. and for treating for the fame to the faid William Steer.'[5]

A little over 80 years later J Head & Son were tanners of 31 Old Town Street and had further premises outside the city, at Ivybridge.[6] It seems there was another tannery here as Henry Greet ran a yard at 87 Old Town Street in 1873.[7] By 1881 John Head had moved to the Stonehouse Lane tannery [qv].

Stonehouse Lane

Location	SX 464545
Operational	to 1881 and later
Bark mill	water-powered

An 18th century tannery existed at Stonehouse Lane; the street also known as Fore Street, East Stone-house in the 19th century, and today named High Street. It was owned by the Yonge family of Puslinch, Newton Ferrers, and was described as 'adjoining fulling and paper mills near Stonehouse Lane' and previously occupied by tanner John Waddon.
Between about 1745[8] and 1765 it was run by John Lewis, a merchant and tanner from Tracey, Honiton. [9] A fire occurred on the premises in June 1765 and Lewis was then indebted to the Rev. J Yonge to the tune of £1000.[10] Ownership continued in the hands of the Newton Ferrers family through to the end of the century. Aaron Hern was the tanner here in 1793 but the yard was offered to let in 1799:

'Tan Yard. To be Let by Private Contract. All that Capital Tan-Yard fituate in Stonehouse-Lane, Plymouth confifting of a good Dwelling-houfe, a Bark Mill, worked by water, running through the yard; with Storehoufes, Drying Lofts, a fufficient number of Pits for carrying on the Tanning Bufinefs to any extent; with a Field adjoining ..'
For further particulars apply to Edmund Granger, Efq, Exeter ..'

A yard fitting this description, using water from the Plymouth Leat, was for auction in November 1813.[11] This was probably one of the five tanneries at work in 1815: it disappears from the record after the Napoleonic era but re-emerges in 1850 when Henry Cridland was listed as tanner, woolstapler and seed merchant of Fore Street, East Stonehouse.[12] John Head, 48, previously at Old Town Street, was established at 26 High Street, East Stonehouse, in 1881 – the modern address for Stonehouse Lane. He was then employing 35 men and youths in this tanyard; quite a large operation by Devon standards.[13]

The Stonehouse tanyard in 1857, with the West of England Fellmongers' Company Works and a slaughterhouse. The Stonehouse Leat is not evident here but was extant in 1593 and ran under the grounds of the nearby Royal Naval Hospital. Water Lane, near the tannery, may or may not be significant in this context. From the Ordnance Survey map 1:500, 1857, sheet 66

Tavistock Road runs north east from Drake Circus continuing towards Tavistock as North Hill.

James Newman Tanner was an active Plymouth leather merchant, born in 1766, who in 1802, with William Prance, offered a fellmongering business – which included a shammy leather mill – for sale by auction. These premises were then occupied by Tanner, Bodkin, Ivory & Co. [14] His Tavistock Road tanyard was active by 1814. [15] Tanner took out a patent in 1819, to preserve or cure raw hides without the necessity of liming. Tanner & Son offered the composition at £16 per ton, said to be half the price of salt. [16]

He had married Margaret Jones, daughter of an Abergavenny clockmaker and a devoted non-conformist, in 1787. [17] Their children were all baptised at Morice Square Baptist Chapel, between 1788 and 1809. [18] Of their eleven offspring, the four sons were all connected with the leather industry. James Jones Tanner, born in 1790, was a currier and glove manufacturer of Exeter. Charles Sheen Tanner, born in 1793, stayed in Plymouth and assisted with the running of the local business. Frederick Tanner, born in 1799, was a currier in Exeter and the youngest, William Tanner, born in 1809, was a leather and glove manufacturer of Westgate, Exeter. At some time he represented family interests in London.

Charles Sheen Tanner in later life

J N Tanner was, it seems, in the upper echelons of Plymouth society; his residence was Sherwell House in 1843. One of his business partners was the banker Simon Radford Strode, from the family that built the mansion at Newnham Park, near Plymouth. [19]

Charles Tanner was listed at the Tavistock Road tanyard in 1844; by this time he was managing the Plymouth business. [20] On 7 November of that year there was a fire at the premises. 1847 must have been a difficult year for Charles and his wife Agnes: Branscombe, Charles' personal clerk and cashier, aged 33, committed suicide in the tanyard. He'd been suffering from depression and drinking heavily. Branscombe was responsible for handling £100 cash per week – about £7,400 in today's money (2005). [21] Woolstapling and glue making were other aspects of the Tanner's business recorded in 1850. Charles and Agnes Tanner lived nearby, at 36 Portland Square. [22] Agnes, who was born in the Nash-designed Cumberland Terrace, London, kept a diary which provided the information for the family tree shown overleaf.

James Newman Tanner died in December 1848 at Sherwell House. He left his fortune to his eldest daughter Ann, a very capable single businesswoman. When she died in 1857, William Tanner inherited much of the property but Charles inherited the Plymouth business and £5000. [23]

Charles Tanner was the administrator and inheritor of the estate of his brother James Jones Tanner, who died at Exeter in 1850. J J Tanner, who had been elected Sheriff of Exeter in 1836, leased premises from that city at Shilhay including lime pits, frizing, grounding, fleshing and pulling shops, glue spread racks and press-house, store and drying lofts with stables and a coach house for £35 rent a year. A large cellar underneath St Edmund, in Exeter, was also used by this concern. And James Tanner rented leather mills at Upton Pyne, just outside Exeter, for

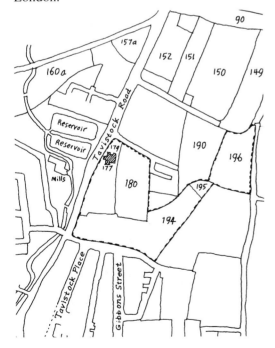

Property owned by James Newman Tanner in 1846, indicated by the heavy dotted line. Entry 177 on this map indicates Sherwell House. From the tithe map, Charles parish

[continued over

£68 a year. He also operated from premises at Well Court, Queen Street, Cheapside, London, where they carried on trade for many years. This was clearly a family of note. [24]

The Tavistock Street premises suffered a serious fire in 1866:

'Extensive Fire at Plymouth. On Monday a fire occurred on premises in the Tavistock-road, resulting

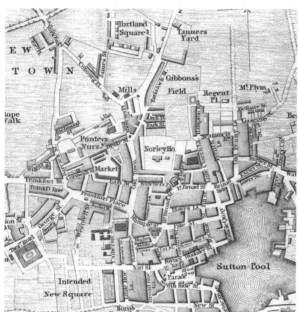

Plymouth in 1820, from an engraving by John Cooke. The 'Tanners Yard' and Portland Square are virtually out in the country

The Tavistock Street area in 1856, heavily urbanised compared with the situation in 1820. The steam-powered tannery is shown in Gibbons Lane and Sherwell House stands by Tavistock Street. From the Ordnance Survey 1:500 map, sheet 46

in the destruction of a large amount of property. The scene of the disaster was the tan-yard of Mr Charles Tanner, opposite the Sherwill Chapel, though the fire itself was alleged to have originated in premises adjoining. The wool and leather contained in the central store is estimated by Messrs Tanner at £22,000 and it is estimated that about two thirds of this has been destroyed. The fire occurred at the worst period of the year, just previous to the great September fairs. The building is the property of Mr William Tanner of Exeter and the damage to it and its contents cannot, if the figures supplied by Messrs Tanner on the spot approach accuracy, be far short of £20,000. The tan-yard premises are insured in the West of England, the European and the Atlas offices .. The origin of the fire is a perfect mystery.' [25]

Charles Sheen Tanner had handed over control to his son Charles Frederick by 1871 – and was now identified as a retired wool merchant, living at 1 Portland Square, having moved from number 36. [26] He died in April 1873 – in his eightieth year – leaving £90,000, having inherited two fortunes. Today's equivalent value (2004) is £6,210,000. [27] The business was being run as C F Tanner & Co; [28] the yard was not listed in 1890 yet is shown on the 1892 Ordnance Survey map. [29] The younger generation had perhaps been a little indulged: Charles Frederick Tanner moved to Stowford House in 1882, [30] a drain on his resources, and in 1889 he bought the less extravagant Filham House. He enjoyed living the life of a gentleman. The tannery was sold and the site redeveloped. His younger brother Edmund Fearnley Tanner, an enthusiastic huntsman, became a lawyer like a number of Devonshire tanner's sons. [31]

The tannery in Gibbons Lane, near Tavistock Street, in 1892, from the Ordnance Survey at 1: 500, sheet 123:8.18. Compared with the 1866 map, the yard has been moved to the east and a mangle factory stands on the old site. The grounds of Sherwell House have been built over

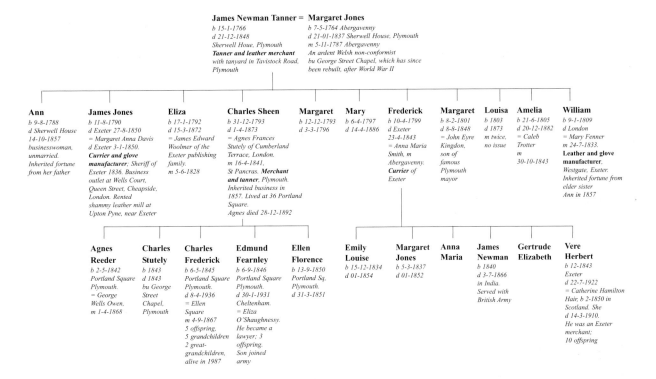

The Tanner family tree

Frankfort Street/ 92 Cambridge Street

Location	SX 473544
Operational	to circa 1875
Output	200 hides a week in 1826
Bark mill	steam-powered in 1826

William Branscombe junior, a Plymouth tanner, was declared bankrupt in 1816. [32] This may later have become his tanyard, as he was listed as tanning at

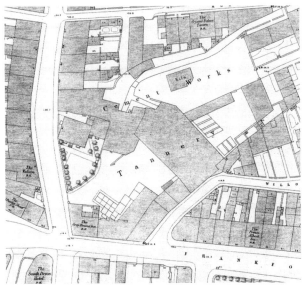

The Frankfort Street/Cambridge Street tannery, last of a line of water-powered sites on the Plymouth Leat. From the 1:500 Ordnance Survey map of 1856 sheet 57

Frankfort Street in 1822 and 1824. [33] Two years later the property was for sale:

'For Sale .. Tanner and Fellmonger's Yard, situate in Frankfort-Street, within the Borough of Plymouth, and recently occupied by Mr William Branscombe, who carried on therein, for many years an extensive and successful Business.
The premises comprise .. space of nearly two Acres, with large channel of water constantly running through them, and possessing a capacity for tanning upwards of two hundred hides per week, and of fellmongering from one to two thousand sheep skins per week; a steam engine of six horse power; and an excellent bark mill and bark-lofts ..' [34]

The steam engine may have powered the the pumps to the tan pits. William Sweet was recorded as the Frankfort Street tanner in 1844. [35]

In 1854 the bark mill was supplied with leat water under a corporation grant of 1612, indicating it was probably water-powered. Several other mills utilised the Plymouth Leat supply before it reached the tannery –

• Drakes Place Mill, Tavistock Road
• Higher Grist Mill, Tavistock Road
• Lower Grist Mill, Pound Street
• Providence Mill, Mill Lane/Mill Street
• Canvas Factory, Mill Lane/Mill Street
• Cement Mill, Mill Lane/Russell Street. [36]

[continued over

The yard listed at 92 Cambridge Street is the same establishment: it is the tannery shown on 1856 and 1867 maps of Plymouth at the junction of Frankfort Street and Cambridge Street. [37] Peter Ashford was tanner at this address at least by 1851 and listed also in 1856. Unmarried, aged 30, he employed eight men at the yard in 1851; his sister Elizabeth kept house. The Ashfords were from Loxbeare, near Tiverton, where Peter's brother, John Henry Ashford, ran another tannery. [38]

Ashford died young, aged 51, in 1872. His wife and his brother from Loxbeare were his executors. [39] He must have been incapacitated before then, as Ward Bros & Co were running the tannery at 92 Cambridge Street by 1866 [40] and were here in 1873; [41] but this firm had relocated to Coxside by 1878.

Mill Street	
Location	not known
Operational	to circa 1875
Bark mill	water powered
Tan pits	73 in 1824, 75 in 1830

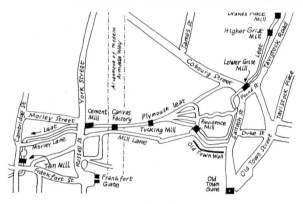

Water-powered sites on the Plymouth Leat. Several of these sites were, aside from the tide mills, the oldest-established watermills in Plymouth. The tan mill shown is the yard at the corner of Frankfort Street and Cambridge Street. The Mill Street or Mill Lane site is not known at present. The area has been totally rebuilt since

W H Dove had a tannery which may have been located in Mill Street, and came onto the market in 1824:
'Valuable Tan-Yard, House, Field and other property in Plymouth. To be Sold by Public Auction .. Lot 1. All that most commodious and desirable Tan-Yard, with the Bark-House, and Mill therein, a Tenement for the Residence of a Foreman, Drying Lofts, Turf Shed, and other buildings thereto belonging. The Tan-Yard contains seventy-three pits, is well supplied with water, and possesses capabilities and facilities for an extensive trade scarcely equalled in the West of England.
Lot 2. All that convenient Dwelling-House and Shrubbery, with the Courtlage, Gig-house .. Situate in Mill-street .. late in the occupation of Mr W H Dove

.. Lot 3. Messuage in Mill street .. in possession of Mr Chapple as tenant .. further particulars .. George Thorn, Esq, Bude Canal Office, Stratton ..' [42]

The yard was occupied by Joseph Brittan in 1830:
'Capital Tan-Yard in Plymouth. To be Sold or Let, by Private Contract, in one or more Lots, all those extensive Freehold Premises situate in Mill-lane, in the borough of Plymouth; consisting of a convenient Dwelling-House, Wash-house and Outhouses, with a small Garden in front. A very compact TAN YARD with 75 pits, drying lofts, 2 open sheds with small copper and press for sheep skins, mill-house with .. bark mill, copper house with a large copper for boiling bark, capacious bark store, turf shed yard, two-stall stable, wall garden and meadow. The whole property stands on about 46,975 superficial feet of land .. the business of a tanner, which has been carried on there for several years by the late Mr Dove, and since by Mr Brittan, .. also 2 other Freehold Dwelling-Houses ..' [43]

The yard may not have survived after that date [44] but it and Frankfort Street may have been the earliest established tanneries in the city, utilising the leat. Mill Street vanished following the redevelopment of this part of the city in the 1950s. It lay south west of Drake Circus near the present Armada Way.

Portland Place/Tavistock Road	
Location	SX 481549
Operational	to circa 1835

Mr Martin, junior, tanner, Plymouth, died in 1821. [45] Richard Martin was listed as tanner at Portland Place, very probably his residence, in 1824. But in 1822 he was also noted as tanner at 'Old-town-without' – see the Old Town Gate entry, possibly his tannery. [46] He was of some standing as his son William's marriage was recorded in an Exeter paper in 1829. [47] Martin was one of three tanners noted operating in Plymouth in 1830, with an address in Tavistock Road; nearby were Tanner & Son of Tavistock Street. [48]

140 Exeter Street	
Location	SX 482544
Operational	circa 1855 – circa 1903

This establishment, like Coxside, was, it seems, a late 19th century development. Thomas Hender was listed at 4 Abbey Place in 1856 – very possibly his residence. [49] He was the tanner listed at Exeter Street in 1873; he ran a tannery at Launceston, just over the border in Cornwall. [50] The Exeter Street business was still active in 1902 and with the concerns at Coxside and Devonport, was one of the last three to survive in greater Plymouth, but closure came before 1906. [51]

Sutton Road, Coxside

Location	SX 4904 5416
Operational	from 1875 to 1897 or later
Bark mill	steam powered

This was a late 19th century, steam-powered yard. It was sited next to the city's gas works. [52]
Ward Brothers & Co came to Coxside from premises in Cambridge Street in the mid 1870s. [53] Tanning was not recorded here in earlier trade directories. William Osmond Ward, the proprietor in 1890, lived in Tavistock and would, when necessary, have commuted to work by train. [54] By 1897 the company was known as Ward & Son and was one of the last two tanneries in the city. Detailed plans of the yard, dated 1895, survive. [55]

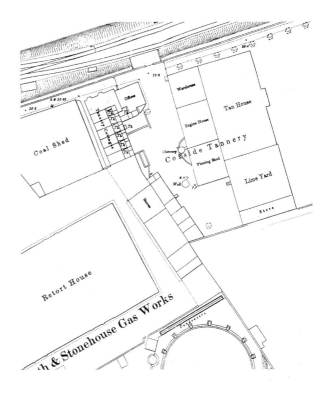

Right: Coxside tannery in 1892, sandwiched between the Sutton Harbour branch railway and the gas works. From the Ordnance Survey 1:500, sheet 123:12.10

Plymouth sources

1 Llewellynn Jewitt, A History of Plymouth, 1873, 635
2 Pigot's General Directory, Devonshire, 1824; Post Office Directory of Devonshire 1866, 1278; Kelly's Directory, Devonshire, 1897, 1111
3 Ray Bush, Plymouth (Drake's) & Stonehouse Leats, The Old Plymouth Society, 2000.
4 For example: Plymouth, October 1808. 'Letters from Corunna .. state the .. arrival there of 136 sail of transports .. from Falmouth .. there was nothing prepared for their reception, such as .. mules for carrying baggage, and other articles, indispensible for landing an army.' Exeter Flying Post 3 November 1808 p 4 col 4
5 Sherborne Mercury 8 November 1784
6 Post Office Directory of Devonshire 1866, 1278
7 The Post Office Directory of Devonshire and Cornwall, Kelly, 1873
8 P&WDRO 107/159, 107/168
9 P&WDRO 107/552 of 1765
10 P&WDRO 107/482
11 Exeter Flying Post 12 December 1799 p 2 col 3, Sherborne Mercury 20 December 1813 p 2
12 White's Directory 1850
13 East Stonehouse census 1881: RG10 2203 f 48 p 4
14 Sherborne Mercury 15 February 1802
15 S Rowe, The Plymouth, Plymouth-Dock and Stonehouse General Directory, 1814, 37
16 Woolmer's Gazette 13 February 1819 p 1 col 3
17 Agnes Frances Tanner, My precious family: Agnes Frances Tanner's own extracts from her diary. 1840-1892. Annotated transcription by E Mary Higman 1987
18 Mormon IGIs
19 Agnes Frances Tanner, op cit; Woolmer's Gazette 9 December 1843 p 3 col 1; Plymouth. Charles the Martyr. Census 1841 – HO107 271/7 f 6 p 5
20 Pigot's General Directory, Devonshire, 1844, 124;
21 Agnes Tanner, op cit
22 White's Directory, 1850
23 Agnes Tanner, op cit
24 The Western Times 26 April 1851 p 1 col 2; Exeter Flying Post 7 January 1836 p 4 cols 4,5
25 The Western Times 17 August 1866 p 5 col 2
26 Plymouth census 1871 – 1 Portland Square, Charles parish – RG10 2116 f 66 p 22
27 Will of Charles Tanner Esq, died 1-4-1873

28 The Post Office Directory of Devonshire and Cornwall, Kelly, 1873
29 White's Devonshire Directory 1890; Kelly's Directory, Devonshire, 1897, 1111
30 Agnes Tanner, op cit; P&WDRO 2519/131
31 Agnes Tanner, op cit
32 Exeter Flying Post 2 May 1816 p 4 col 1
33 Taperell's Plymouth .. Directory 1822, 4; Pigot's General Directory, Devonshire, 1824
34 Exeter Flying Post 13 April 1826 p 1 col 2
35 Pigot's General Directory, Devonshire, 1844, 124
36 David J Hawkings, Water from the Moor. An illustrated history of the Plymouth, Stonehouse and Devonport Leats. Devon Books, 1987. 14, 72
37 Ordnance Survey maps, Plymouth, 1: 500, sheet 57 of 1856 and sheet 123:7,8 of 1867
38 Plymouth St Andrews census, 1851 – HO 107 1879 f 408 p 30; Post Office Directory, Devon and Cornwall, 1856
39 Will. Peter Sharland Ashford, late of Plymouth, died 11-8-1872. Proved by Mary Cook Ashford, widow, and John Henry Ashford of Loxbeare, tanner, brother
40 Post Office Directory of Devonshire 1866, 1278
41 The Post Office Directory of Devonshire and Cornwall, Kelly, 1873
42 The Alfred 20 April 1824 p 1 col 3
43 Exeter Flying Post 25 March 1830 p 2 col 1
44 Mill Street was never listed in trade directories
45 Exeter Flying Post 1 April 1821 p 4 col 4
46 Pigot's General Directory, Devonshire, 1824; N Taperell, The Plymouth, Plymouth Dock, Stonehouse, Morice-Town & Stoke Directory, 1822, 20
47 Exeter Flying Post 24 September 1829 p 2 col 4
48 Pigot's General Directory, Devonshire, 1830, 111
49 Post Office Directory, Devon and Cornwall, 1856
50 The Post Office Directory of Devonshire and Cornwall, Kelly, 1873
51 Kelly's Directory, Devonshire, 1883, 345 and 784; 1897, 1111; and 1902, 1906 editions
52 OS sheet 123.12.10, surveyed 1892-3
53 Ward Brothers and Co, tanners, Coxside, Plymouth – Harrod's Devonshire Directory, 1878, 558
54 White's Devonshire Directory 1890
55 Kelly's Directory, Devonshire, 1897, 1111; plans dated 1895 – P&WDRO 114/47/57

Plympton

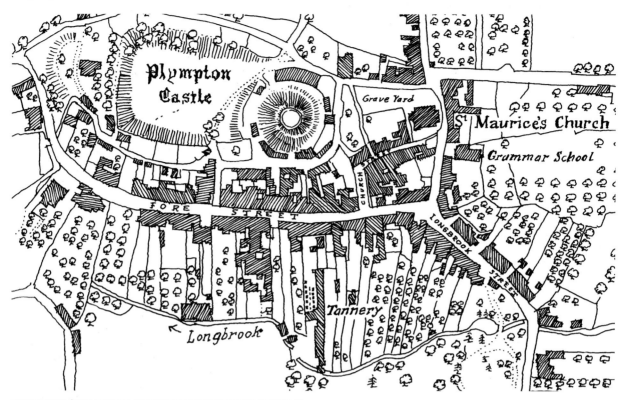

Tan Street

Location	SX 5447 5553
Operational	to circa 1865
Bark mills	two, water-powered
Tan pits	about 100
Staff	12 in 1851

The tannery stood on a strip of land south of Fore Street and bordering the Longbrook. There doesn't appear to be a leat to serve the bark mills but a pond is shown on the tanyard site on the earlier tithe map. Fore Street was once the main highway from Exeter to Plymouth. From the Ordnance Survey map of 1866

There are two Plympton parishes – Plympton Earl, otherwise known as Plympton St Maurice and the much larger Plympton St Mary. The little town of Plympton St Maurice was a medieval borough from 1194, with a market and fair, close to the castle constructed by Richard de Redvers at the beginning of the 12th century, the ruins of which remain. It was one of four Devon stannary towns from 1328. Tanning was recorded as one of the trades here in the 16th-18th centuries, together with wool-combing, brewing, coopering and hat-making. [1]

A 16th century tannery appears to have existed at Plympton Underwood, in Plympton St Mary parish: Thomas Adams was the tanner in 1588. [2] Plympton St Maurice was represented in the early eighteenth century by Roger Watts, tanner in 1719, and by William Port in 1739. [3] Another St Maurice tanner was Emanuel Burnell: reference was made to a dwelling house, tanyard, stable and garden and then to six fields at Underwood, over the parish boundary, in 1758. [4]

John Maddock, a Plympton St Maurice tanner, had property at Underwood in 1773. [5] The tanyard he used – parish undefined – was advertised in 1779:

'TAN-YARD. To be Lett .. from Midfummer next .. late in the poffeffion of John Maddick, tanner, deceasfed, fituate in Plympton, in the county of Devon, for fuch terms as fhall be agreed on ..
For particulars apply to John Culme, Efq, near Plymouth .. Dated 25 May 1779.' [6]

Joseph Burnell, very possibly a relation of Emanuel, and also a tanner, was bankrupt in 1785. [7]

Before the turn of the century Joseph Weekes had settled at Plympton and was the town's representative at a meeting of tanners at Exeter, all concerned about the *'.. free exportation of oak bark, injurious to the home industry'.* [8] Weekes was clearly active in 1800, advertising for staff:
'To Tanners. Wanted TWO JOURNEYMEN, to WORK at the BEAM - Apply to Joseph Weeks, Plympton, near Plymouth, who will give good wages according to merit and sobriety .. Plympton, January 8, 1800.' [9]

Four years later he was dead. [10] The next recorded event was the sale of tanyards at Plympton in 1827. The bark mills here were worked by water; one of the yards was still for sale in 1829. [11]

William Eales was tanning in Plympton in 1830. [12] A tanyard was again on the market in 1831: *'.. the Bark Mills are worked and the oozes pumped by water, and the greater part of the pits are under cover..'* [13]

By the middle of the 19th century one tanyard survived in Plympton. This was run by Thomas Brown from at least 1841. [14] He was very possibly the Thomas Brown, tanner of Buckland Monachorum from c 1822 to 1825 or later.

In 1851 the premises were in Fore Street, Plympton Earl, and Brown, aged 51, employed 12 men – more staff than at many Devon tanyards. [15] He was involved in property at Beaworthy in north Devon in 1857. [16] Thomas Brown, gentleman of Plympton St Maurice, died in August 1871. His nephew, George Drew of Plympton, also a tanner, was executor. Brown left an estate valued at about £2000. [17]

The tanyard came onto the market:
'Auction. Lot 1. All that .. freehold Dwelling-house, situate adjoining Fore-street, Plympton, with two large Gardens behind the same; adjoining is a spacious Tan-Yard which contains about 100 pits, with extensive drying houses and lofts, bark stores, stable and other convenient offices, bark mill, pumps and gear complete. Zinc bed roller, stable, with a never failing stream of water.
Also with the above will be offered for sale a Leasehold Cottage, and Coach-house adjoining, with a garden and roadway behind the same (forming an entrance to the tanyard) .. the whole being formerly in the occupation of the late Mr Thomas Brown, who for many years carried on an extensive tanning trade on the above premises ..' [18]

But no more is heard of tanning here. Presumably George Drew had enough money to retire on and by the 1870s tanning was a declining industry in Devon.

The Plympton Earl or Plympton St Maurice tanyard stood on the south side of Fore Street, directly south from the eastern end of Plympton Castle. [19]

'Tan Street' is still shown on a modern town centre A-Z, running south from Fore Street, although it is not indicated as such on the ground. In 2004 at the foot of a back lane, by the Long Brook, stands a curious little building, its wooden louvred openings in a clerestory now screened off and preserved behind glass. On one corner stood a kiln or stove with chimney. It may well be the last remnant of the tannery and may have served as a drying shed.

Plympton sources
1   W G Hoskins, Devon, Devon Books 1992, 461-463
2   Property at Easton Park – P&WDRO 69/M/2/433
3   1719 – Roger Watts, tanner of Plympton St Maurice. Copy will – P&WDRO 552/425; 1739 – William Port, tanner, estate at Furseball – P&WDRO 552/34
4   P&WDRO 69/M/2/200 of 1758
5   P&WDRO 69/M/2/487 of 1773
6   Sherborne Mercury 28 June 1779
7   Exeter Flying Post 21 July 1785 p 2 col 1
8   Bristol Mercury 30 August 1790; Joseph Weeks, tanner, Plympton – Universal British Directory, 1792, 281
9   Sherborne Mercury 13 January 1800
10 Exeter Flying Post 17 May 1804 p 4 col 3; Weekes' estate mentioned Exeter Flying Post 7 January 1808 p 1 col 3
11 Sherborne Mercury 24 March 1827 p 1; Sherborne Mercury 23 February 1829 p 4
12 Pigot's Directory, 1830, 123
13 Sherborne Mercury 4 July 1831 p1
14 DRO: Plympton St Maurice Tithe Map and Tithe Apportionment of 1841. Thomas Brown owned two houses, a garden and tanyard, items 56, 57, and leased land 54, 58, which included the building illustrated below
15 Plympton St Maurice or Earl's Plympton census, 1851 Fore Street – HO107 1877 f 393 p 9; Thomas Brown, tanner and farmer, Plympton Earl's, 1856. Post Office Directory of Devonshire and Cornwall, 1856, 257
16 NDRO 178B/M/T115
17 Thomas Brown's will of 1871
18 The Western Times 5 January 1872 p 1 col 1
19 OS Devonshire 25" sheet 124:7,2,3 of 1866

A building on the edge of the tannery site at Plympton, and adjoining the Longbrook, extant in 2004. It appears to have had a kiln and louvred openings in the clerestory roof. These are now preserved behind glass. Possibly a building for drying hides

Rewe

Chowns

Location	SX 9473 9957
Operational	to 1839
Output	200 butts a week
Bark mills	two, horse-powered
Pumps	horse-powered
Tan pits	45 handlers,
	34 troughs, 32 latches

Rewe's tannery may well have existed in the 18th century, but at present no evidence exists for it before 1807. Thomas Cleeve was the sole tanner from at least 1807 to 1839, [1] when he probably ceased trading.

The tanyard was part of an estate owned jointly by the Earl of Egremont and Lord Ilchester, and stood quite close to the Exeter-Tiverton road, overlooking the valley of the Culm to the east. It was known then as Chowns and covered just over 30 acres. [2]

In 1839 the property was offered for sale by auction: *'Auction .. Leasehold Estate and Capital Tanyard .. at Rewe. Lot 1. All that commodious Dwelling House, Pound-House, Barn, Courtlage, Garden and Orchard known as and forming part of Chown's Estate, situate at Rewe, with a first-rate Tanyard, Bark Sheds, Lofts and all necessary buildings, capable of tanning 200 Butts per week .. Three Acres .. situate in a good bark country .. The intended Bristol and Exeter Railroad will pass through this Estate .. Five-twelfths of the above Property is held under a lease from the Earl of Ilchester, for the*

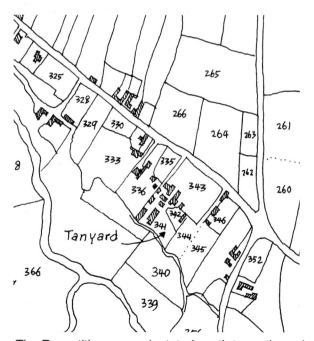

The Rewe tithe map, orientated south to north, and surveyed and drawn in 1840, before the Bristol & Exeter Railway arrived in the parish. By 1889 most of the tanyard buildings had gone

Residue of a term of 99 years .. and the remaining seven twelfths is held under a Lease from the Earl of Egremont .. Mr Cleeve, the owner ..' [3]

A further auction was attempted in 1840 [4] but the yard remained unsold. In 1845 the materials were put up for sale and the notice in the local press gives considerable detail:

'Rewe, Devon. To Tanners, Builders, &c. Mr Webber begs to announce that he has received instructions to sell by Public Auction .. all the Materials of that Extensive Tan Yard, Lately in the occupation of Mr Thos. Cleeve; Comprising one capital bark mill and cutters, nearly new, by Northam; one other ditto; iron pump, by horse power, tan burner, on an improved principle; tan pits, under cover are 45 handlers, 34 troughs and latches, 32 ditto; extensive leather house and serging loft, 70 ft long by 24 ft; slate roof; one thatch ditto, 70 by 24, with flooring balk, beams, and deal joice; boarded bark sheds, 50 ft by 12 ft; one other ditto, same size; an excellent double screw cider press and apple engine, with stone bruisers; half hogshead copper furnace, with many other useful lots.' [5]

Northam was an Exeter ironfounder and rival to Bodley. In fact several of the Exeter founders manufactured bark mills for the tanning trade.

Almost all of the buildings associated with the tannery have been demolished and had gone by 1889. A leat from the Culm may have existed, but if so this was probably only to supply water. Milling bark and pumping the tan pits were both horse-powered operations – this is what the 1845 sale notice implies.

The tannery was close to the Bristol and Exeter Railway, which opened in 1844, but while the 1839 notice indicates that it would run through the estate, it doesn't appear to have affected the buildings and yard which stood above the Culm flood plain. Leather production probably came to an end here in 1839 when Cleeve retired. He was not to be found in the parish in 1841. [6]

Rewe sources
1   1807 – Thomas Cleeve, tanner, Rewe, an assignee of William Kelland, currier of Exeter.
    Exeter Flying Post 23 July 1807 p 1 col 4; 1814 – Thomas Cleeve, tanner: offspring baptised. A H Shorter transcription from Devon & Cornwall Society records, Rewe parish registers; 1836 – Thomas Cleeve, tanner, Rewe. His son married. Exeter Flying Post 4 February 1836 p 2 col 5
2   DRO – Rewe tithe map and apportionment, 1837. Chowns included 341 = House, Tan Yard & Buildings 1a 1r 2p
    289 = Cottages, Buildings 0a 0r 6p; 286, 287, 288 = Garden. All arable; 343 = Orchard 1a 3r 19p
3   Exeter Flying Post 2 May 1839 p 1 col 3
4   Exeter Flying Post 10 September 1840 p 2 col 3
5   Exeter Flying Post 3 April 1845 p 1 col 1
6   Rewe census, 1841

Sampford Courtenay

Halford Manor

Location	SX 6490 9777
Tan pits	30
Operational	until circa 1795

Halford Manor. The porch carries the date 1615 and the initials 'T H'. This was the home of the Snell family, tanners in the 18th century, who later leased it to others. The tanyard site was nearby, a little to the north

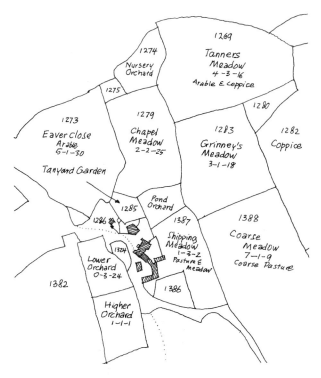

Great Halford in 1844, from the Sampford Courtenay tithe map and apportionment. Tanyard Garden and Tanners Meadow point to the 18th century tanyard here. Note also Pond Orchard just to the north of the house: tanneries needed water

Halford Manor house, otherwise known as Great Halford, dates from 1615. The Snell family owned Halford from some time in the 18th century until the mid 19th century or later. The Snells were tanners in the parish in the 18th century – John Snell, senior and junior, were making leather in 1720; [1] John Snell, tanner, had property interests at Higher Holland in 1735. [2] Mrs Snell was probably the owner when the yard was to let in 1784 with John Westaway then the tanner:

'Tan-Yard. To be Lett by PRIVATE CONTRACT, for a term of 14 or 21 years from Lady-day or Midsummer next, All that commodious TAN-YARD, with a good dwelling-houfe, ftable and outbuildings, adjoining .. situate at Halford, in the parifh of Sampford Courtenay, in the County of Devon .. and about five miles from Oakhampton [sic]..
The yard consists of upwards of Thirty Pits, and may be enlarged if required .. apply to Mr John Westaway on the premises .. or to Mrs Snell at Sampford Courtenay ..' [3]

Halford tanyard was again offered to let in 1796 [4] and that is the last that is heard of it. There were no tanners or tannery recorded in the 1841 census for the parish. [5] In 1844 the Great Halford Estate was owned by John Snell and occupied by John Hill senior. A little to the north of Halford manor, the building itself dating from 1610, was Tanyard Garden. Pond Orchard adjoined and two fields away, by a stream, was Tanners Meadow. The whole estate was a little over 293 acres. [6] It had increased to 298 acres in 1854, when again offered to let by tender, and still owned by a member of the Snell family – another John Snell. There is no mention of the tanyard, which had probably closed at the end of the 18th century. [7]

While close to the Taw, Halford stands on higher ground and the small stream on its land may have been inadequate for a 19th century yard – Halford would have had to compete with tanneries at North Tawton and Bow. At Sampford bark may have been ground in a horse mill rather than by a water-powered mechanism. The Snells appear to have made enough money from tanning in the 18th century to become landowners and lease the estate to others.

Sampford Courtenay sources
1. The Apprentices of Great Britain 1710-1762, transcription by Society of Genealogists from IR/PRO records 1921-8. Book 47 f 71. [Shorter]
2. NDRO – 2309/T55/12
3. Sherborne Mercury 15 March 1784
4. Exeter Flying Post 12 May 1796 p 1 col 1
5. Sampford Courtenay census 1841
6. DRO – Sampford Courtenay tithe map and apportionment
7. The Western Times 27 May 1854 p 1 col 2

Sampford Peverell

Location	ST 031 142
Output	50 hides a week in 1819
Operational	closed by 1841
Bark mill	water powered
Tan pits	40 handlers, 6 latches, 24 troughs, 4 stone pits, 3 lime pits and 2 masonry pits in 1831

Leather was made here at the beginning of the 17th century: John Combe was a Sampford tanner in 1605 and Thomas Morrell in 1608. [1] John Jones, tanner in 1648, was renting property in the parish at 18 shillings annually. [2] In 1784 the tanyard was offered to let [3] and by 1798 it was occupied by James Webber, who was then advertising for a journeyman tanner. He was looking for a *'Perfon who is qualified to take the Management and Care of a Tan Yard and Dry Leather. Alfo a Man who underftands the Business to work in the Yard and affift at the Beam occafionally. Conftant Employment and good Wages will be given ..'* [4] Webber was probably fully occupied during the wars with France but as early as 1816, less than a year after Waterloo, he was in difficulties and declared bankrupt. [5] The yard was then for sale. It was still for sale in 1819, indicating that the recession had hit. The contact at this date was William Webber, a successful tanner in Wiveliscombe, and very probably related to Samuel. An extensive notice in the local press gives a good outline of the property:

'To be SOLD, in Fee, by PRIVATE CONTRACT, A Newly erected and substantial DWELLING-HOUSE, with an eligible TAN-YARD behind the same, capable of tanning upwards of 50 hides per week. On the premises are a Patent Bark-Mill driven by a never-failing stream of water, a large Bark-barn, and two large Turf-Racks, with other necessary appendages, and Stabling for five horses. There is also a Walled Garden and Orchard, well stocked with fruit-trees, adjoining the tan-yard ..
The Dwelling House has a handsome front, with a southerly aspect, and comprises two good parlours eighteen feet square, a large Vestibule, with a Handsome Staircase, Kitchen, Brewhouse, and other necessary Offices, with a suitable number of good Lodging Rooms .. Sampford Peverell is situated on the Great Western Road, from London to the North of Devon, about five miles from Tiverton .. the premises close adjoin the Grand Western Canal, which is about to be extended to Taunton, which will enable the proprietor to convey his goods to Bristol and other markets ..'
Further particulars may be known on application to Mr. WILLIAM WEBBER, of Wiveliscombe, Tanner, Mr. HENRY PULLEN, of Kentisbeer ..' [6]

The construction of the new residence may well have drained Samuel Webber's funds. Tanning continued here as the tanyard was on the market again in 1831. John Payne may then have been the tanner. At this date details of the yard's capacity are given:
'A Tan Yard to be let with immediate possession, situate in the village of Sampford Peverell .. comprising a dwelling-house, bark shed, bark mill by water, 40 handlers under sheds, 6 latches, 24 troughs, 4 stone pits, 3 lime pits, 2 masonry pits covered and necessary lofts, stables, outhouses and walled garden.
To view the same apply to Mr Cowlen, attorney-at-law, Sampford Peverell, or John Payne, on the premises. The tenant to pay the Taxes and keep the Premises in Repair.' [7]

It is not clear whether a further tenant took the lease. No tanners were found in the parish in 1841 and the tithe map provides no clue as to the location of the yard. [8] We know it was close to the canal, that the house was built circa 1810 and was substantial, and faced south and that the bark mill was water-powered.

Members of the local history society have now identified the site, close to the Globe public house. The house and yard were later adapted as Saint Boniface's home for orphaned children and further demolition and clearance took place in the 1960s.[9] Court Way, a modern estate now overlies the site.

The stream that worked Sampford Peverell Mill also provided the power to turn the tannery's waterwheel, and when the canal was built, was culverted under it. A leat would have been provided to serve the tannery – for the waterwheel and also to provide water to the tanpits. When Sampford Mill was built the streams from Whitnage were found to be inadequate and the mill was built on a dam allowing the creation of a millpond behind it. To increase the supply of water, a long leat was dug, running all the way from the river Lowman. It still runs today, and can be seen running under outbuildings at the inn at Uplowman Cross.

Sampford Peverell sources
1 1605 – Terrier regarding tenements in the parish refers to John Combe, tanner of Sampford. Fursdon, Devon Parishes. DRO – 1198addA/PZ 9 of 1608
2 DRO – 1198addA/PF 11 of 1648
3 Exeter Flying Post 22 January 1784
4 Exeter Flying Post 27 December 1798 p 1 col 2
5 Sherborne Mercury 1 April 1816 [sale]; Sherborne Mercury 13 May 1816 [bankruptcy notice].
6 Sherborne Mercury 23 August 1819
7 Exeter Flying Post 15 September 1831 p 2 col 2
8 Sampford Peverell census, 1841; Sampford tithe map and apportionment
9 Personal communication from David King of Sampford Peverell, 9 May 2005. An old Sampfordian, once a boy at the orphanage, recalls swimming in a pool adapted from the tanpits.

Sandford

Doggetsbeer

Location	SS 818 044
Operational	closed between 1816 and 1839

Sandford possessed a tannery throughout the 18th century; it was at Doggetsbeer, some way north of the village. [1]

It was offered to let in 1787:

'All that Eftate and Tan-Yard called DOGGETSBIER fituate in the parifh of Sandford, in the county of Devon, about a mile and half from Sandford Town ..The premifes comprife a good Dwelling-houfe with all the neceffary Barns, Stables, Pound-houfe for grinding Bark, Cyder-pound, Cellars, Rind-houfe, working-houfe, tan-yard, in which hath been carried a confiderable Trade for many Years by the Owner, and which is fupplied with the beft of water from a spring which never fails; a cottage adjoining .. Further particulars may be known by applying to Mr Hamlyn at Pafchoe, near Crediton.' [2]

Yelland was a nearby property and Andrew Snell, of Yelland, a tanner, died in 1794. [3]

Whether there were two tanneries or whether Yelland and Doggetsbeer were at one time worked as a single estate has yet to be established. While Doggetsbeer stands beside a small stream, Yelland is beside the Binneford Water which may have provided power for a bark mill. It is clear from the 1787 lease notice that Doggetsbeer then had a pound house rather than a bark mill to grind its bark; a spring was deemed sufficient for water supply. However the tithe apportionment of 1839 does not indicate a tannery at Yelland. [4]

Richard Kelland was tanner at Doggetsbeer at least from 1807: in that year his wife died. [5] In 1810 his apprentice John Arthur absconded. [6] Business appeared to be picking up as Kelland advertised for three journeymen tanners. [7] But in the same year Kelland was declared bankrupt: [8] he died in 1811. [9] The tannery was offered to let, or failing that, was to be sold by auction at 'Yeoland' – clearly Yelland. [10] The Sandford tanyard was again for sale in 1816 and it seems to have ceased work following the Napoleonic wars. [11]

Doggetsbeer tannery had gone by 1839 when the property was owned and occupied by William Lake. It is worth noting that item 435 on the tithe map, by the stream, was listed as Tanney Orchard. [12]

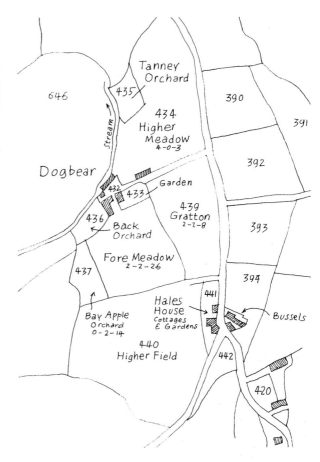

Doggetsbear or Dogbear as it was recorded on the Sandford tithe map. The 24-acre estate was owned and occupied by William Lake in 1839

A visit to Doggetsbeer in 2003 provided no evidence for this establishment. It may be that a restricted water supply led to its demise early in the 19th century. The place is now a smallholding.

Sandford sources
1 Robert Lane, tanner in 1721: Daphne Munday, Sandford, A Parish Patchwork, privately published, 1985, 198; tanyard to let 1725: Brice's Weekly Journal 21 January 1725-6; Thomas Pope, tanner, 1752: Munday op cit
2 Exeter Flying Post 11 October 1787
3 Exeter Flying Post 19 June 1794 p 3 col 2
4 DRO – Sandford tithe map and apportionment of 1839
5 Exeter Flying Post 12 May 1807 p 4 col 3; Doggetsbeer: 'In 1808 we find that Richard Kelland was there ..' Daphne Munday, op cit, 75
6 Exeter Flying Post 22 March 1810 p 1 col 5
7 Exeter Flying Post 28 June 1810 p 1 col 4
8 Exeter Flying Post 4 October 1810 p 1 col 4 and p 4 col 1
9 Exeter Flying Post 23 May 1811 p 4 col 2
10 Sherborne Mercury 3 June 1811
11 Exeter Flying Post 14 March 1816 p 1 col 4
12 DRO – Sandford tithe map and apportionment of 1839

Shobrooke

Week or Tanner's Wyke
Location   SX 8728 9972
Operational   closed after 1815

Sanctuary
Location   SS 8889 0258
Bark mill   steam powered
Operational   from circa 1816 to circa 1821

Sanctuary or Sanctuaries in 2007. This house dates from after Richard Reynolds' time but the parkland location illustrates his ambitions

Mathew Frost, the tanner here in 1691, spent a small fortune buying oaks – 500 for £900 – from the city of Exeter. [1] Relatively close to the city and to Crediton, the tannery may have had some market advantage, in buying hides and selling the tanned product.

By the end of the 18th century Richard Reynolds was actively seeking additional hands, expanding his business. [2] In 1799, the same year as he was advertising for journeymen, he married. Richard's bride was Maria, the second daughter of Lewis Hole, Esq, four times mayor of South Molton. [3] In 1801 he sought a further *'Two or Three Journeymen Tanners'*. [4] At a meeting chaired by George Barne of Tiverton in 1812, Reynolds was one of 16 tanners appointed to a committee charged with sending a memorandum to the Board of Trade on the undesirability of the new leather tax. [5]

His tannery was at Week, or Wyke as it was then known, at the foot of Wyke Hill and known as 'Tanners Wyke' 80 years later. But in 1815 he was the tenant here and his agreement appears to have come to an end:
'To be Let, by Auction, at the White Hart Inn, in Crediton .. for a term of ten years, from Lady-day next .. a Messuage or Tenement, with its appurtenances, called WEEKE, in the parish of Shobrooke, between five and six miles from Exeter, and about three from Crediton; comprising a dwelling-house and necessary offices for the farming business, with about 60 acres .. and a large and commodious TAN-YARD, with suitable buildings for carrying on an extensive business in the tanning line, all now in the occupation of Mr Richard Reynolds, as tenant ..' [6]

Reynolds remained in Shobrooke, building, as far as can be ascertained, a new house and associated tan yard at Raddon Hills, then known as 'Sanctuaries' and now as 'Sanctuary'. And so he became a proprietor. Tanners Wyke had possibly not been an ideal location – there was no major stream of water, so useful for production. Sanctuaries did have a stream but Reynolds installed one of the earliest steam engines to be used in the industry in Devon, to work the pumps that circulated the liquour – various strengths of tannic acid – and to grind the oak bark.

Reynolds looked set to go on to greater things; no longer content with the Exeter and Crediton markets, in 1817 he experimented with sending his tanned hides to London by Russell's flying waggons. [7] These waggons were not the cheapest means of transport and nor was the steam engine the cheapest power source. It seems Reynolds hadn't anticipated the slump that followed the Napoleonic wars and by 1821, over-extended on credit, he was bankrupt and the tannery was on the market:
' .. 'Sanctuaries' – lying in the parish of Shobrooke .. 40 acres meadow, pasture, orchard and arable land with an excellent new-built Dwelling-House, Farm-yard and Tan-yard .. worked by a steam engine with steam apparatus for heating the oozes. The tan-yard is considered one of the best in the kingdom .. Premises on an eminence, commanding very extensive views and sheltered from the north winds by the surrounding hills .. 3 cottages for labourers ..' [8]

The materials of the tanyard at Wyke were for sale in 1826 as it was no longer required – no other tenant tanner had taken it on. [9] Buildings here survived until later in the century. Sanctuaries became a parkland residence, the tanpits seemingly converted for use as a walled garden. [10]

Shobrooke sources
1   Michael Havinden, The Woollen, Lime, Tanning and Leather Working and Paper-Making Industries c. 1500 – c. 1800, in Kain and Ravenhill, Historical Atlas of South-West England, University of Exeter Press, 1999, 342, citing Robert Newton, Eighteenth Century Exeter, Exeter, 1984, 4
2   Exeter Flying Post 24 January 1799 p 1 col 3
3   Exeter Flying Post 14 February 1799 p 3 col 4
4   Sherborne Mercury 6 April 1801
5   Exeter Flying Post 20 August 1812 p 4 col 5
6   Exeter Flying Post 24 August 1815 p 2 col 3
7   Dorian Gerhold, Road transport before the railways. Russell's London Flying Waggons. Cambridge University Press, 1993, 102, citing L/1816/132 and 1817/510: Russell letters in PRO under C112/91 and C/112/92 respectively. Records of Chancery
8   Exeter Flying Post 26 April 1821 p 1 col 2
9   Exeter Flying Post 26 January 1826 p 1 col 4
10 Ordnance Survey 25" of 1889, sheets 67.8 and 55.16

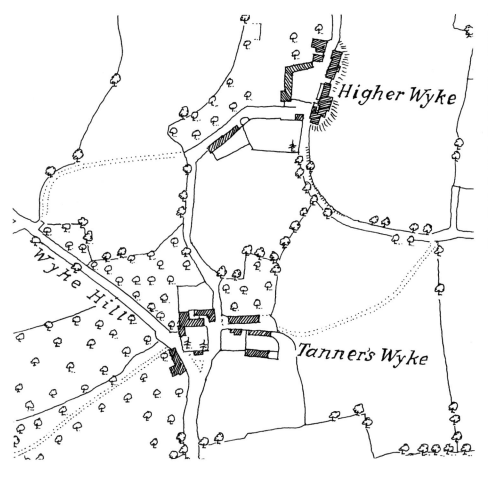

The tannery at Week or Tanner's Wyke was located at the foot of Wyke Hill. Most of the buildings shown on the Ordnance Survey map of 1889 have since been demolished. The tannery may have ceased trading here as early as 1815. From Ordnance Survey sheet 67.8, 25" = 1 mile

Sidbury

Sidford

Location	not known
Operational	circa 1808 to circa 1857
Tanpits	34 in 1810

Members of the Symonds or Simmons family were tanning at Sidbury in the 18th century. [1]
Joseph Weeks ran the Sidford tannery in 1808, when he married Miss Hodge, daughter of the surgeon Thomas Hodge, Esq, of Sidmouth. [2] His business came unstuck in 1810, when he was declared bankrupt and his stock-in-trade was auctioned. [3] His house and grounds, adjoining the Lyme Regis – Exeter turnpike, and close, the evidence indicates, to Sidford watermill, were also sold off:
'To Tanners and Others. To be Sold by Auction at the Royal Oak Inn in Sidbury .. Lot 1. All that Messuage or Dwelling House with the Tan-Yard, Drying Houses, Stables, Garden, and about two acres of excellent Orchard, late the residence of .. Joseph Weekes, and lying in the village of Sidford on the Lime Turnpike to Exeter .. The dwelling-house has lately been decently fitted up and the tan-yard, drying-houses &c, are entirely new built; there are thirty-four pits of different descriptions in the yard and a continual stream of water runs through it .. Lot 2. Mill Meadow ..' [4]

Expenditure on the new tanyard probably caused the bankruptcy. The premises may have utilised water power, but this is not explicitly stated. Downstream, at Sidmouth, an 18th century tanyard did have a water-powered bark mill. [5]

Sidford's tannery was again for sale in 1819 when owned by Thomas Jenkins Esq and occupied by Thomas Pitfield. [6] Thomas Pinn was later listed as tanner, but in the 1851 census the only individual of that name in the parish was recorded as a carpenter. [7] Nevertheless, while Thomas Pinn disappears from the record, Mrs M Pinn – presumably his widow – was running the tanyard in 1856. [8] Leather making in the parish probably terminated soon after that date. The yard does not appear on the tithe map.

Sidbury sources
1   1732 – William Simmons, tanner, married:
     A H Shorter, D&CNQ, from D&CRS transcriptions:
     1774 – William Symonds, tanner. Debtor applying for relief: Exeter Flying Post 8 July 1774 p 3 col 4
2   Sherborne Mercury 11 July 1808, Exeter Flying Post 14 July 1808 p 4 col 2
3   Sherborne Mercury 20 August 1810
4   Sherborne Mercury 3 September 1810
5   Sherborne Mercury 2 April 1770
6   Sherborne Mercury 17 May 1819
7   White's Directory 1850; Sidbury census 1851
8   Post Office Directory, Devon and Cornwall, 1856

South Molton
Two tanyards at East Street

South Molton has been home to tanners since at least the late sixteenth century. Seventeenth century tanners included Robert Pearce and Richard Barons. [1] In the eighteenth century John Gay, George Gay, John Upton, Jonathan Brooks, Thomas Smyth and William Berry were all involved in the industry. [2]

In 1802 a site for a tannery was offered adjoining Mole Mills, on the river Mole, to the east:
'There is a very convenient place adjoining for a Tan-Yard, and there is plenty of water to run conftantly through the Yard, and for foaking hides. Bark is always to be had in great plenty, and ground by water, and all the tan liquor pumped from one pit to another by the fame water-wheel. Hides and fkins may be always had from Ireland, Plymouth, or Briftol, befides Southmolton and the adjoining markets. There is about one acre of ground adjoining ..' [3]

East Street	
Location	SS 7165 2586
Operational	to 1853
Tan pits	6 taps and spenders, 19 layers, 44 handlers, 3 limers, 2 watering pits, 2 grainers in 1821 and 1853
Staff	3 men in 1851

Whether a tanyard already existed or was merely proposed for the site at Mole Mills is not clear. The Smyth family was established at 73 East Street – later renumbered 77. But there was a second yard at East Street – near New Road – which was for sale in 1821:

All that commodious Dwelling-House, and Tan-Yard behind the same, situate in East-street, in the town of Southmolton, Devon; now in the occupation of Mr F Trix, who is about to leave .. The house consists of two parlours .. each 17 feet by 11, an office or counting house, two kitchens, cellars and 6 bed-rooms, with convenient stables, and offices. There is a walled Garden well stocked with choice fruit trees, a small Orchard, and an extensive Kitchen Garden. The Tan Yard contains 6 taps and spenders, 19 layers, 44 handlers, 3 limers, 2 watering pits, 2 grainers, mill-house, leather-house, barn and spacious bark and drying sheds .. For further information apply .. to Mr N Gould, Southmolton ...' [4]

The yard was for sale again in 1826 when John Cox was tenant. And it was to let in 1839 when owned by Robert Furse, a South Molton surgeon. [5] His elder brother George Furse ran the tannery in the period 1844 to 1853, when he appears to have been declared bankrupt and the premises were offered for sale. George was then aged about 65. [6] The tan pits were unchanged in number from the time the yard was previously for sale in 1821:

'To Tanners and Curriers, To be Let, for such Term and from such time as shall be arrived on, a convenient TAN-YARD, situate in East Street, in the Town of South Molton .. together with several Cottages adjoining .. The Tan-Yard (which is now and has for many years been in full work) contains 6 Tapps and Spenders, 19 Layers, 44 Handlers, 5 Limers, 2 Watering Pitts, 2 Grainers, Mill House, Leather House and spacious Bark and Drying Sheds .. Tenders to be addressed to Mr Furse, Surgeon, Southmolton, the Proprietor ..'

To be .. sold by Public Auction under the provisions of an assignment for the benefit of creditors, the whole of the Stock-in-Trade and other Personal Effects of Mr George Furse, Tanner, on Wednesday 22nd day of June next .. in the Tan Yard in the occupation of Mr Furse, in East-street, Southmolton, consisting of 300 prime Foreign Butts and 600 Bellies, in course of manufacture, a quantity of English Hides, several tons of Bark, Rolling Machine, Bark Mill, and various other Articles and Tools which have been used in the Business of a Tanner. Dated 31st May 1853.' [7]

By 1856 William Gould Smyth was running the sole surviving tannery in South Molton and this second East Street site appeared to have come to the end of its working life. [8]

77 East Street	
Location	SS 7197 2586
Operational	to 1965
Bark mill	horse-power, then steam-power and latterly diesel engine
Output	100 heavy hides a week in 1880
Staff	28 in 1851

Entrance to the tannery in East Street. Sections of old bark mill edge runners stand here

The buildings here represent the most complete tannery structures now extant in the county, with the yard at Colyton excepted. While these date from the 18th and late 19th centuries, it is thought that a tannery has existed in this site since the 16th century.

Thomas Smyth was a South Molton tanner in 1759 [9] and when the property was advertised for sale in 1880 it was noted that it had been in the family's possession for over a century. For this reason there are scant records relating to its facilities and output.

The bark mill was originally horse powered and in the late 19th century steam power was used. A

Blackstone diesel engine was subsequently employed to grind the oak bark. [10]

William Smyth, probably the son of Grace Smyth –who died aged 76 in 1833, a tanner's widow – was tanner in the early to mid century, but died in 1836, in his fiftieth year, having recently been appointed an alderman for the borough. [11]

William G Smyth, born in the town, was tanning in East Street in 1851. Aged 36, he employed 28 hands. His wife Elizabeth, was somewhat younger – aged 24 – and was born in Porlock, Somerset. A son and a daughter and three servants were living in the household on census day. [12] Smyth was the only South Molton tanner listed in directories for 1856 and 1866; the other East Street tannery had now closed. In 1871 he was also recorded as a magistrate, living with two teenage daughters. [13] In 1873 Smyth's business address was 73 East Street; he was still listed as tanner in 1878. [14] He died on 1 June 1880:
'William Gould Smyth Esq, late of South Molton, JP, died 1 June 1880 at Fort House, South Molton. Left £25,000. Executors – daughters Elizabeth Alma Smyth and Maria Louisa Smyth, spinsters. Proved 9 September1880.' [15]
There is a tanner's house by the entrance to the yard, but by the mid 19th century the town's mayor chose to live at Fort House .

The yard was put up for sale:
'Southmolton – North Devon. An old-established tannery to be disposed of on advantageous terms in consequence of the death of the late owner – To be Let for a Term or Sold, with immediate possession, all those extensive premises situate in East Street, Southmolton, late in the possession of W G Smyth, Esq, and in which a large tanning business has been conducted by him and his predecessors for above a century past. The premises comprise a convenient Dwelling-house, with suitable outbuildings, Tan pits, Drying Lofts, Warehouses, and all accommodation capable of tanning 100 heavy hides per week. The taker may have the whole of the stock on the premises at a valuation, if desired. There are several cottages for labourers .. further information may be obtained from John Smyth Esq, Swimbridge, Barnstaple ..' [16]

George Southcomb was tanner manager in 1881, [17] while the yard remained on the market. Two years later it was taken on by two brothers from Porlock experienced in the trade – Thomas and Charles Pearce. They may have been relatives of William Smyth's wife, also from Porlock. Thomas returned to run the tannery at Porlock and one at Crewkerne while the South Molton business belonged to Charles Pearce and Sons (South Molton) Ltd. [18]

Charles Pearce was responsible for the construction of the late 19th century buildings. He married Elizabeth Hayward of Calne in 1884 and they had six children, including three sons, two of whom later became directors of the company. Having twice

followed in Smyth's footsteps as mayor of South Molton, Charles Pearce moved to Barnstaple, where he was also mayor and a justice of the peace; his cousin Walter became manager at South Molton early in the 20th century. [19]

In 1900 the firm's customers, mostly saddlers, ranged from Penzance to Swanage and Bristol. [20] South Molton leather also went to Northampton and London; in World War I it was used for Sam Brownes and leggings. Tanning ceased in 1965; due to restrictions on effluent. The Pearce family still owns the yard which is now given over to other uses. [21]

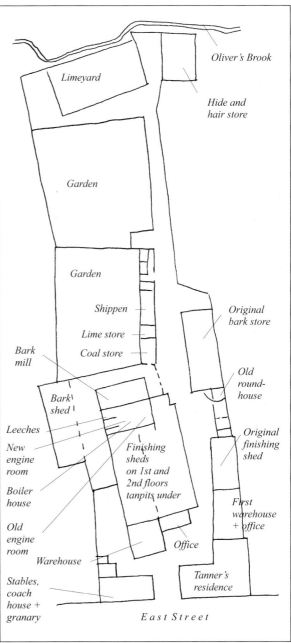

East Street Tannery, not to scale, adapted from a survey by Dick Pearce. A spring on Brook Meadow was piped over Oliver's Brook and into the limeyard. The original bark mill here was horse-powered, evidenced by the round house. In the 19th century steam power was used; this was in turn superseded by a Blackstone diesel engine

South Molton

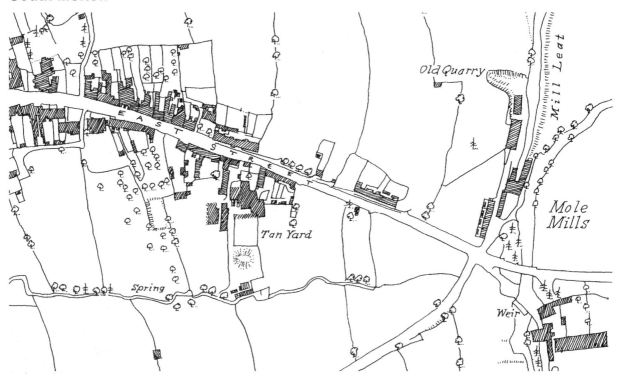

The tannery at 77, previously 73, East Street in 1889. To the east, by Mole Bridge, the Mole Mills were still manufacturing woollen cloth, powered by leats from the river. From the Ordnance Survey map, 25" = 1 mile, sheet 22.5. The second East Street tannery was to the west, near its junction with New Road

South Molton sources
1   DRO 1148Madd/2/L27/29, L28/65
2   DRO 1148Madd/2/L930, 2309B/T52/2; NDRO 1142B/
    T3/42, 2309 add3/2/20/1, B1/2812, B1/2818, B1/2851;
    Exeter Flying Post 14 July 1796 p 2 col 4
3   Sherborne Mercury 17 May 1802
4   The Alfred – West of England Journal, 11 December 1821
    p 3 col 2
5   The Alfred 28 March 1826 p 3 col 1 and the Exeter Flying
    Post 12 September 1839 p 2 col 4. DRO: the tanyard is
    shown on the South Molton tithe map and apportionment,
    item 1151, with orchard 1152. Owned and occupied by
    Robert Furse in 1846.
6   Pigot's Directory, Devonshire, 1844, 77, South Molton
    census 1851, East Street, HO 107 1891 f 458 p 26
7   The Western Times 11 June 1853 p 1 col 2
8   Post Office Directory, Devon and Cornwall, 1856
9   NDRO B1/2812
10 Shirley Bray, South Molton Tannery, The South Molton
    Archive 2002, 2, 9
11 Grace Smyth: Woolmers Gazette 7 September 1833
    p 2 col 3; William Smyth: Exeter Flying Post
    10 March 1836 p 2 col 6
12 South Molton census, 1851. East Street.
    HO 107 1891 f 479 p 17
13 South Molton census, 1871. RG10 2180 f 40 p 1
14 The Post Office Directory of Devonshire
    and Cornwall, Kelly, 1873; Harrods Directory,
    Devonshire, 1878, p 399
15 Exeter Flying Post 9 February 1881, p 7 col 5
16 The Western Times 23 July 1880 p 4 col 1
17 Shirley Bray, op cit, 11
18 Shirley Bray, op cit, 11; Leather Trades Review
    16 September 1953
19 Shirley Bray, op cit, 12
20 NDRO B729/1, tannery ledger
21 Dick Pearce in meeting with author, 21-09-2007

18th century warehouse and office adjoining the original tanner's house

A view south showing part of the late 19th century complex with chimney indicating a steam-powered site. The tan pits were located here, on the ground floor

The original tanner's residence in East Street, by the yard entrance. The complex was completely enclosed, a typical feature of tanyards

Right: a view north with the older range of buildings on the left; late 19th century structures on the right

This view shows workers and tan pits in the single-storey limeyard. The roof beams are visible. Hides are suspended in the water pit or sink, foreground. With three beams for fleshing or scudding hides

Men working the tan pits on the ground floor of the building. Duck boards or similar cover some of the pits to provide access. Note the moveable trough in the centre, bringing tan liquor to one of the pits

An upper floor: notice the worn floorboards. The men are working revolving rollers used in conjunction with a flat bed to finish leather by compressing it to give an even, shiny surface. These photographs date from the twentieth century when the tannery was run by the Pearce family

More worn floorboards. A stack of finished half hides or bends stand in the foreground, with bellies to the left. The latter were used for handbags or straps. These four images courtesy of Devon Library and Information Services

Swimbridge

Swimbridge Tannery	
Location	SS 6196 2994
Operational	until 1965
Bark mill	steam powered by 1863
Staff	9 in 1851, 20 in circa 1960

Tannery House and adjoining derelict remains of a part of the tannery in 2004. Other sections of the factory have been taken over by light industry

Tanning was central to Swimbridge. The tannery was the leading employer here in the nineteenth century and it was located within the village; not ideally placed for the prevailing south westerly winds. It almost certainly utilised water from a tributary of the Taw that rises on Stoodleigh Down, West Buckland.

We know there was a tanyard at Swimbridge in the eighteenth century – Mr Upham, the tanner in 1773, was robbed returning from South Molton market. [1]

The Smyth family ran the tanyard throughout the Victorian period, from as early as 1825, it is thought, to 1911. John Smyth was born in South Molton in 1796 [2] and was recorded as tanner in 1841: [3] he very probably relates to the South Molton tanning family of that name. In 1851 Smyth employed eight men and three women; one was no doubt his son John, an apprentice tanner, aged 19. His household on census night included two servants and a visitor – Richard Dunn, a South Molton currier, possibly one of his customers. [4] Ten years later – in March 1861– John Smyth senior died, leaving £7000. [5] His son John was now recorded as farmer and tanner and a younger son, William, aged 21, was learning the trade. [6]

John Smyth introduced or upgraded steam power at Swimbridge. The Old Quay Foundry at Exeter, run by the Bodley family, undertook work for him in 1863. A new 10" cylinder horizontal steam engine was supplied by the foundry and engine works in January for £85-5s-5d. An additional £35-14s-4d was paid for the driving gear to the bark mill and in November the liquor and water pumps were powered at a cost of £19-8s-1d. [7] Coal for the steam engine was probably shipped to Barnstaple and then hauled by road to Swimbridge as the railway didn't reach the village until 1873. [8]

William Smyth continued to assist his elder brother in the business until about 1873 when he moved to Barnstaple to run the Rackfield Tannery. John was on his own in 1881, supported however, by two unmarried sisters in their forties and four servants. They lived in Tannery House, built in about 1827 and right next door to the works, and were respected members of the parish, contributing the organ, a new marble reredos and other furnishings to the church.[9]

By the turn of the century the tannery was employing between 30 and 40 staff, many of whom had worked there all their lives. William Smyth's son John, born

circa 1873, was running the business in 1910. [10] The company product at Swimbridge and Barnstaple was the manufacture of sole leather; Swimbridge used hides imported from the Argentine and Uruguay. Barnstaple relied on hides from Europe. Trade was uncertain in the 20th century and by 1910 it was depressed, seriously affecting the Swimbridge yard: the work force was on short time, effectively working only four days out of six. The cost of raw hides had risen and sales were slow – the business was being undercut by cheap American imports. After lengthy consultations, John and William Smyth took the decision to close the Swimbridge yard in 1911; Barnstaple's Rackfield was able to continue in operation for the time being.

The Exeter press voiced concern, the Gazette railing against 'free trade':
'.. the unrestricted import of manufactured leather into this country is increasing every year, with the result that other tanners will be obliged to follow the example of Swimbridge. From 1895 to 1899 our net imports of manufactured leather – that is after allowing for re-exports – totalled £5,900,000, whilst in the period covered by the years 1905-09 the total rose to £7,569,000 – or an increase of over £1,600,000 worth of imported leather for consumption in this country .. every million pounds worth of imported manufactured goods means a loss of 30s a week for a whole year to 6,400 British working men ..' [11]

But closure, which must have had a major impact on the village, was short lived. In 1916 the British Electric Tanning Syndicate of Langport took over the Court de Wyck tannery at Yatton, in north Somerset and Swimbridge. If the economic climate was so dismal for Devon tanners in 1911, what induced the Langport firm to restart operations? World War I *'created an enormous demand for leather of all descriptions'*. In addition *'.. British Electric Tanning Syndicate does not set out to make a long, expensive tannage, it claims to produce a leather – made on the latest scientific lines – of good quality and a*

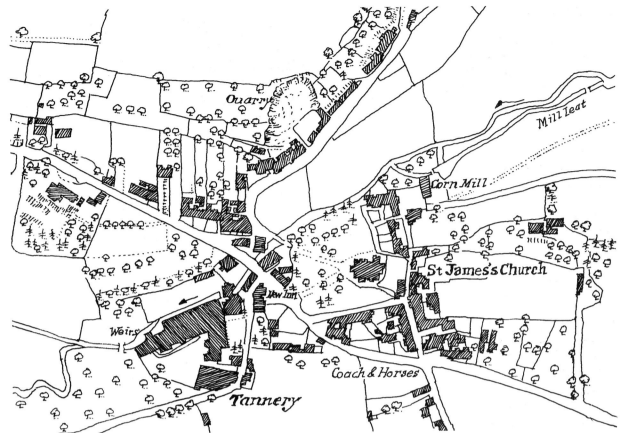

The Swimbridge tannery dominated the village by 1889; the buildings' 'footprint' much larger than, for instance, St James's Church. Note that the New Inn has since been renamed the Jack Russell and the water powered corn mill no longer exists. From the Ordnance Survey map, 25" = 1 mile, sheet 14.9

moderate price. Modern machinery is to be erected at Swymbridge, and the company hopes to be in full work there before the end of the year ..'
This statement implies the company intended to introduce a faster and more competitive tanning process: however oak bark tanning was probably still used for sole leather. According to Andrew Parr of Colyton: *'chrome tanning produces a very 'open' leather with poor water-resistance and wear properties .. they may have used a mixed vegetable tannage based on mimosa and myrobalan'*. [12]

The tannery re-opened in March 1917, [13] but the Langport management only survived until 1921.

In that year H Fulford arrived at Swimbridge and *'found the factory poorly equipped and the workmen far more skilled in farming than tanning ..'* Fulford continued to use imported wet-salted hides but also bought local hides: *'.. The Devonshire cattle yield a raw material which cannot be bettered in any part of England, and it is indeed fortunate that such fine plump hides are found so close at hand'*. Gradually the Fulford family resuscitated the concern, producing leather *'according to modern principles'*. The tanpits were located in and under long drying sheds, their upper floors supported on massive wooden beams. There was no ironwork, hence no rust and the danger of it affecting the hides. To control

the tanning processes H Fulford and his brother A A Fulford installed a well-equipped laboratory. Mains electricity didn't arrive until 1937 and until then the old waterwheel was used to generate lighting, the steam engine providing the rest of the motive power.

One factor was beyond the Fulfords control and ultimately led to the demise of the business: the local sewers were not able to deal with trade effluents from the chemicals involved in the chrome tanning

Unloading hides at the tannery in the 1950s. Imported hides came by rail – goods train to Swimbridge station and then by lorry to the yard. Bert Liverton, the then foreman, on the right. Photograph courtesy Mervyn Dalling

Swimbridge

process, which appears to have been adopted here. Had trunk sewers and large-scale treatment plants existed then the tannery might have survived beyond 1965, the year of closure. Pollution and attendant health and safety concerns sealed its fate. [14]

This was an unsettling time for the parish – the Taunton-Barnstaple railway closed in the same period. [15] Jeff Patton brewed Swimbridge Bitter on part of the premises from 1981 but big combines with tied houses restricted sales potential and the brewery closed in 1983. [16] Swimbridge was a large establishment but major structures have been demolished; [17] various buildings still stand, adapted to light industries and businesses. Tannery House, a Grade II listed residence, was on the market for £450,000 in 2003.

Swimbridge sources

1   Exeter Flying Post 29 January 1773 p 3 col 4
2   IGI Mormon indexes: John Smyth married Mary Shapland, 26-3-1831, Swimbridge. He was baptised 6-12-1796, son of William and Ann Smyth of South Molton. Offspring: Anna baptised 15-7-1834; Grace 6-1-1836; Mary 1-11-1837 and William 18-3-1840.
3   Swimbridge census, 1841. HO107 236/3 f 5 p 6; DRO tithe map and apportionment 1845-6 – House and Tanyard item 1405, owned and occupied by John Smith [sic]
4   Swimbridge census, 1851. HO 107 1892 f 9 p 11
5   Will of John Smyth, 1861
6   Swimbridge census, 1861. RG9 1488 f 5 p 3
7   DRO Exeter – Bodley journals 67/5/2/1 folios 461-466
8   The Taunton-Barnstaple railway opened throughout in November 1873. David St John Thomas. A Regional History of the Railways of Great Britain. Volume 1. The West Country. Phoenix House, 1960, 27;
9   Swimbridge census 1871 – RG10 2182 f 10 p 13; The Post Office Directory of Devonshire and Cornwall, Kelly, 1873; Swimbridge census 1881 – RG11 2243 f 7 p 8; information from Mary Balment, a Swimbridge resident, 31 October 2003
10 Kelly's Directory of Devonshire and Cornwall, 1910, 1143
11 Gazette 1911
12 Gazette October 1916; Andrew Parr of Colyton tannery, personal communication 24 May 2006
13 Gazette March 1917, Kelly's Directory of Devonshire and Cornwall, 1919, 1116
14 John Fulford, article on Swimbridge tannery, Leather Trades Review, 19 August 1953
15 Information from Mary Balment
16 Lois Lamplugh, A look at the Past of Swimbridge. Wellspring, Swimbridge, 1993, 42
17 Tom Bartlett, Postcard Views of North Devon, Volume II, Barnstaple and Around, Badger Books, Bideford, 1988, 85

Members of the Smyth family on the down to the south of Swimbridge. Possible candidates are sisters Grace and Mary Smyth with their brother John Smyth, right, and village children. The photograph was taken before 1877, the year houses to the left of the church were demolished to make way for an enlarged churchyard. The tannery is hidden behind trees on the extreme left, but Tannery House can be seen between two trees. Photograph courtesy Mary Balment

Swimbridge tannery staff at the end of the Smyth era, before the first closure in 1911. The bearded man in the middle of the front row, wearing a 'pork pie' hat, is John Morrish, the tannery foreman. Photograph courtesy of Mervyn Dalling

Looking south to Dennington Lane on the hill beyond the tannery, with the derelict three-storey drying shed in the foreground, shortly before its demolition in the 1960s. Photograph courtesy Mervyn Dalling

Tavistock

Taviton
Vigo Bridge
Bannawell Street
Parkwood Road

Tanning was an early Tavistock industry, along with weaving and cloth making. Tavistock Abbey, the heart of the town in the medieval period, was probably responsible for the introduction of the leather-making trades. A 'tan-mill' and an alder bed, the latter used instead of oak for tannic acid, were in existence at Taviton in the late 14th century. The mill was then converted, fulling stocks were installed and it operated for the benefit of the woollen industry. [1]

In the first half of the eighteenth century leather workers represented 13% of the town's leaseholders and by 1752, 15% or 102 of Tavistock's 652 workers were engaged in the trade. And these statistics do not include the farmers, slaughtermen and fellmongers associated with the production of leather.

In 1751 Tavistock was shipping shoes and pumps to the West Indies. Dozens of shoes at £2 5s to £2 8s per dozen were sent by coaster from Exeter to London for export to Kingston, Jamaica. Clearly the industry in the town was then, as Crediton's was to become in the 19th century, quite an extensive one and not merely meeting local needs. [2]

Despite the 'tan-mill' conversion to fulling circa 1400, Taviton was involved in leather making in the 18th and early 19th centuries. [3] The other 19th century tanneries were concentrated near Lower Brook Street and Bannawell Street: there are references to tanners living at Exeter Street in 1844 and Whitchurch Road in 1890, but these are residential addresses.

The nineteenth century witnessed an upsurge of mining activity in the hills and valleys around the town. With the opening of the Tavistock Canal providing access to the sea via the river Tamar, Tavistock was able to establish support industries such as ironfounding and tanning declined in importance, especially after the arrival of the railway from Plymouth.

Taviton
Location	SX 4937 7455
Bark mill	probably water powered
Operational	to circa 1823

The precentor of Tavistock Abbey owned a tan-mill at Taviton until the period 1400-1413, when it was converted to full cloth. [4] There was a large woollen mill here in the 18th century or early 19th century,

together with a leather mill and bark mill. So tanning had been reinstated at some point in the intervening centuries. Like many properties in the neighbourhood, this was owned by the Duke of Bedford when offered for sale in 1823:

'To be Sold by Private Contract, with immediate Possession. All the very desirable Factory and Premises called Taviton Mills, situate within half a mile of the flourishing and excellent market town of Tavistock .. lofty and spacious Building lately used as a Woollen Factory, 3 stories high, and 73 feet long by 24 wide, to which is attached an overshot wheel of very superior construction, 40 feet in diameter, and four abreast, recently built of the best materials, and plentifully supplied with water.
Another roomy building, used as a Leather Mill, being 41 feet by 25 feet 6 inches, with an overshot water wheel therein, 16 feet diameter, and 4 feet 8 inches abreast.
Also another spacious building, heretofore a Bark Mill, having drying lofts above and attached and a shed capable of containing forty tons of bark. Together with two Cottages adjoining the same. The whole forming a compact and connected range of buildings, well adapted to the above branches of business .. easily convertible to Paper or Grist Mills. The premises are held by lease of his Grace the Duke of Bedford for the remainder of a term absolute, of which 42 years are unexpired at the moderate yearly rent of 10l. ..' [5]

Milling continued at Taviton but on present evidence this was the end of the line for the leather industry here. Taviton mill has survived, converted to private housing.

Taviton Mill in 1908, some time after shammy leather dressing production had ceased here. The waterwheel is a large high breast-shot type; the leather mill used a smaller 16' overshot waterwheel. Image courtesy of Roderick Martin, taken from a postcard. Photographer Sydney Pierce

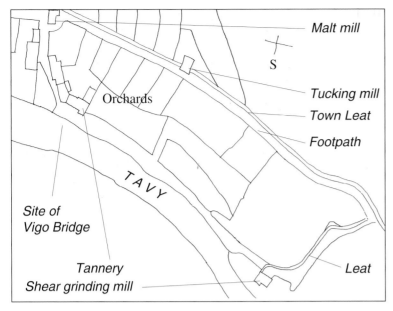

Tavistock's east end in 1753: very different from today. The Town Leat, then also known as Drake's Pool, served several watermills including the tucking mill and malt mill, shown here. The tannery stood near the site of Vigo Bridge; the latter not built until 1772. A subsidiary leat powered the shear grinding mill near the Tavy. This was to adjoin a later tannery.
An earlier tannery site, Glanville's Tannery, existed further west along Brook Street in the 18th century
From Wynne's survey, 1753, DRO TD273

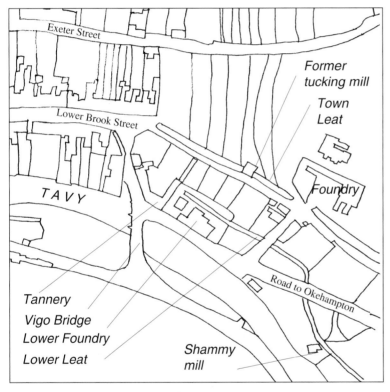

Tavistock's east end in 1842. Still significantly different from the present day. The railway has yet to arrive. But Vigo Bridge has been in existence for 70 years. The Mount Foundry, the Lower Foundry and the Lower Leat all feature. This second leat was utilised by the Vigo Bridge tan yard as well as the Lower Foundry and was cut by Mr Isaac of the lower foundry in 1800.
A third leat, not shown – Higher Leat – was made in 1804 to serve Gill & Co's main foundry.
The tucking mill had ceased to function; the shear mill became a shammy mill about 1800 and later a cottage. It adjoined the tannery site shown in the 1885 map by which time Parkwood Road had replaced the 'Road to Okehampton'.
From John Wood's 'Plan of the Town of Tavistock', 1842, DRO T1258M/E10

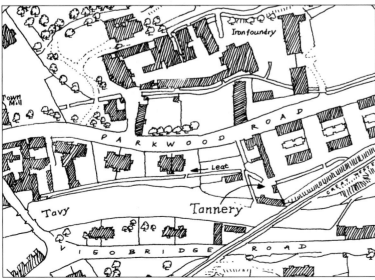

1885. Orientation is now due north rather than north-north-west. The tannery at Vigo Bridge had ceased operations by 1857. The railway has arrived. Parkwood Road continues from Lower Brook Street and the Lower Leat has been moved nearer the river. The surviving tannery is evident adjoining the river and the Great Western Railway's Tavistock branch. Two water-powered ironfoundries are also close by, the larger of the two, originally Gill & Co's foundry, making use of the Higher Leat. The second is largely off the map on the lower right. From the Ordnance Survey map 1:500, sheet 105: 8.13

Tavistock

Tannery by Vigo Bridge

Location	SX 484 746
Bark mill	water-powered from circa 1808
Operational	until 1844 or so

This tannery was in existence in the 18th century and before Vigo Bridge was built in 1772. In 1752 it was leased to Richard Prideaux and occupied by a Mr Beauford. It may have replaced Glanville's tannery, which stood further west, about 200 yards towards the centre of Tavistock, off Brook Street. [6] By 1803 the Vigo Bridge site was described merely as an 'office' for partners Samuel Carter and Richard Abbott, who had established a second tannery in Bannawell Street. A lease of 1808 concerning the adjoining, recently built, lower foundry stated that the water in the foundry's leat: *'shall be permitted to run on to the bark mill or machine lately erected by Messrs Rd Abbott and Samuel Carter'*. [7]

By 1817 Abbott and Carter's operation at Vigo Bridge had been extended with a new house and a lease from the Duke of Bedford made reference to a drying house and other outbuildings. [8] In 1827, following the death of Richard Abbott, [9] the partnership became Carter and Martin. The younger Carters were not dedicated tanners and Richard Martin, still a young man, was looking to retire from the business in 1844. He was then living in Exeter Street, [10] now known as Old Exeter Road. He married the youngest daughter of Mr Poole, a chandler of Pembroke Street, Devonport. [11]

He appears to have had difficulties disposing of his lease of the tannery; he was in dispute with Gill & Co concerning payments for leat water. Christopher Haedy of the Duke of Bedford's estate office voiced concerns over the exact status of one of the two waterwheels: *'Mr Martin must defend his own rights - My notion is, as you are aware, that his waterwheel is on the Foundry Premises ..'* [12] Martin was declared bankrupt in 1848. [13] By 1857 the site had become a coachbuilder's yard. The bark mill water-wheelpit was dug out in recent years by Exeter Archaeology when Vigo Mews was under construction. [14]

Bannawell Street

Location	SX 479 746
Operational	from 1794 until circa 1845

Bannawell Street tanyard is said to have been founded in 1794 by Samuel Carter and Richard Abbott. [15] Abbott was summonsed in 1806, accused of attempting to sell inadequately tanned hides in Plymouth market. [16]

Samuel Carter's three sons each ran the business in succession, which included the yard by Vigo Bridge. [17] William Carter was involved in a slander case in 1818, winning damages. [18] His partner Richard Abbott died in 1827 and Carter formed a new partnership with Richard Martin in that year. Martin was a minor, but he was also executor of Abbott's will. [19] The partnership was listed at Bannawell Street in 1830 [20] but was later dissolved.

John Carter, Samuel's third son, inherited the tannery in that decade. He'd lived the life of Riley for thirty years, never having worked. His management of the concern was a disaster and his son, another Samuel, who was due to study law, found himself in charge of the industry. In 1844 he was listed as the Bannawell Street tanner but managed to relinquish control and headed off to pursue his legal studies. In 1847 he was called to the bar and later became a politician. [21]

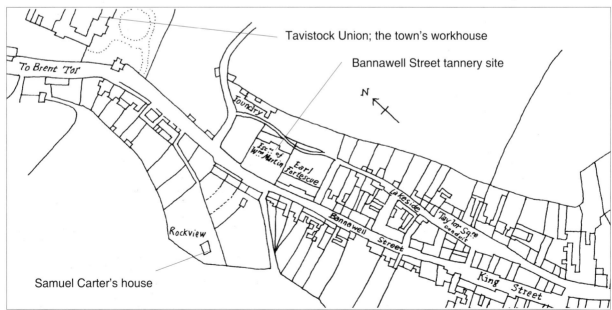

The site of the Bannawell Street tannery. The Bedford Foundry later occupied the site. From John Wood's 'Plan of the Town of Tavistock', 1842, here orientated east-north-east. Source: DRO T1258M/E10

Tannery plan in 1825

In 1825 the yard was described as: *'Messuage or Tenement Buildings and Tanyard situate on the East side of Bannawell Street abutting partly on a house and garden'* [22] Samuel, 36, was listed living at Rock View House in 1851, overlooking the tannery, together with his father John, a 'retired farmer'. [23]

The tanyard site disappeared when the nearby Bedford Foundry was extended by 1848. It was bounded by the Fishlake, a small Tavy tributary, which would have supplied the water for the tanpits and might have turned a waterwheel [24]

Tanyard by Brook Street / Parkwood Road

Location	SX 4857 7457
Bark mill	water powered
Operational	19th century, c1846 or earlier until 1885 or later

One of the Tavistock yards was leased to Joel Blanchard, who had previously been a Brook Street bootmaker. [25] Mary Blanchard, Joel's widow, was living at Brook Street in 1851. Her husband had died in 1846. She was listed as tanner here in the trade directory for 1850. [26] The Vigo Bridge site was occupied by coachbuilders Randle & Smith by 1857 [27] but another tannery stood to the east, reached from Parkwood Road. It adjoined a site which had been a

shear grinding mill in 1753 but was a shammy mill in about 1800, by Tavistock's lower leat, the latter constructed in 1800. [28] So it would appear that it was this yard that was offered for sale in 1858:

'Tavistock, Devon. To Tanners and others. An old-established Tanning Business which has been in the occupation of the late Mr J C Blanchard and Mrs Blanchard upwards of twelve years, is to be disposed of by Private Contract. The premises consist of a Dwelling-house, Bark Barn, Drying-Lofts and Tan-Yard, in excellent repair .. The above has been carried on successfully by the late and present occupier, the latter being about to retire from business .. For particulars apply to Mrs Blanchard, Brook Street, or to Mr H Blanchard, currier, Tavistock.' [29]

Mary Blanchard was still listed as a tanner living in Brook Street in 1861, aged 63; [30] the tannery was in operation in 1887, making use of the lower leat, but it is not presently known who ran it. [31]

Candidates are John Clifton, a tanner, living at 4 King Street in 1878 [32] and William Osmond Ward of St John's House, Old Plymouth Road, later renamed Whitchurch Road, in 1881. Ward was 34 at that date; his birthplace Ottery St Mary. He employed 40 men and it is quite probable that he was a partner in Ward Brothers, Coxside – a Plymouth tannery. But equally he may have run the tannery off Parkwood Road as a separate business. Ward was still living here in 1891, a widower with two teenage daughters. [33]

Parts of the site recently survived as warehousing but it has since been redeveloped for residential housing.

Tavistock sources
I am indebted to Mary Freeman for considerable advice.
1   Whitchurch Down. A Study by Members of the Tavistock LHS. 1990. – Helen Harris, Industrial Archaeology, 11-14, citing 1 – H P R Finberg, Tavistock Abbey, D&C 1969, 153; 2 – DRO W.D. Bdle 27 no 3
2   D M Trethowan, The Leather Trade of Tavistock, Devon and Cornwall Notes & Queries, 1965-7, 220-221
3   The Alfred 18 March 1823 p 1 col 3
Taviton
4   Whitchurch Down text – op cit.
5   The Alfred 18 March 1823 p 1 col 3
Vigo Bridge
6   Personal communications from Mary Freeman of Tavistock, June 2007, citing John Wynne's survey of the town of 1753, DRO TD273
7   Mary Freeman, citing foundry lease of 1808
8   DRO L1258M/L/L1/5: Indenture of 1 October 1817
9   Exeter Flying Post 26 April 1827 p 3 col 5
10 Pigot & Co's Directory, Devonshire, 1844, 141
11 Exeter Flying Post 29 February 1844 p 2 col 5
12 DRO L1258M/L/L1/5: attached letter from C Haedy
13 Exeter Flying Post 24 February 1848 p 3 col 7
14 Mary Freeman, in a letter, June 2007, citing Exeter Archaeology report 97, 39
Bannawell Street
15 G Woodcock. Tavistock's Yesterdays. Episodes From Her History. Volume 1, privately published 1985, 33; the tanyard is not shown on William Wynne's map of 1753

16 P&WDRO 1/695/80
17 G Woodcock, op cit, 33
18 Exeter Flying Post 26 March 1818 p 1 col 2
19 Exeter Flying Post 26 April 1827 p 3 col 5; Tavistock census 1841 – HO107 249\13 f 8 p 10;
20 Pigot & Co's Directory, Devonshire, 1830, 128
21 Pigot & Co's Directory, Devonshire, 1844, 141, G Woodcock, op cit, 33
22 DRO T1258M/L1, item 21
23 Tavistock Census, 1851, Bannawell Street HO107 1883 f488 p 7
24 Communications from Mary Freeman, June 2007
Brook Street/Parkwood Road
25 G Woodcock, op cit, 33
26 Tavistock census 1851 – index and HO107 1883 f 567; White's Directory, 1850
27 Communications from Mary Freeman, June 2007
28 DRO TD273 – John Wynne's survey of Tavistock, 1753; DRO T1258M/E10 – John Wood's 'Plan of the Town of Tavistock', 1842; Mary Freeman. The First Iron Foundry in Tavistock. Devon Historian 57, 1998, 28-29
29 The Western Times 13 March 1858 p 1 col 2
30 Tavistock census for 1861 – RG9 1461 f 20 p 32
31 Ordnance Survey map, 1885, 1:500, sheet 105: 8,13
32 White's Directory 1878, 1090
33 Tavistock census for 1881 – RG11 2217 f 60 p 16, White's Devonshire Directory 1890, Tavistock census for 1891 – RG12 1749 f 49 p 11

Tiverton

Manley – Tanpitt Close or Woodlands
Fairby
New Place
Town's End

In the late 14th century, Tiverton tanners traded at Exeter, buying hides and selling their leather in the city's markets. [1] The town became a chartered borough in 1615. There were 25 burgesses initially, of whom eight were merchants and a further eight were clothiers. Of the rest, two were known to be yeomen, two were gentlemen and the leather trade was represented by, it appears, a single tanner. [2] Tanning was never a mainstream activity in Tiverton; it was associated, however, with the talented George Barne. He came from Bickleigh and Butterleigh and was involved in Tiverton affairs from at least 1791.

Both 18th century Tiverton tanneries were on the outskirts of the town – George Barne's New Place tannery was at West Exe, out beyond Wellbrook Street and the second tannery was near the Town Leat, not far from Town's End, and now the garden of Brunswick House.

Manley – Tanpitt Close or Woodlands
Location	SS 983 118
Operational	early 17th century

A 17th century yard existed just outside the parish at Manley. The tan pits were in a field just inside the parish: in 1670 the tanner's house was known as *'The Tanhouse, or Cruddles house, as it was let to one Cruddle a tanner about 50 or 60 years ago, and the field called Woodlands to make his tan pitts in because there was water there; belong to Kings College ..'* Ownership was disputed between Kings College, Cambridge, and Richard Newte. [3]

Fairby
Location	SS 944 173
Operational	18th century

Fairby stands by the turnpike road to Bampton which opened along the Exe valley in 1819.
Tanning appears to have been undertaken here as late as 1789. The Tiverton historian, Martin Dunsford, provides this account:
'On Friday 19 May John Newton, a farmer and his son, attempting to ride across the river Exe, about eleven at night, from a coppice on the Washfield side of the river, where they had been barking oak, to their dwelling at Lower Fairby in the parish of Tiverton, were swept away by the violence of the current, swelled by a heavy rain a few hours before, and drowned.' [4]

At Lower Fairby a ground known as Tanpit Orchard was part of the property when the tithe map and apportionment were drawn up c 1840. [5]
Presumably the rain came after the Newtons had been stripping the bark – it is not an activity to be undertaken in the wet.

Fairby, on the road to Bampton

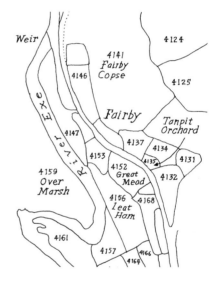

A section of the Tiverton tithe map, showing Tanpit Orchard at Fairby. The house overlooks the river Exe and the now vanished leat to Rock Mill

New Place
Location	SS 947 127
Operational	18th century to circa 1840
Bark mills	One water-powered, one horse-powered
Tan pits	56 handlers, 32 layers or troughs, and 3 other pits

In the late eighteenth century Barne owned a farm at Combe, Butterleigh [6] and ran a tannery at Higher Brithayes, in the Burn valley, Bickleigh. His father – also George, a gentleman of Bickleigh – died in 1788. [7] By 1793 George had re-established in Tiverton. [8] Higher Brithayes was offered to let in 1789. [9]

The house at New Place survives and was listed Grade III in 1946. It is almost a mansion: a two-

New Place, George Barne's Tiverton home, seen through a screen of trees from Seven Crosses Road

storey structure of five bays dating from the 18th century and stands in its own gardens. It may well have been built by Barne following his father's death. When built it probably stood isolated in the country. Today it is surrounded by housing.

The tanyard was probably nearby; the Cottey brook would have provided power for a bark mill and water for the tanpits. At present it's exact location is not known, nor its capacity, but it is safe to assume that capacity and output exceeded the 18th century tanyard at Higher Brithayes, Bickleigh.

It is not unreasonable to surmise that Barne was educated at University: one imagines him going up to Oxford, following schooling, say, at Blundells. He was clearly an able man, an organiser and networker with many contacts, and was to become the leading representative of the trade in Devon. In 1790 he called a meeting of tanners at Exeter; proceedings were reported in the Bristol press. Oak bark was being exported from the country and this was creating serious problems for the expanding home trade, no doubt through scarcity and rising prices. Tanners from Dorset and Cornwall were also present. [10]

Tiverton Corporation – an influential body in that era – was also to involve much of his time: George was elected an assistant in 1791 and two years later entertained members of the Corporation at the Angel. The Angel was one of Tiverton's leading inns, standing in Angel Hill near the junction with St Peter Street, on a site occupied by the library from 1928 to 2004. In 1793 the party went on some time: *'the day and evening were spent very agreeably ..'* [11]

George no doubt was one of those organising the illuminations in the town following Nelson's victory

at the Battle of the Nile in 1798. His brother John had recently been appointed rector of Butterleigh and George served as churchwarden for a number of years. [12] In 1798, too, George married Mary Baker, a farmer's daughter from Chettiscombe; they had six known offspring – two sons and four daughters. [13]

George Barne's inheritance, his tanning activities and his work for the Corporation provided an income such that he was able to become a partner in the Tiverton and Devonshire Bank in 1808. The bank had been established in 1787 by Dickinson, Lewis and Besly. Lewis had withdrawn and in 1808 Besly wished to retire. Henry Dunsford the younger, a Tiverton mercer, and George Barne each bought $^3/_{10}$ths of the shares, with the new partnership authorised to run for 14 years. [14]

A duty was now imposed on leather. In 1812 Barne called and chaired a meeting of tanners at the London Inn, Exeter, to oppose the government's new tax. A committee was formed to co-ordinate activities and draft a memorandum to the Board of Trade on the damage this would do to the tanning industry. The sixteen members included Richard Reynolds of Shobrooke, Peter and William Sharland of Cheriton Fitzpaine, Samuel Wreford of Chulmleigh and the Exeter tanners James Rew and William Underhay. [15] Concerns over taxation continued and George Barne chaired further meetings in Exeter in 1817 and 1818. [16]

1818 was a high point in his career: George was elected Mayor of the Borough of Tiverton and his predecessor held a dinner in his honour at the Angel in August attended by 57 individuals including Sir Charles Chalmers, Sir John Duntze, Messrs Hay of Collipriest and Dickinson, his fellow banker: *'The day passed with the greatest hilarity and harmony ..'* [17]

Tiverton

New Place tannery was still functioning: in 1825 a ten-year-old boy, Robert Carter of Butterleigh, was apprenticed. [18] By 1830 the tannery was operating under the trading name of Barne & Son. [19] With Barne's many other activities, it is probable that the day-to-day operation was supervised by a manager or foreman.

Cullompton suffered its great fire in 1839, and Barne, who owned property in the parish at East Butterleigh, subscribed £5 towards the rebuilding subscription, as did Cullompton tanners Mortimore and Sellwood. [20] This was the year when sheep stealing became prevalent in the neighbourhood and Barne suffered losses from his flock, probably from Cottey House Farm. A West Exe butcher was being sought for the crimes. [21]

George Barne died in 1842, aged 75, and a memorial survives in St Peter's church. He left a substantial estate with property in Tiverton, Cullompton, Butterleigh and East Anstey. Mary Barne, his wife, inherited New Place house and a controlling interest in Cottey House Farm and other property. His son John, a banker, was sole executor and became owner of New Place tanyard. [22]

A rival, John Ware, tanner of Town's End, had been declared bankrupt in 1841. [23] New Place tanyard was never listed again in local directories and tanning came to an end in Tiverton. Only Aplins, the Fore Street glovers and fellmongers, continued. Devon's tanning boom, which had coincided with George Barne's lifespan, had largely run its course.

The New Place tannery was offered for sale in 1842. It had a water-powered bark mill, probably worked by the Cottey brook, an Exe tributary, and also a horse-powered mill:

'Tiverton, Devon. Sale of Valuable Bark Mills, Iron Water Wheel, Bone Mill, Tan Pits, the property of G. Barne, Esq. To be Sold by Auction .. on the Premises, at New Place .. Bark Mill, by Underhill .. driven by an iron water wheel, with gear work and fender complete. A capital Bark and Coffee Mill, driven by horse power .. a good Bone Mill and a large Waggon, capable of carrying from 4 to 5 tons, almost new, with patent axles and boxes. The Tan Pits comprise 56 handlers, 32 layers or troughs, and 3 pits – Also the roofing, flooring, beams, joists, posts, partitions, doors, boarding &c of several extensive sheds; a large beam linhay, turf house, turf frame, large beam and scales for weighing bark .. Dated Tiverton, 26th March 1842.' [24]

This notice indicates the materials of the tannery buildings were to be recycled. The site was probably levelled subsequently.

Town's End

Location	SS 958 131
Operational	18th century

Town's End tannery was at Brunswick House near the old road out of Tiverton to Bampton. The Ware family was in residence in 1821, when rates were paid on a house and tanyard here. [25] In 1824 John Ware junior was listed at St Andrew's Street, but no tannery is known to have existed there, and this may have been his residence; [26] by 1830 he was at Town's End and in 1841 he went out of business, bankrupt. [27] No further activity is recorded here although J B Aplin was recorded as a tanner of Fore Street in 1856, [28] possibly utilising the Town's End premises. However the Aplins had been long established as glovers and fellmongers in Fore Street and Gold Street and most probably made use of their existing facilities. The tannery adjoined the Town Leat and may have used its water. Its proximity to the town's water supply may have caused concern to the health authority of the time and the construction of the workhouse in Belmont Road may have removed the last traces of this operation.

Tiverton sources

1 Maryanne Kowaleski, Local Markets and Regional Trade in Medieval Exeter, Cambridge University Press, 1995, 302
2 Mike Sampson, A History of Tiverton, Tiverton War Memorial Trust, 2004, 89
3 PRO – C5/529/40 of 1670, Newte v Kings College Cambridge; C8/295/25 also of 1670
4 Dunsford, Historical Memoirs of the Town and Parish of Tiverton, 1790, 263
5 Tiverton tithe map and apportionment, c 1840. Tanpit Orchard, item 4135. Lower Fairby – owned by Thomas Daniel Esq; tenant – Peter Newton
6 Jill Neusinger. A History of St Matthew's Church, Butterleigh, c 2000, 15
7 Exeter Flying Post 18 September 1788 p 3 col 4
8 Universal British Directory 1793-1798, 619
9 Exeter Flying Post 19 February 1789 p 3 col 1
10 Bristol Mercury 30 August 1790
11 Georgian Tiverton, D&CRS, 1986, 123 and 135
12 Neusinger, op cit, 18-19
13 IGIs and John Bourne, ed, Georgian Tiverton. D&CRS, New Series vol 29, 1986, 158.
14 DRO – 1926 B/D/B/1/7
15 Exeter Flying Post 20 August 1812 p 4 col 5
16 Exeter Flying Post 29 May 1817 p 1 col 3
   Exeter Flying Post 12 February 1818 p 4 col 4
17 Exeter Flying Post 27 August 1818 p 4 col 2
18 DRO – 3357A-2/PO 3/19
19 Pigot's General Directory, Devonshire, 1830
20 Woolmer's Gazette 20 July 1839 p 2 col 4
21 Woolmer's Gazette 10 August 1839 p 3 col 4
22 PROB 11/1973 Q6. George Barne's will, proved 14 January 1843
23 Exeter Flying Post 1 April 1841 p 3 col 6
24 Woolmer's Gazette 9 April 1842 p 1 col 4
25 Plan with deed of 11 September 1845; New Poors Rate, Tiverton, 1821
26 Pigot & Co's Directory, Devonshire, 1824
27 Pigot & Co's Directory, Devonshire, 1830, Exeter Flying Post 1 April 1841 p 3 col 6
28 Post Office Directory, Devon and Cornwall, 1856

Totnes
Bridgetown
Lake Garden

Totnes has a long history of tanning. Other towns may rival it, but the tanners here are on record from the 13th century. In 1244 the abbot of Torre was allowed to buy 60 hides a year, free of toll, in exchange for two pairs of boots for the lord of the manor at Michaelmas. Sixteen Totnes tanners were required to pay the thangavell, an annual levy, at twopence each in 1255. [1]

Export was the main driver for the town's merchants in the 1520s. Normandy, Brittany, northern Spain and the Channel Islands provided linen, canvas, wine and fruit in exchange for cloth, tin and leather shipped from the quays at the foot of the High Street. [2]
One of the 16th century tanners was Robert Nayle, whose offspring were baptised in St Mary's church. [3]

In 1792 a meeting was called in Totnes to deal with concerns over the price of leather in Devon:
'.. the Tanners in this County, as well as many other parts of the Kingdom, have abundantly COMBINED together and enhanced the PRICE of LEATHER to an immoderate Degree, to the great Prejudice of the Public ..' [4]
By the 19th century tanning had become concentrated at two yards – at Bridgetown on the Berry Pomeroy bank of the river Dart and at Lake Garden, by Maudlin Road, south east from Leechwell Street, where the cattle market was established in the 1830s.

Bridgetown
Location	SX 8075 6032
Operational	to circa 1875
Bark mill	If it existed, water-powered

The Bridgetown tannery in Rowsell's Lane was advertised as 'old-established' when offered for auction in 1826:
'.. to be Sold by Public Auction .. Tan Yard, called Langworthy's, together with a Garden-Plot, and 4 Marshes adjoining .. situate in Bridgetown .. late in the occupation of Mr Windeatt, deceased .. The above premises adjoin the navigable river Dart ..' [5]
John Windeatt was established here by 1813; he also occupied an early iron foundry nearby, on the Dart. George Hayward was tanner in 1830. [6] John Rouswill was leaseholder in 1841 when the premises were owned by the Duke of Somerset, followed by tanner Thomas J Searle in 1844. [7] Searle was a native of the town; aged 55 in 1851, he employed two men here. [8] The impression is that the yard was quite small by Devon standards. In 1866 Searle's business address was 'Bridge Town Quay, Totnes'. [9]

Matters are complicated by the appearance of a second Thomas Searle, who was aged 41, farmer of 110 acres, and tanner, and employing four men and one boy in 1861. He was then living at Plymouth Road, by Leechwell Street. As the son of Thomas J Searle, it would be reasonable to suppose that they were in partnership at Bridgetown, but this is not certain; possibly another tannery existed on the outskirts of Totnes. Searle the son had moved to Fore Street by 1871 and the household included his 78-year-old father, still listed as 'tanner'. Bridgetown was now run by the younger Thomas Searle. [10] There is no evidence for the yard here in 1885, [11] and when Thomas Searle retired it probably closed.

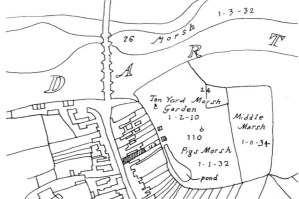

Bridgetown in 1813, the map orientated to the west with Totnes across the bridge. Tannery at Pig's Marsh with tanner's house, hatched, at 113. DRO 1392M/Estate maps 11

Lake Garden
Location	SX 8023 5995
Operational	to circa 1875
Steam powered by 1870	

A stream, a tributary of the Dart, which powered an overshot waterwheel at Snail Mill at the foot of Orchard Terrace, provided the water for the tanpits here, above the mill and on the edge of the town.

Andrew Langman was a Totnes tanner who died in 1824: as John Langman later owned Lake Garden, it is reasonable to suppose that Andrew Langman ran the yard in the early 19th century. Members of the family had been tanners in the town in the 18th century. [12] Andrew Langman's will had been lost and in 1824, Richard Langman was appealing for news of it in a newspaper notice. [13]

John Langman offered the tanyard for sale in 1830; it appears there were effectively two yards on site:
'To be sold by Public Auction .. premises situate in the parish of Totnes called Lake Garden ..
Lot 1 .. Dwelling-House, Courtlage, Stable, Cowhouses, and Loft over, and Garden adjoining thereto, having a stream of water constantly running through and forming very desirable property.
Lot 2. All that part of the Tan-Yard, Tan-Pits, and Orchard on the western side of the stream of water.
Lot 3 - All that other part of the Tan-Yard with the

Totnes

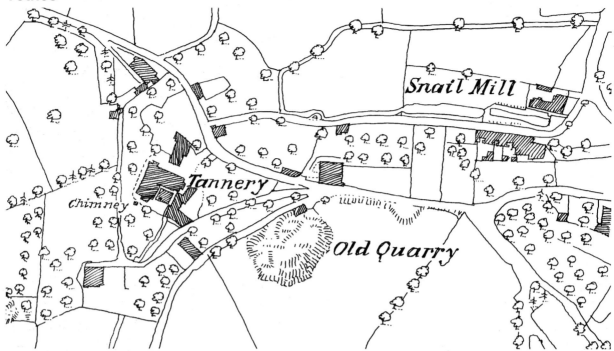

Lake Garden Tannery, on the stream which ran on to power Snail Mill. From the Ordnance Survey map, first edition 25", sheet 121.9

Dry-house, Pound-house and Turf Stand thereon situate and lying on the eastern side of the said stream. This lot capable at a small expense of being converted into an overshot Grist Mill.
These last lots form two good Tan-Yards, and are well adapted for carrying on the Tanning Business, and have at all times a sufficient supply of water ..
For viewing the Premises, and for further particulars application to be made to Mr John Langman, of Totnes (the Proprietor) ..' [14]

John Webber Chaster leased Lake Garden from 1839. He was born on 10 June 1816. Shortly after his twenty-first birthday he inherited £50 from an uncle [worth £3,550 in 2004]:
'.. the first sum of consequence I was ever master of. I received it with uncle John's sage advice to keep it and add a trifle continually to it, the which if I am able to effect will without doubt effectually keep me for ever from the fangs of Pauperism'.

Chaster took possession of Lake Garden on Lady Day 1839 – March 25. Repairs were virtually complete on 10 June and a week later he:
'Commenced operation at Lake Garden this day having taken on a man who has lately been working at Cridlands. He is very steady and understands his business well. I hope to be so much occupied in business now as to have no time for politics ..'
The Lake Garden premises were rented from Mrs Prideaux for 30 guineas a year. Cridland may have been the tanner at Modbury, but there was also a Cridland in Totnes.

John Chaster was a strong supporter of the whig or liberal party in the town and favoured the Reform Act. When not involved in politics, fishing and beekeeping were his pursuits. John's parents were Walter Preston and Mary Chaster; Walter was a saddler. In 1851 John married Susanne Gidley, daughter of Nicholas Gidley, Esq, whom it would seem from the diary, he was courting in 1837, when they took at trip to Dartmouth on an early river steamer. They had three sons.

The year before he leased the tannery John Chaster spent three months in London. He travelled up by coach – via Exeter, Honiton, Ilchester, Salisbury Plain, Andover, Basingstoke, Staines and Brentford. Theatre and opera at Drury Lane and Covent Garden and a concert at Hanover Square were cultural high points, as were visits to the National Gallery and the British Museum and the collection which later formed the gallery at Dulwich. Sightseeing encompassed the City, Regent's Park, including the Zoo, and Greenwich, reached by steamer and from whence Chaster returned by train. The Thames Tunnel was viewed, still under construction. A trip to Windsor Castle involved a return rail journey from Slough: *'The remainder, 20 miles by steam, was accomplished in forty minutes! A system of cracking on which I highly relish and approve!'*

Chaster left London on 2 August, taking the paddle-steamer Eclipse from a wharf at Tooley Street to Portsmouth, which was reached *'after a terrible 38 or 40 hours labouring'*. The small vessel was barely able to cope against the heavy seas and rather than continue, Chaster got coaches home from Portsmouth. In London he had attempted to find

The Lake Garden Tannery site: buildings once covered the ground between the greenhouse and residence beyond

The tanner's house, but tanner John Chaster lived elsewhere – in the house next to the Kingsbridge Inn

Left: the chimney associated with steam power on this site still stands in the grounds of a private house in 2004

work, with the most hopeful posting on offer as a Landing Waiter in the Port of London at £160 per annum. But nothing came of it. [15]

John Webber Chaster was listed as a master tanner in 1851; he employed two men. His wife Susanne or Susannah, incidentally, was a professor of music. [16] Once again, operations at Totnes appear to have been on a small scale. Chaster's address was given as Leechwell Street in 1856. [17] The family was here in 1861 with a live-in servant: John Chaster was now employing nine men. It is clear that operations had been significantly expanded within a decade. In 1830 the site had been offered as two yards: in 1861 there were two managers or foremen at Lake Garden – Richard Skinner and Samuel Mitchell, both tanners. [18]

Parts of the tanyard were destroyed by a fire in 1865, one of the major hazards for the leather industry. The Western Times published the following report: *'Totnes. The premises of Mr J W Chaster took fire about six o'clock on Saturday evening. The West of England Fire Insurance Company's engine was called out and rendered valuable assistance. The leather was removed without any damage. About 115 tons of bark and a large building were totally destroyed. The premises were insured in the Sun Office and the bark in the Globe.'* According to the rival Exeter Flying Post *'There was a strong breeze blowing at the time and the fire was not subdued till a rick of bark and the building were destroyed.'* [19]

This event may have prompted a rebuild for Chaster is listed as a client of Bodley Brothers of the Old Quay Foundry, Exeter in the period 1860-1877. This ironfoundry specialised in making bark mills for tanners, but also built steam engines and may have re-equipped the premises: a tall square random-stone built chimney survives in the garden of Brookvale today. Chaster's enthusiasm for steam power, experienced travelling on Brunel's Great Western in 1838, may have led to the early installation of a steam engine at Lake Garden. [20]

Following the fire, Chaster's focus was elsewhere. He was listed as a magistrate in 1866 and was the mayor of Totnes in 1870-1871, when recorded as

Totnes

The building next to the Kingsbridge Inn, Leechwell Street, is thought to be John Webber Chaster's home in 1871

a landowner rather than a tanner. His house was at West Hill, next to the Kingsbridge Inn, in Leechwell Street, at the top of the town. His eldest son was a banker's clerk, not a tanner, and the household included his sister Mary Webber and uncle, Nicholas Sumpter, a retired officer in the Royal Navy, and his wife Bridget, and two servants. Chaster was 54 in 1871. Samuel Setter ran the tanyard at Lake Garden, but the tannery by this time has ceased to warrant an entry in the local trade directories. [21]

Ten years later Chaster was still at Leechwell Street, now recorded as 'Retired Tanner'. [22] Quite a large covered yard existed at Lake Garden, still marked 'Tannery' in 1889. [23] But as yet there is no evidence for survival of the business into the 20th century.

When was the steam engine installed? The thick walls of a nearby building might suggest that a rotative beam engine worked here, the walls carrying the weight of the beam. It was almost certainly operating before November 1873, when a tramway from Totnes station to the quays, nearer to the tanyard than the station, opened. [24] Most probably coal was shipped in by sailing vessel from the North East or South Wales, rather than being sent by rail. But Totnes was an expensive port, certainly by 1854, as this item in the Western Times indicates:
'The heavy quay dues at Totnes have compelled the woollen manufacturers at Buckfastleigh to send to Newton for culm, where that article can be purchased at 3s per ton cheaper than at Totnes. Newton is ten miles from Buckfastleigh, Totnes is six.' [25]

Today the cart shed and what may have been the bark mill have been converted into the house 'Brookvale'. The stream, canalised, runs alongside the building where once stood a lean-to shed with a partially slate-floored walkway by the water; a higher level leat may have powered a waterwheel here, before being superseded by the steam engine, whose existence is evidenced by the surviving chimney. Its coal store

survives, as does the thick-walled structure, which may have housed it. Other linhays or stores have been converted into greenhouses. A neighbouring 20th century house is named 'The Tannery': it once stood in the grounds of the yard and was built at a time when the tannery buildings, now 'Brookvale', were derelict. The entrance to the latter retains imposing stone entrance pillars. By the entrance was an office where a clerk controlled the carter's waggons, bringing hides and oak bark, and in some cases whole carcases. The present owner has dug up plenty of cattle teeth in the grounds. The whole site was enclosed by a stone wall, built with rock from a nearby quarry. [26]

Lake Garden, the tanner's house – used by the manager rather than the owner in John Chaster's day – survives today as a residence, with its own private drive overlooking the tannery site.

Totnes sources
1   Percy Russell, The Good Town of Totnes. The Devonshire Association, 1984, 22
2   Totnes Elizabethan House Museum leaflet and guide
3   A H Shorter, D&CNQ, 1952, from D&CRS transcriptions from Totnes parish register
4   Exeter Flying Post 26 July 1792 p 1 col 2
5   Exeter Flying Post 30 March 1826 p 1 col 3
6   DRO 1392M/Estate maps 11; Pigot's Directory, 1830, 140
7   DRO - Berry Pomeroy tithe map and tithe apportionment 1841, item 1132 = Tan Yards, Lofts and Garden ; Pigot's General Directory, Devonshire, 1844
8   Totnes census, 1851– HO 107 1874 f 195 p 13
9   Post Office Directory of Devonshire 1866, 1277-1278
10 Totnes census, 1861 – RG9 1417 f 46 p 2
    Totnes census, 1861 – RG10 2095 f 53 p 12
11 Ordnance Survey map, Totnes, 25"= 1 mile, sheet 121
12 DRO 1579A/2/297 – Andrew Langman, tanner, 1743; DRO 1579A/2/179 – Edward Langman, tanner, 1790
13 Exeter Flying Post 5 February 1824 p 4 col 5
14 Woolmer's Gazette 2 October 1830 p 3 col 5
15 Personal communication from owner David Holman, October 2004 and sourced from Adobe Acrobat copy of Chaster's diary – the original is in Totnes Museum.
16 Totnes census 1851 – HO 107 1874 f 83 p 1
17 Post Office Directory, Devon and Cornwall, 1856
18 Totnes census, 1861
    John Webber Chaster, Leechwell Street
    RG9 1417 f 50 p 9
    Lake Garden – Richard Skinner and Samuel Mitchell
    RG9 1418 f 41 p 35 entries 225 and 226
19 The Western Times 14 March 1865 p 4 col 2,
    Exeter Flying Post 15 March 1865 p 7 col 6
20 DRO. Bodley Foundry Ledgers– 67/5/22A and B; Journal – 67/5/2/2
21 Post Office Directory of Devonshire 1866, 1048 and 1278; Totnes census, 1871
    John Webber Chaster, Leechwell Street
    RG10 2095 f 40 p 22
    Samuel Setter, tanner, Lake Garden
    RG10 2095 f 81 p 34 entry 192
22 Totnes census, 1881
    RG11 2176 f 112 p 23
23 Tannery shown on OS 25" map sheet 121.9, above Snail Mill, in 1865 and 1889
24 The Western Times 14 November 1873 p 7 col 2
25 The Western Times 12 October 1854 p 7 col 6
26 Visit by the author to Brookvale, September 2004

Uffculme

Tannery in village	
Location	ST 0680 1267
Operational	closed after 1840

Bodmiscombe	
Location	ST 1075 0968
Bark mill	water powered
Operational	from circa 1799 to 1849
Output	35 hides a week

Tanning was an Uffculme trade from at least the sixteenth century; Richard Hussey, a tanner of Craddock, died in 1568/9. In his will he left tanning vats, thought to be portable, to his brother Thomas and to his servant Robert Keyst. [1]

Permanent yards had been established by the eighteenth century and one existed in the heart of the village, between church and school. It is shown on the parish tithe map for c1840 but the site has since been levelled and built over. [2]

A second tanyard was constructed at Bodmiscombe, near boundaries with Kentisbeare and Sheldon parishes, south from the village. It was worked – together with the adjoining 166 acre farm – by the Broom family from about 1799 to 1849. [3] Francis Broom, baptised on 7 July 1795, the son of Francis and Mary Broom, was active here in 1839 and 1841

when the estate was known as Brooms Bodmiscombe [4] but he died in 1849. His wife then offered the farm and tanyard to let. [5] Today a ruined, roofless, bark mill and the remains of its mill leat survive in the grounds of Bodmiscombe house. The bark mill would have been powered by an overshot waterwheel. The layout was such that the leat ran on to serve tan pits, which have since been filled in and landscaped to lawn. This leat then also powered barn machinery in the farm, possibly introduced after the tannery had closed.

Francis Broom senior, who it is thought was also tanner here, had a close association with Edward Richards, the Whimple tanner, as in 1808 they jointly advertised for one journeyman tanner. [6] Bodmiscombe was a small country yard with an output of 35 hides a week: [7] a member of the Broom family was later to run the larger yard at Whimple, [8] which Edward Richards sought to lease from 1838. [9]

Uffculme sources

1. Peter Wyatt and Robin Stanes, Editors. Uffculme: a Peculiar Parish. A Devon Town from Tudor Times, Uffculme Archive Group, 1997, 231
2. Uffculme. A Culm Valley Parish. Uffculme Local History Group 2002, 27
3. Woolmer's Gazette 3 November 1849 p 1 col 1
4. Mormon IGI; DRO Uffculme tithe map and apportionment 1839 - item 810 House and Garden, 809 Tanyard, the estate, owned and occupied by Francis Broom junior totalled 174 acres; Uffculme census 1841 – HO107 202/19 f 15
5. Woolmer's Gazette 3 November 1849 p 1 col 1
6. Sherborne Mercury 21 April 1808; Broom was still at Uffculme in 1818 – DRO 146B/T98-99
7. Woolmer's Gazette 3 November 1849 p 1 col 1
8. Edward Broom was tanner at Whimple in 1856 – Post Office Directory, Devon and Cornwall, 1856
9. Exeter Flying Post 21 June 1838 p 2 col 2

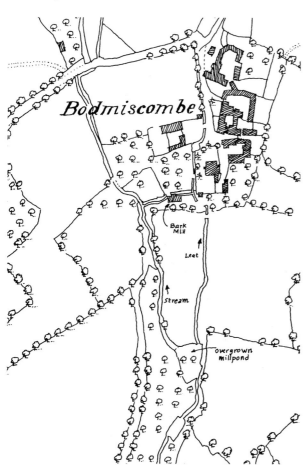

Above: Bodmiscombe House – the tanner's residence in the 19th century. A ruined water-powered bark mill survives in the grounds

Left: Bodmiscombe, showing the leat, bark mill and old mill ponds in 1889. The tannery buildings may have been adapted for farm use: the leat ran on to power agricultural equipment in the later 19th century. From the Ordnance Survey map, 25" = 1 mile of 1889, sheet 47.9

Whimple

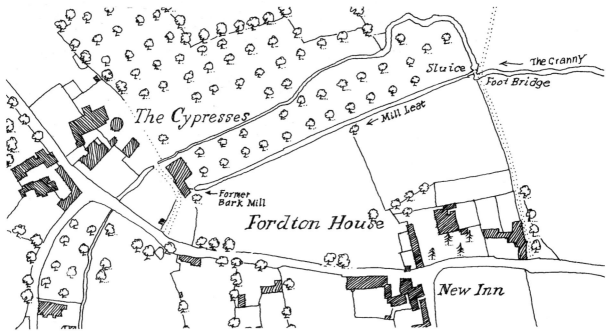

The Cypresses, previously known as Lower Fordton, the site of Whimple tannery. The former water-powered bark mill – fed by a leat from the Cranny – has been converted into a modern private residence. The Cypresses is now known as The White House, bought in the 1890s by Henry Whiteway, the founder of the cider company. A second – horse-powered – bark mill may be indicated by the round structure near the Cypresses. From the Ordnance Survey map, Devonshire, 1889, sheet 69.11

Lower Fordton

Location	SY 0425 9751 – the bark mill
Operational	to circa 1885
Output	80 hides a week in 1838
Bark mills	Two, one water-powered
Tan pits	60 handlers, 29 layers, 15 spenders, 6 limes, 2 grainers
Staff	4 employed in 1861

Nathaniel Salter was the Whimple tanner towards the end of the 18th century. He was leasing Lower Fordton tanyard in 1778 when it was offered for sale:

'..Whimple, near Ottery St Mary. To be Sold by Private Contract, All that Eftate lying in Whimple, called FOADTON [sic], and Part of SANDFORD'S, HAYMAN'S, and a Part of HAVIL'S, all lying together, with a good tan-yard on the premifes, and about four acres of orchard, fix acres of very good meadow, and about twenty six acres of good arable and pafture land; barn and pound-houfe, with a horfe-engine, and two fpill preffes; now in the poffeffion of James Cook; and the tanyard in the poffeffion of Nathaniel Salter as tenants .. now lett for upwards of fifty pounds per annum .. For further particulars apply to John Sanders, of Whimple, the owner.'

Salter was still here in 1786 when he married. [1] However, by 1797 he may have moved and was running or owned a tanyard at Rawridge in Upottery

parish. [2] The Whimple owner, John Sanders, was probably descended from Richard Sanders, the tanner in 1728. [3]

As the new century dawned, Edward Richards took on the yard at Whimple. He was advertising for a journeyman tanner here in 1801, 1805 and again in 1809, [4] suggesting aside from a rapid turnover of staff, that business was brisk during the years the country was at war with France. In 1808 Richards jointly advertised for a journeyman tanner with Francis Broom of Bodmiscombe tannery, Uffculme: it is thought the two families may have been related. [5] Clearly Richards ran a successful business as he advertised the premises to let in 1838, no doubt intending to retire. The notice in the local press gives an outline of the facilities:

'To Tanners. To be Let, for a term of 18 years, with possession at Lady-Day next, a most desirable TAN-YARD, capable of carrying from 70 to 80 hides per week, situate in the parish of Whimple ..
The yard consists of 60 Handlers, 29 Layers, 15 Spenders, 6 Lime Pits, and 2 Grainers, and has a stream of water running through it. Also two Drying Lofts, Store Rooms, Bark Barns .. The Yard is now in full work and the business has been carried on by the owner for the last forty years .. There are two bark mills in the Yard, one of which is driven by water, which mills must be taken by the Lessee at a valuation .. For a view apply to the Owner, Mr Edward Richards, Whimple ..' [6]

Lower Fordton, alias The Cypresses, and now known as The White House. Some rebuilding was evidently undertaken in 1868

Nearby, 'The Old Tanyard' is a modern rebuilding of the water-powered bark mill that once served Lower Fordton tanyard

The stream of water is known as the Cranny, a tributary of the Clyst. A leat from the Cranny powered the water-wheel working one of the bark mills. The leat may also have provided water for some of the tan pits. The second bark mill was probably horse powered. In March 1840 the tanyard was still to let, but was now advertised for a term of 26 years. Capacity had apparently increased from the *'70 to 80 hides'* of 1838 to *'100 butts a week'*.[7] By 1842 Richards had found a tenant and John Sanders occupied the estate at Lower Fordton, a little over 4 acres. [8] He stayed for roughly a decade, leaving Whimple early in 1851. [9]

Edward Broom, who had been farming Burn Rew, at Willand, in 1841, [10] moved to Whimple and was occupying the tannery in 1856. [11] He may have been a relative of Richards and also probably related to the Broom family who tanned at Bodmiscombe, Uffculme. Offered for sale or lease in 1859, the tannery then contained layers, handlers and lime pits mostly under cover; two pumps were worked by horse-power. The bark shed could hold 50 tons of bark, and adjoined the water-powered bark mill. [12] In the event Edward's son, Edward Richard Broom succeded to the business and employed four men in 1861. [13] It was no doubt this family who built the wall surrounding the estate which survives today. The date 1868 is picked out in white brick. The evidence is that Tanyard House, as it was then – also known as Lower Fordton, later the Cypresses and today divided in two, now part known as 'The White House' – was built at the same time. [14]

Edward Broom senior was listed as 'landowner, retired farmer and tanner' in 1871, and aged 66 and widowed, lived at Fordton. [15] His grandson, also Edward Richard, died an infant in the same year. [16] Edward Broom jnr put Lower Fordton and its tanyard on the market in 1878. [17] Broom moved to Littlesham and became an hotel keeper. [18] John Trump was probably the last Whimple tanner. He was at Lower Fordton in 1881, tanning and farming 60 acres with the assistance of four men and a boy. [19] Trump was related to William Trump Wish, the tanner at Beare from about 1854 to 1875 in nearby Broadclyst parish.

By 1889 the tannery had ceased production and Lower Fordton was known as 'The Cypresses'. [20] Henry Whiteway, the founder of the well-known cider company, bought the premises in the late 1890s. He installed a steam engine to power his cider mill and press, ignoring the water-powered bark mill. [21] This building, for some time derelict, was entirely rebuilt in 1998 and is now known as 'The Old Tanyard'. Little else remains today as evidence of this 19th century industry. Whiteway expanded his business, moving to a new site nearer the railway, recently redeveloped as modern housing.

Whimple sources
1   Sale of estate in 1778 – Sherborne Mercury 6 April 1778 p 3 col 3; Nathaniel Salter, tanner, married Miss Shepton at Whimple – Exeter Flying Post 30 March 1786 p 3 col 2
2   Diversion of footpath beside tanpits worked or owned by Nathaniel Salter at 'Rowridge' [Rawridge] DRO QS/113A/208/1. September 1797
3   DRO 146B/add/E11 – Richard Sanders, tanner, 1728
4   Exeter Flying Post 5 February 1801 p 1 col 3; Exeter Flying Post 12 December 1805 p 2 col 2; Exeter Flying Post 27 April 1809 p 4 col 4
5   Sherborne Mercury 21 April 1808
6   Exeter Flying Post 21 June 1838 p 2 col 2
7   Woolmer's Gazette 28 March 1840 p 1 col 1
8   DRO – Whimple tithe map and apportionment, 1842. Items 201, 202 and 203
9   Exeter Flying Post 27 March 1851 p 1 col 3
10   Willand census 1841. Burn Rew farm. HO107 222\8 f 4 p2
11   Post Office Directory, Devon and Cornwall, 1856
12   The Western Times 21 January 1860 p 1 col 2
13   Whimple census, 1861. Fordton House. RG9 1385 f 104 p 6
14   Exeter Flying Post 6 March 1878 p 1 col 2
15   Whimple census 1871. RG10 2050 f 109 p 12
16   Exeter Flying Post 24 April 1871 p 5 col 6
17   Exeter Flying Post 6 March 1878 p 1 col 2
18   Census 1881
19   Whimple census 1881, RG11 2141 f 106 p 4
20   Ordnance Survey map 1889. Devonshire sheet 69.11, 25" = 1 mile. Tannery not shown, indicating disuse
21   E V M Whiteway, Whiteway's Cyder. David & Charles, Newton Abbot, 1990, 20-21

Winkleigh

Woodterrill	
Location	SS 6260 1073 – the bark mill
Operational	to circa 1850
Bark mill	water-powered
Tan pits	details not known
Staff	possibly 4 in 1850

Remote from Winkleigh village and some way too, from the nearest hamlet, at Hollocombe, the tannery at Woodterrill may have existed in 1691 when Anthony Bowden was recorded as tanner in the parish. [1]

Members of the Dunning family, long established in the parish and hinterland – a Dunning memorial is the only one evident inside St Mary's, Honeychurch – were running Woodterrill by the late 18th century: a Richard Dunning was tanner in 1777 [2] and John Dunning in 1787. [3] His son Richard was baptised in 1795 [4] and was the last known Winkleigh tanner. Tanning was undertaken in conjunction with farming and in 1839 the tannery stood by the entrance to the farm with the water-powered bark mill in the valley below, accessible only by crossing the Hollocombe Water on a bridge and then through a ford. [5]

Richard Dunning was listed as tanner here in 1850 [6] but was described as a *'farmer and freeholder of 158 acres, employing 4 men and 4 labourers, plus one woman, one boy and one man'* in 1851. [7] He was then aged 56. Tanning operations appear to have ceased and the farm was advertised to let in 1855 with no reference to the tannery:

'To be Let, by Tender, for a Term of fourteen years, from Lady-day 1856, a desirable farm called 'WOODTERRIL': comprising a commodious farm-house, barns, stables and other outhouses; a labourer's cottage and about 141 acres of good arable, meadow, orchard and pasture land; situated in the parish of Winkleigh; the whole is within a ring fence. The tenant will be required to pay the tithe rent charge, land tax, insurance .. A person on the premises will be in attendance and show the estate; and for further particulars apply to Mr Dunning, Woodterrill, to whom tenders .. may be sent ..' [8]

By 1889 the tannery had been levelled – the buildings seen on the tithe map had disappeared and only the shell of the bark mill remained. [9] The farmhouse, which one might have expected to be pleasantly Georgian, is undistinguished. Today the mill – on private property – is mere humps and bumps, although the high level leat which once drove an overshot water-wheel is still evident running along the hillside.

The Dunnings are commemorated in Winkleigh church.

Winkleigh sources
1 A H Shorter, D&CNQ, 1952, from Devon and Cornwall Record Society transcriptions from parish register
2 DRO 1909B/T/64
3 Exeter Flying Post 27 September 1787 p 4 cols 1 & 2
4 Mormon records - IGI
5 DRO – Winkleigh Tithe map and apportionment, c 1839
6 White's Directory, 1850
7 Winkleigh census, 1851 – PRO – HO 107 1894 f 229 p 12
8 Exeter Flying Post 2 August 1855 p 1 col 2
9 Ordnance Survey map, 25" Devonshire, 1888: sheet 42.9

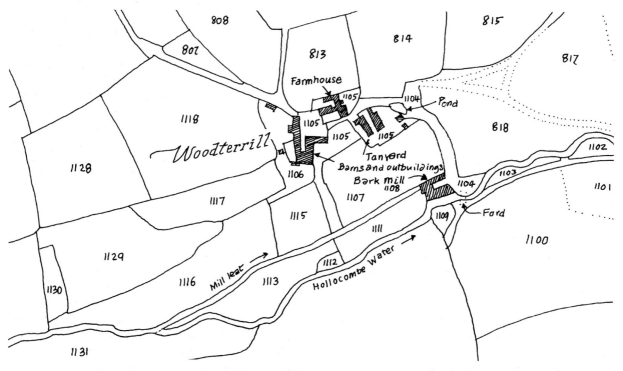

Woodterrill in 1839, drawn from the Winkleigh parish tithe map. By 1888 the tannery buildings had been demolished and the bark mill was derelict. Today only the line of the embanked leat running along the valley side remains as evidence of this remote site.

Woodbury

Copplestones, Broadway
Gilbrook
The Green

Woodbury parish had no less than three tanneries but they were not all operational concurrently.

Copplestones, Broadway
Operational   18th century

William Collings was a Woodbury tanner in 1654 who died in 1696. [1] It is thought that his tannery was at Broadway, as Anthony Copplestone had established his business there by 1699.[2] He was still active in 1715, but in 1729 John Copplestone was the tenant, with four acres of ground, a house, garden and tanyard. The property was in the ownership of the Rolle Estate. [3] Various other 18th century leaseholders are recorded here, but it is not known if they were operating the tanyard. [4] The yard was still extant when part of an estate made up of a dwelling house, two gardens, two orchards and a meadow adjoining, on Broadway, was leased to Thomas Weeks in 1767. [5] Weeks was still resident in 1798, but the tannery was not listed and it must be assumed it had ceased to function. [6]

Gilbrook
Location	SY 0078 8655
Operational	to 1913
Bark mill	horse powered
Staff	11 in 1871

Gilbrook formed part of the Rectory Manor estate and belonged to the Vicars Choral. Thomas Weeks was listed here in 1756 [7]– as we have seen he also leased the yard on Broadway a decade later. Weeks was succeeded by William Hole in 1790. [8] Hole was advertising for staff in 1808, at the height of the wars with France. [9] Following his death, the tannery passed to his son Thomas Hole in 1818. [10] (A possible relative – William Mengery Hole – owned a tannery at Kingkerswell from at least 1808 until bankrupt in 1822, and then was active again as a tenant at Ottery St Mary in 1825). [11] Thomas was selling livestock here in 1824 [12] and was bankrupt in October 1829. [13] He was probably over-extended on credit and Gilbrook was put on the market at the beginning of the year:

'To be sold, by Private Contract, all that Messuage, Tenement or Dwelling House, Tan-Yard, Gardens .. called GILBROOKE .. 10 acres .. well-suited for the business of a tanner, in which the same has been carried on for a great number of years, is in a good country for bark, and distant only 3 miles from Topsham Quay and 7 from Exeter .. For viewing

apply to Mr Thomas Hole, on the premises.' [14]

In April a sale of the stock-in-trade included:
'.. 100 hides and skins, iron and wood striking beams & pins, Bodley's bark mill nearly new, brass roller & bed, 6 pumps, shutes, barrows, buckets .. a cart horse, a hackney horse, two carts & harness .. a double cider screw press & horse engine .. variety of other articles in the farming line ..' [15]

Thomas Hole's chest tomb stands in Woodbury churchyard. He may have died in 1831 – the decade numeral on the inscription has broken away.

From 1829 Gilbrook became the responsibility of the tanner William Sanders; in 1839 the yard was owned by the Priest Vicars of Exeter Cathedral. [16] William later ran the yard in partnership with members of the Ware family, who assumed control in 1856, when Sanders retired to Heavitree. [17]

He was almost certainly the younger brother of James Lee Sanders, who ran the yard at Exeter St Thomas and later occupied the tannery at Bow. [18] The Ware family produced three generations of tanners. With a significant number of male births, Woodbury was to prove merely a stepping stone to careers elsewhere.

Thomas Ware, born in Woodbury in 1791, was farming the 340-acre Venn Farm, at Sowton, near Exeter in 1851. [19] In 1856 he returned to Woodbury and Thomas and four of his sons, William Walter, Thomas junior, Edward and Henry all became tanners. Thomas senior and William Walter Ware were partners in 1861. [20] At some point in the 1860s William left to run a tannery at Newnham in Gloucestershire where, in 1871, he employed 23 men and two women. [21] Thomas junior was then running Gilbrook tannery with 9 men and two boys. [22] But he also departed Woodbury and in 1881 was running the large Clift House tannery at Bedminster on the outskirts of Bristol. This concern has survived to the present day. [23] Edward Ware was a Woodbury tanner in 1861 but twenty years later was a leather merchant of Milton near Salisbury, Wiltshire, employing 42 men, six women and eight boys. Henry, the youngest son, stayed in Woodbury. [24]

Ware & Sons were the only tanners listed for Woodbury in 1870. [25] Thomas Ware jnr was then in charge of Gilbrooke tannery with eleven hands and his brother Henry managed a second tannery at The Green with a further eleven. By late 19th century standards these were small concerns and when Henry moved to run Gilbrooke, [26] the tannery at The Green closed. As we have seen, Thomas saw a brighter future at Bedminster and moved away.

By 1878 Ware & Sons had offices at 3 Waterbeer Street, Exeter, with the tannery listed at Woodbury. [27] In

Woodbury

due course Harold Ware became tanner, taking over from his father Henry – who was variously listed as farmer and tanner in successive census returns – and the concern lasted into the twentieth century, closing in 1913 after Harold had rather overcommitted on imported hides from Argentina. According to Ursula Brighouse, *'the Wares had been a driving force in the parish for over a century'*. [28]

Certainly this particular branch played a large part in the parish's tanning activities from 1856 to 1913.

*Gilbrook House.
The tanner's residence remains beside the stream. Some outbuildings and walls of the old tannery stand beyond the residence*

Thomas Hole's chest tomb in Woodbury churchyard

Gilbrook Tannery lay to the south west of the village. From the Ordnance Survey map, 25" = 1 mile, 1889, sheets 93.5 and 93.6

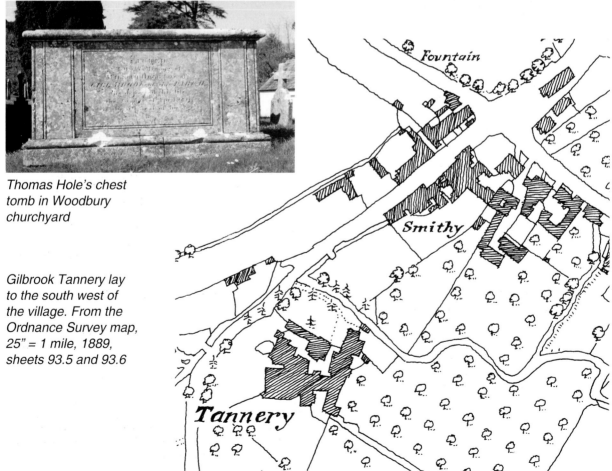

Woodbury's third tannery was a latecomer, established by Peter Sharland and Henry Wippell in 1808 when they bought New House. [29] This was during the wars with France when demand for leather was high.

The tannery was set up in the yard of Thorn Farm. This had belonged to Philip Lempiere, who had acquired it through marriage to Thomas Weeks' daughter. Lempiere had been Attorney General in Jersey and had fled the island in 1769. Mark Rolle obtained the property in 1807, but Philip White, previously Lempiere's tenant, was forced to sell stock in trade and household goods *'under distress for rent'*. [30] This was not an ideal location for a tannery – it was in the centre of the village and the small stream nearby would have been a barely adequate source of water. Bark mills and pumps were probably operated by horse power.

In 1830 Peter Sharland married Elizabeth Campbell, the widow of the licensee of Woodbury's Globe Inn, and so became the inn's leaseholder. [31] His partnership with Henry Wippell was dissolved in 1837 and Wippell continued to operate the tannery independently. [32] Sharland died in 1842, aged 64. [33]

By 1847 Thomas Gibbings, who had married Henrietta, Henry Wippell's daughter, was running the tannery. [34] Henry died in 1848 and in 1857 Thomas Gibbings sold the business to Thomas Ware. [35] Gibbings had decided to re-establish at Chichester in Sussex. With Henry Sharland, tanner of Fareham and George Wippell jnr, ironmonger of Exeter, he acted as an executor to the will of Thomas M C Sharland, tanner of Cheriton Fitzpaine, in 1863. [36]

An old photograph from the 1860s indicates the tanyard buildings in Thorn farmyard. New House was probably the tanner's residence, although Peter Sharland lived in Izel Cottage, previously Critchards. In the 1870s the Woodbury tanneries at Gilbrook and at the The Green were run by trustees [37] – several of the Ware brothers, now tanning in Gloucestershire and Woodbury or dealing in leather in Wiltshire.

Edwin Berry took on the lease of a rather dilapidated set of buildings here in 1884. [38] His family were agricultural machinists and millwrights. They constructed and installed acorn-milling machinery at the Gilbrook tannery, driven by horsepower. [39]

Woodbury sources

Copplestones, Broadway
I am indebted to Mrs Gill Selley for the sources here:
1. DRO Quarter Sessions QS box 58, for 1654; William Collings' will, 1696
   – DRO Rolle estate papers 96M 48/14
2. PRO E134/12E WM3/Trin 2
3. DRO Quarter Sessions QS Box 174; Rolle Estate Office Rental, East Budleigh, for 1729
4. Rolle Estate Office Rentals, East Budleigh
5. DRO 96M/50/2 and 96M/6/7 Manor Court
6. Rolle Estate Survey, 1798

Gilbrook
I am indebted to Mrs Gill Selley for a number of the sources:
7. Churchwardens accounts, Woodbury, 1756
8. Vicars Choral Manor Court Presentation, 1790
9. Exeter Flying Post 29 September 1808 p 1 col 4
10. Personal communication, Mrs Gill Selley, 15-09-2004
11. Exeter Flying Post 2 June 1808 p 4 col 3, Sherborne Mercury 15 April 1811, Exeter Flying Post 30 April 1818 p 4 col 4, Exeter Flying Post 28 February 1822 p 1 col 3; Exeter Flying Post 5 May 1825 p 1 col 5
12. Exeter Flying Post 28 October 1824 p 4 col 4
13. Exeter Flying Post 1 October 1829 p 3 col 4
14. Exeter Flying Post 8 January 1829 p 3 col 5
15. Exeter Flying Post 24 April 1829
16. Land tax accounts, Gilbrook – DRO VC/6/123.016 9/10 of 20-10-1835; DRO tithe map 1839-40, item 1395
17. Deeds belonging to Esme Thomson of Gilbrook House – sale of estate to Thomas Ware, gent, of Sowton, 1856
18. Note from Mrs Gill Selley: 'John Sanders of Salcombe married Grace Lee on 2 April 1779 and had three sons, John (b 1779), James Lee (b 1786) and William (b 1788). John and James were baptised at Salcombe but there seems to be confusion as to whether William was baptised at Salcombe or Bradninch – perhaps he was born in Bradninch but baptised at Salcombe. The 1851 entry on the census for Woodbury records William (aged 61) born at Bradninch, but his later children were certainly born at Salcombe. This seems too much of a coincidence that William Sanders of Woodbury and James Sanders of Bow are not brothers.' Communication 15-9-2004
19. Sowton census 1851 – HO107 1866 f 173 p 15
20. Woodbury census 1861– RG9 1384 f 62 p 6 and RG9 1384 f 81 p 21
21. Newnham census 1881 – RG11 2524 f 92 p 46
22. Woodbury census 1871 – RG10 2049 f 62 p 11 and f 99 p 20
23. Bedminster, Somerset, census, 1881 – RG11 2451 f 71 p 17; advice from Mike Bone, February 2008
24. Woodbury census 1861– RG9 1384 f 100 p 20 and Milton, Salisbury, census 1881 – RG11 2070 f 37 p 1
25. Devon Directory 1870
26. Woodbury census 1881 – RG11 2140 f 69 p 5
27. Harrod's Devonshire Directory, 1878
28. Ursula W Brighouse, Woodbury. A View from the Beacon. 1998, 192

The Green
29. Personal communication, Mrs Gill Selley, 15-09-2004
30. ibid
31. ibid
32. Exeter Flying Post 14 December 1837 p 2 col 4; DRO tithe map and apportionment 1839-40, item 1210 - owner Lord Rolle, occupier Henry Wippell
33. Exeter Flying Post 26 May 1842 p 2 col 5
34. See 29; DRO 346M /T764
35. See 29; and sale poster of 1857
36. Will of Thomas M C Sharland, died 24 February 1863
37. Personal communication, Mrs Gill Selley, 15-09-2004
38. Rolle Estate Office, East Budleigh - letter book entry 1887
39. Ursula W Brighouse, op cit, 168-169

Other nineteenth century sites

It has not been possible to determine the sites of all the tanneries at work in the county after 1800. The following yards, together with a few of those listed in the gazetteer, have as yet only the barest of information and most of their locations have yet to be discovered.

Atherington

Anthony Snell was an Atherington tanner in 1691. [1] A tanyard was to let in the parish in 1814:

'.. for a term of years, a TAN YARD .. with a dwelling-houfe and .. outbuildings .. well supplied with water and bark .. For viewing the premises and for further particulars apply to Mr Robert Mayne, the owner, on the premises .. Atherington, Sept 10th, 1814.' [2]

The tannery is not indicated on the tithe map and apportionment of 1839-1840. [3]

Braunton

James Darracott was a tanner in the parish in 1850. [1] The tanyard has not been located, although James Darracott was living at Darracott's, a farm outside the town, in 1844. [2]

Culmstock

Robert Fry was a Culmstock sergemaker and tanner who insured his property in 1766. [1] A tannery in the parish possibly just lasted into the nineteenth century: Charles Baker was bankrupt in 1801. It is thought, but not confirmed, that Baker's tanyard was at Prescott. [2] It may have been Baker who placed the following item in the press in 1810:

'To tanners. Wants a situation, as superintendent, or active Partner, in the Tanning Business, a perfon who has many years experience, and is perfect mafter of all its branches. Letters, poft-paid, addreffed to C. B. at the printers will meet with immediate attention.' [3]

Gittisham

In 1828 Gittisham tanner William Branscombe, was discharged from debt. [1]

Newton Ferrers

A H Shorter refers to a tannery here in 1829.

Newton St Cyres

Location SX 8812 9728. In 1728 tanner John Bidgood married. [1] Nearly a hundred years later George Ponsford was tanner when the tanner's house was destroyed by fire. The premises were not insured. [2] The yard was offered to let in 1829:

'A TAN YARD with a convenient Dwelling-House and Out-Buildings, well adapted for Business, situate in Newton St Cyres; together with about 21 Acres of Arable, Meadow and Pasture Land, late in the possession of Mr George Ponsford, but now of Mr Robt. Lane, called COLD HARBOUR, otherwise

WESTLAKE's. For which purpose a survey will be held at the Crown & Sceptre Inn in Newton St Cyres. For viewing the same apply to Mr Thomas Helmore of Newton St Cyres.' [3]

Robert Lane died in 1831 and the tannery apparently remained in operation to mid century. [4] Coldharbour is a somewhat unlikely site above the village, but close to a small stream.

Paignton

The town supported nine shoemakers in the decade 1820-1830, although it seems some were itinerant. John Codner was tanner from 1816 to 1823 when his wife Elizabeth died, aged 40. Two of their offspring had previously died as infants. [1]

Payhembury

In 1738 John Parrock, tanner, was married [1] and in 1799 Henry Venn, also a tanner, married. [2] One of the Venn family, another tanner, died in 1806. [3] Henry Venn was one of the tanners appointed to serve on George Barne's committee at Exeter in 1812. It was formed to lobby the Board of Trade on the undesirability of the new leather tax. [4]

Plymtree

A H Shorter refers to a tannery in 1827.

Stoke Canon

A H Shorter refers to a tannery here in 1801.

Stoke Gabriel

Mr Churchward, tanner of Stoke Gabriel, died in 1816. The Churchward family were farmers here and the parish's most famous son, George Jackson Churchward, was locomotive engineer of the Great Western Railway in the first quarter of the 20th century. [1]

Willand

Location ST 0425 1080. In 1831 what is now known as Weir Mill Farm was offered on lease:

'.. All that Messuage or Tenement, called or commonly known as SUMMERS MILL consisting of a good farmhouse, tan yard, well supplied with water, with a good drying loft, 27 handlers, 6 troughs or lathes, the beam contains 2 lime, 2 grainers and water pit; the bark mill is driven by a never failing stream of water – barn, stable and cottages adjoin with store rooms and 13 acres (more or less) of rich orchard and pasture land, situate at Summers Mill within the parish of Welland aforesaid and now in the occupation of Mr Thomas Osmond, the owner, who is about to retire from business ..' [1]

There is no record of a tanner here in mid century and this was a dairy farm by 1889, although when advertised to let, known as 'Were and Summers Mill', reference was made to a tannery and a mill previously on the site. [2]

Sources

Atherington
1 NDRO 2309B/T49/1
2 Exeter Flying Post 15 September 1814
3 DRO – Atherington tithe map and apportionment 1840

Braunton
1 White's Directory, 1850
2 DRO – Braunton tithe map and apportionment 1844

Culmstock
1 Stanley D Chapman, The Devon Cloth Industry in the Eighteenth Century. Sun Fire Office Inventories .. Devon & Cornwall Record Society, 1978, 50-51
2 Exeter Flying Post 5 March 1801 p 1 col 1; an earlier, 1800, item in the London Gazette apparently refers to the yard at Prescott
3 Exeter Flying Post 11 October 1810 p 1 col 3

Gittisham
1 Exeter Flying Post 13 March 1828 p 3 col 1

Newton Ferrers, Plymtree, Stoke Canon
1 D&CRS transcription from parish records

Newton St Cyres
1 D&CRS transcription from parish records
2 Exeter Flying Post 22 April 1824 p 4 col 3
3 Exeter Flying Post 9 July 1829 p 2 col 2
4 Exeter Flying Post 17 February 1831 p 2 col 5, Mid Devon Country Walks and Villages. 11 – Newton St Cyres, Mid Devon DC, Tiverton, 1994.

Paignton
1 Paignton parish records. Transcriptions from D&CRS

Payhembury
1 D&CRS transcriptions from parish registers
2 Exeter Flying Post 14 March 1799 p 3 col 2
3 Exeter Flying Post 14 August 1806 p 4 col 2
4 Exeter Flying Post 20 August 1812 p 4 col 5

Stoke Gabriel
1 Exeter Flying Post 17 October 1816 p 4 col 2

Willand
1 Exeter Flying Post 10 February 1831 p 1 col 4
2 The Western Times 31 May 1889 p 1 col 1

Earlier sites

Parishes known or believed to possess tanneries in earlier centuries: dates given are the earliest known record.

Awliscombe	1703	Kenn	1705
Aylesbeare	1727	Kenton	1707
Beaford	1753	Kentisbeare	1694
Bovey Tracey	1722	Kilmington	1673
Bratton Clovelly	1786	Kingsteignton	1727
Bridford	1732	Lamerton	1750
Brixham	1706	Matford	1382
Burlescombe	1715	Morebath	1675
Calverleigh	1706	Pinhoe	1755
Chagford	1753	Rattery	1723
Chawleigh	1672	Rockbeare	1703
Churchstanton	1723	Rose Ash	1720
Churston Ferrers	1694	Sampford Spiney	1721
Clawton	1740	St Giles	1724
Clyst Hydon	1731	Sidmouth	1762
Combe Martin	1620	Silverton	1731
Combe Raleigh	1710	South Brent	1650
Cotleigh	1744	South Tawton	1716
Dartington	1725	Stockland	1689
Denbury	1738	Sydenham Damarel	1720
Dolton	1737	Tamerton Foliot	1656
Dunsford	1694	Tawstock	1712
Exminster	1736	Thorverton	1697
Fremington	1615	Upottery	1797
Gidleigh	1712	West Anstey	1703
Hennock	1712	Whitchurch	1711
		Witheridge	1721
		Zeal Monachorum	1732

Glossary

Bark barn – a store for oak bark, capable of retaining 100-200 tons of bark in a medium sized tannery. Oak bark had to be kept dry until required: rain would cause the tannic acid to leach out and lessen the potency of the bark.

Barking – removing oak bark from trees. Usually done with a barking iron.

Bark harvest – barking was carried out in May and June, as far as possible in dry weather.

Bark mill – horse-, oxen- or water-powered mill often using a serrated upright- or edge-runner stone in a stone trough to grind oak bark to powder, to create, as required, tanning acid or ouse or liquor.

Basil – a sheep skin tanned in bark; distinguished from roan, which is tanned in shumac.

Beam, Beam house – Flesh and hair were removed from hides in the beam house. Hides and skins were worked on over a beam, using curved scudding knives. One of the less pleasant tannery tasks.

Butt – thicker or hinder part of a hide or skin, as calf-butt, kip-butt, and especially the hide of the back and flanks of an ox or cow, reduced to a rough rectangle by rounding. Also refers to thick leathers such as sole leather.

Cape hides – South African hides, imported and tanned in England.

Chamois – Or 'shammy' leather made from pelts – from sheep, goats, calves and deer skins. Work done by fellmongers and skiver dressers rather than tanners, involving tanning with shumac, and fulling with cod oil.

Chrome tanning – Hides tanned in chromium salts. This process was not introduced until the end of the nineteenth century. It now accounts for most tannage and is particularly suitable for handbags, garments and shoe uppers. Tanning is undertaken in days rather than months and so chrome tanning was one of the main agents in the decline and closure of many local tanneries at the beginning of the 20th century. A drawback is that leather produced by this process is not particularly water proof. The much slower processes involved in oak bark tanning made it largely obsolete; uncompetitive with chrome tanning.

Courtlage, curtilage – a small court, yard or piece of ground attached to a dwelling house and, in law, forming one enclosure with it. Pronounced and often written 'courtledge' in the south west, where its use was still current early in the 20th century.

Currier – one who dresses and colours tanned leather. Work involves cleaning, reducing in thickness and softening of the leather by the impregnation of oils. Leather is dressed by 'whitening', a scraping process adopted to unify the material thickness. 'Staining' is a secondary procedure, using water-borne stains. 'Finishing' or 'softening' involves the application of tallow-based dubbin.

Drying lofts, drying-house, drying-linhay – After processing in pits, which took 18 months or more, leather hides were dried in near darkness in a well ventilated loft to prevent discolouration. Drying lofts were often built over or adjacent to the tan pits.

Fellmonger – a dealer in skins or hides of animals, especially sheep skins. But often also a fuller of chamois leather.

Floater pit – pit in which butts are laid flat and moved up to three times a day, through increasing strengths of liquor, over a six to eight week period.

Frizer – leather dresser producing thinned goat or sheep skins of uniform thickness for shammy leather, using a pumice stone or a blunt knife. A worker in a leather dresser's or fellmonger's yard.

Grainer – Another term for a mastering pit.

Handler – tan pit where the leather acquired its colour. Here the hides would be moved regularly from pit to pit.

Hide – skin of animals such as oxen, used for shoe leather and for harness. Butts [qv] were used for shoe leather, bellies for handbags and straps. Nothing was wasted: offal was used for belts, the top wedge of an animal's tail was very hard and used for heels. Cheeks – facial skin – were suitable for billiard cues and football studs. Body hair was used in mortar in the building trade; tail hair was used to stuff furniture. See diagram on page 18; see also welt.

Kieve – A term used in the 18th century, relating to hides or skins, but one which is which is unknown today.

Kip – hide or skin of calf or young animal used for leather; in particular shoe uppers.

Latches – tanning pits, also known as spenders.

Layer – tanning pit. Here hides or butts were laid flat alternating between layers of ground bark and the pit filled with water. A process that took up to 18 months, involving the strongest liquors.

Leaching pit – pit in which ground oak bark mixed with water was allowed to stand for six to eight weeks. Elsewhere defined as vats for mixing liquor in.

Leat – man made channel available in some tanneries to bring the essential water from a weir on a stream or river to the tan pits.

Lime pit – slaked lime and water were used to loosen epidermis and fats from hides, a process taking up to six weeks and known as 'liming'.

Linhay – hay barn and animal shelter; the livestock area on the lower level. A term favoured in the west country.

Liquor – or ouse: a solution of water and tannic acid.

Mastering pit – hides processed at the beam would then be immersed in mastering pits to remove all traces of lime. The pits contained a mixture of warm water, hen, pigeon and dog excreta.

Myrobalan – Indian acorn used in tanning leather.

Oak bark leather – both firm and flexible, hard wearing. Used for boot soles, direct from the tanyard; for boot uppers and harness it also required processing by a currier.

Ouse or ouze – a solution of water and tannic acid. Also known as tanning liquor.

Pelts – A general term for a hide or skin that has been limed and de-haired and is ready for tanning.

Rounding – large hides, each comprising varying qualities of skin were cut up into 'butts' and other pieces prior to tanning, a process known as rounding. Inferior parts of hide were removed with a rounding knife. See also diagram on page 18.

Pumps, lifting pumps – used to circulate the liquor or ouzes or water, powered by a water wheel or steam engine, or by hand.

Sam Browne – wide belt, usually of leather, used by the military in the UK and the USA and by the police, as a means of carrying a sword or a pistol. Named after General Sir Samuel James Browne, VC GCB KCSI, 1824-1901, although a sample survives from 1812 in a museum in New Jersey.

Scudding – hides were washed and scraped with a scudding knife to remove all impurities.

Shammy leather – See Chamois.

Shumac or sumac – a preparation of dried and chopped leaves and shoots of plants of the genus Rhus, especially Rhus Coriaria. Imported from Sicily and used in the production of shammy leather. Also used in re-tanning harness, bridle and stirrup butts as it softens the leather and improves the colour.

Skins – obtained from smaller animals such as sheep and used by fellmongers and glovers.

Spender or suspender pit – pits in which hides were hung vertically on bars in tanning liquor. These were continually agitated, often worked by water power. Hides would be moved daily from pit to pit through increasing strength of liquor. These pits prepared hides to absorb stronger liquors at subsequent stages of the process in handler and layer pits.

Tan, to – convert (raw hide) into leather by soaking in liquid containing tannic acid or by use of mineral salts.

Tannic acid – astringent substance obtained chiefly from the ground bark of oak trees, but also from alders.

Tawer – a tanner who steeps skins in a solution of alum and salt to produce white or Hungarian leather.

Troughs or trows – lime pits with sloping sides in which hides could be pulled in or out easily. Hides would be layered flat on top of each other and moved daily.

Turf frame - A term familiar to nineteenth century tanners but one which is unknown today.

Valonia – soluble powder made from crushed acorn cups and acorns from a species of oak, Quercus aegilops which contains concentrated tannin and is imported from the north east Mediterranean. Leather made with valonia is said to be heavier and firmer than that which has been tanned with oak bark.

Water pit – where hides were washed to remove salt preservatives or traces of blood.

Water power, water-wheel – used to power an edge-runner stone or bark mill to grind oak bark and/or to pump water/liquor in/from/to tan pits. In some locations a water wheel was employed to raise and lower hides in suspender pits. Horses and oxen also provided motive power.

Welt – shoemaker's or saddler's term. Strip of leather sewn to the edge of the sole and the turned in edge of the upper; or a strip of leather stretched between the skirts and the seat in saddle. Made from shoulder or scraps of a hide.

Appendix
Devon-born tannery workers living in Bermondsey in 1871

From the Bermondsey census 1871
Research undertaken by Frank Clements,
151 Longhill Road, Catford SE6, circa 1980

Bermondsey covers an area on the south bank of the Thames, roughly from London Bridge in the west to Canada Wharf in the east, and is bounded by the Old Kent Road on the south and south-west. It was the country's main centre for tanning leather in the nineteenth century. A notable number of Devonians moved here from their native west country parishes to work in the London industry, in the two decades immediately preceeding the census of 1871.

The following text re-groups Mr Clements' research into the Devon parishes the tanners were born in, and estimates are made of the years when they moved from Devon to London.

Further research – from the 1841 and 1851 census for the Devon parishes concerned – indicates that many of these workers were agricultural labourers or sons of agricultural labourers in Devon, and had not learnt their trade or served apprenticeships in the county.

Alphington

Finnimore, Richard HM 60 tanner 16 Brook Street
 wife Elizabeth, 62, born Winkleigh. No offspring resident. Mary Woolacott, niece, 11, born Exeter, staying with them.

Ashburton

Morse, Richard HM 48 leather finisher 16 Riley Street
 wife Mary Ann, 45, also from Ashburton. Two sons, both born Sittingbourne, Kent. Eldest Harry [?], leather finisher's lad, 14, Younger brother John, 12. So moved to London from Kent sometime after 1862. When was the move to Kent?

Barnstaple

Buckingham, William HM 41 tanner Wilds Rents Long Lane
 wife Sarah 34, born Bishops Stortford [Hertfordshire]. No offspring so no indication of date of move, but probably after 1858.

Berry Pomeroy

Smerden, Thomas HM 53 leather dresser 73 Spa Road, Bermondsey [St Olave parish]
 wife Betsy, 50, born Kingston, Devon. Daughters Emma and Clara born Broad Hampton – possibly Broadhempston, Devon, and aged 23 and 22 respectively. So London move was after 1851.
 Smerden could have gained experience at a currier's shop, or at one of the two Totnes tanneries.

Bow

Battershell? Thomas HM 28 leatherdresser 68 Grange Road
 wife Sophia, 25, born Sires? Devon. No offspring listed.
Clemeints, William lodger 23 tanner 3 Paulin Street
 Probably moved to London after 1867. Surname is probably Clements.
Clements, John HM 50 tanner 2 Alice Street
 wife Elizabeth, 49, born Zeal [Monachorum]. Three sons, eldest John, 19, tanner, born Bermondsey. So moved to London circa 1851 or a little earlier.
Clements, John HM 31 tanner ? Richmoor Street
 wife Alice, 27, born Stevenage [Hertfordshire]. Son George, 7, born Bermondsey. Moved to London by 1863.
Clements, William HM 34 tanner 61 Albert Street
 wife Mary A, 40, born 'Zale', which probably means Zeal Monachorum, near Bow. Four children; William the eldest, 10, born Bermondsey. So moved to London in 1860 or earlier.
Cochran, John HM 34 tanners labourer 27 Alderminster Road
 wife Mary, 32, born North Tawton. Eldest son resident, William, 10, born Bermondsey, so in London by circa 1860.
Cochran, William HM 32 tanners labourer 27 Alderminster Road
 wife, Agnes 35, born North Tawton. Daughter Annie, 4, born Bermondsey. Moved to London in period before 1866; possibly followed elder brother or cousin [qv] to London.
Davey, John HM 32 tanner 17 Ernest Street
 wife Elizabeth, 30, b Bow, too. Son John, 4, born Bermondsey. So probably moved to London by 1866.

Household included father in law, John Waldorn [?], 61, tanner, b Bow, and relative
Samuel Davey, unm, 19, tanner, born Bow.

Davy, Samuel HM 25 tanner 5 Paulin Street
wife Hannah, 24, machinist, born Bermondsey. No offspring. But Samuel probably moved to London
after 1865.

Davy, Samuel HM 25 tanner 3 Maltby Street
wife Hannah M, 24, machinist, born Bermondsey. Moved to London after 1865.
[Interesting: same couple at two different addresses!]

Davies, Robert HM 25 tanner 28 Ernest Street
wife's Christian name unclear or not recorded, but age 42, born Plymouth. Their son Samuel, aged 1,
born Bermondsey. Robert may have worked in Plymouth before moving to London, but at 25, we can
assume the move to London was within the last five years, ie in the period 1866-1869.

Dilve? William HM 27 tanner 24 Alderminster Road
wife Elizabeth, 30, born Bermondsey. Son William, 3, born Bermondsey. Moved to London circa 1867
or earlier.

Foley, William HM 41 tanner 60 Albert Street
wife Mary A, 41, born Bow. Four daughters, ages 19-9, and son, aged 2. Eldest dau Elizabeth, 19, unm,
a hat trimmer, born Bow. Next dau Selina, 17, assistant in a biscuit factory, born Bermondsey.
So a good estimate for the date for the move to London would be 1855.

Head, Henry HM 39 leatherdresser 17 Prince Street
wife Ellen, 40, born Berkshire. Eldest of 6 offspring, Henry, 13, born Bermondsey. Moved to London
before 1857. Also resident: Thomas Head, tanner, 18, younger brother of Henry, born Bermondsey.

Heard, George HM 35 tanner 57 Albert Street
wife Jane, 33, born North Tawton. No offspring with them. Jane Avery, 14, niece, resident, b North
Tawton. Also a lodger, George Merchant, tanner, 32, unm, born North Tawton. They probably moved to
London in the 1860s.

Heard, John HM 31 tanner 13 Alice Street
wife Harriett, born Pinhoe [near Exeter]. Son Harry, 6, born Bermondsey. Moved to London by circa
1864.

Heard, Thomas HM 38 tanner 1 Stainton Terrace
wife Emma, 32, also b Bow. 5 offspring recorded at census night. Eldest Ophilia 9, b Bermondsey
So moved from Devon by 1861.

Howard, William HM 26 tanner 64 Albert Street
wife Elizabeth, 28, born Oxfordshire. Two offspring. Son Alfred, 3, born Bermondsey. Move to London
was perhaps in 1867, when William Howard was 22, or earlier.

Kelland, William HM 33 tanner 5 Willow Street
wife Mary A, 28, born Bow. Eldest child Elizabeth D, 7, born Bermondsey. Moved to London
sometime before 1863. Son William, 5, listed as 'imbicile'.

Middlewick, Frederick HM 34 tanner 10 Mint Street
wife Eliza, 37, born Middlesex. No offspring resident. No clue as to move date, but probably after 1856.

Mugford, John HM 38 tanner 6 Balaclava Road
Mary A, wife, 28, born Bow. Two offspring born Bermondsey. Eldest, James, 9. So in London
before 1861.

Northam, John HM 26 tanner 20 Spa Road
wife Jane, 30, b North Tawton. Eldest son Robert, 5, born Bermondsey. So move to London
came circa 1865.

Perkins, Francis HM 25 tanners labourer 27 Alderminster Road
wife Charlotte, 28, from Cheriton Bishop. Daughter Emma, 3, born Bow. Son Frederick, 5 months,
born Bermondsey. So arrived in London after 1868. *[Sharing house with Cochran family, qv]*

Pike, John HM 37 tanner 10 Steven Street
wife Elizabeth, 40, born Bow. 6 children, all born Bermondsey. Eldest Emma, 13. So London move was
by 1857 or 1858.

Pike, Samuel HM 44 tanner 12 Steven Street
wife Elizabeth, 58, born Bow. Daughter Sophia [?], 21, costumemaker, also born Bow. So moved to
London some time after 1850.

Pike, Samuel HM 32 tanner 46 Willow Street
wife Elizabeth, 31, from Andover. Eldest son David, 11, born Hampshire. 4 other children, eldest
Mary, 8, born Bermondsey. Moved to London circa 1861-2.

Stanlake, Robert H, HM 49 tanner 3 Cadbury Road, Bermondsey [St Olave parish]
wife Mary Ann born Exeter. Eldest dau b Plymouth circa 1849, so left Bow 1848 or earlier
six offspring recorded. Rest born in Hertfordshire. Moved to London after youngest born, circa 1865.

Stoneman, Richard   HM   32   leatherdresser   13 Rock Grove, Blue Anchor Lane
> wife Mary, 32, born Tiverton. 4 offspring. Eldest Eliza, 9, born Bow. Richard, son, 5, born
> Bermondsey. Move to London 1863-1865.

Stoutman [?] James   HM   62   tanner   15 Riley Street
> wife Susan, 50, also born Bow. Their daughter Jane, 12, born Bermondsey. So in London at least
> by 1858.

Woodman, James   HM   42   tanner   149 Church Street
> wife Maria, 37, born 'Stockley' – possibly Stockleigh Pomeroy. Eldest dau listed Annie M, 14,
> born Bermondsey. Suggests moved to London circa 1856.

Woodman, John   HM   51   tanner   13 Alscot Street
> wife Fanny, 52, also from Bow. No offspring listed here so date of move from Devon unknown.
> John possibly the elder brother of James, so possibly moved to London by 1856.

The number of tanners and associated tradesmen – 30 odd – born in Bow and moving to London has to be significant. One pointer is the death of the foreman at Halse tannery, John Stanlake, who had been in charge there since 1814. He died in October 1854. The exodus seems to have largely occurred after that date. His relative, presumably, Robert H Stanlake, doesn't play a part, as he left Bow probably before John's death and only reached Bermondsey in the mid 1860s. Money was better in London, although the quality of life was debatably worse. The arrival of the railways and lack of opportunities in Devon may have encouraged this movement of workers. This exodus must have affected the economy of the village. Those living in Bow were, it seems, labourers or sons of labourers, and so may not have affected the running of the local tannery.

Bradninch

Anstery, Aaron   HM   33   tanner   7 Dips Buildings
> wide Catherine, 35, from Ireland. Two sons and a daughter. Eldest Thomas, 9, born
> Bermondsey, so had moved to London by 1861, but probably not much earlier, either.

Cadeleigh

Bisley [?], James   HM   33   leather dryer   26 Maltby Street
> wife Martha, 31, born Cornish?, Devon. No such place. They had a lodger, Thomas Ellis, widower, 42,
> tanner, born Cadeleigh

Chawleigh

Parsons, George   lodger 35   tanner   19 New Street
> no other details

Webber, Robert   HM   59   tanner   1 Neckinger Street
> wife Sarah, 52, born Overton, Gloucestershire. 7 offspring listed. Eldest Walter H, fish porter, 19,
> born Bermondsey. So family moved to London by about 1851. No known tannery at Chawleigh but
> there was one at neighbouring Chulmleigh.

Cheriton Bishop

Gossland, William   HM   45   tanner   21 Steven Street
> wife Eliza, 45, born Devon. No offspring resident so unable to estimate move date

Haywood, Thomas   HM   33   tanner   4 West Street, Neckinger
> wife Mary Jane, 31, also born Cheriton Bishop. five offspring. Eldest Elizabeth S, 8, b Bermondsey
> so move from Devon circa 1861 or so. Henry Haywood, 25, brother of Thomas,
> also born Cheriton Bishop, also a tanner, living in household.

Pillar, John   HM   38   tanner   5 Mary's Old Court
> wife Harriett, 39, also from Cheriton parish, as too eldest two sons, one of whom, George, 15, is a
> tanner. Second son William, aged 11. Eldest offspring born Bermondsey is Jane, aged 4. So came to
> London between 1860 and 1866. In same household is John Cook, HM, 24, tanner, born Spreyton, and
> his wife Harriett, 22, born Cheriton.

Heywood, Robert   HM   27   tanner   1 Little Tailia Street
> Susan, his wife, 26, born Bow. Their first son Henry, 4, born Bermondsey. Suggests they moved to
> London in about 1866. Samuel Heywood, father, also resident, aged 51.

Cheriton Fitzpaine

McGuire, Abraham [or Negrace - name not certain]
                    HM   47   tanner   24 Maltby Street

wife Mary, 46, also born Cheriton [could be Cheriton Bishop, but Cheriton Fitzpaine had the tannery]. Son John, unm, 20, labourer in rice mill, also born Cheriton. Move to London anytime after 1852.

Slee, Thomas   HM   35   tanners labourer   69 Aves Road

wife Charlotte, 33, born Cadeleigh. Four offspring. Eldest, John, 10, born Cadeleigh. Rhoda Ann, 8, born Bermondsey. Suggests move to London by 1862, possibly earlier – Charlotte may have returned to Cadeleigh to have first birth. In the household were her brother John Davy, 27, tanner, born Cadeleigh and her husband's brother John Slee, 38, a tanner, born Cheriton Fitzpaine.

Tothill, Benjamin   HM   30   tanner   22 Steven Street

wife Harriett, 46, born Wencaston, Suffolk. Two offspring. Eldest Adelade M [?], 11, born Bermondsey. Move to London probably before 1860. Was Tothill from C Fitzpaine or C Bishop?

Chudleigh

Bowden, Charles   HM   44   tanner   6 Saxon Street

wife Margaret, 40, born Chudleigh, too. 4 daughters and one son all born Surrey. Eldest dau Mary Ann, 16. So taking Surrey to mean Bermondsey [as in Surrey docks], move to London could have been before 1854.

Clannaborough

Heard, Richard   HM   38   tanner   9 Alice Street

wife Eliza, 33, born Exeter. Eldest son William H, 10, born St George, Surrey. Daughter Eliza, 8, born Bermondsey. Move to London c 1860. (Clannaborough given as 'Clanbors, Devon', by Enumerator).

Clovelly

Harvey, Edward   HM   50   tanner   9 Mary's Old Court

wife Elizabeth, 49, born Hartland, where there was a tannery. None at Clovelly or otherwise nearby. Son Edward, 18, born Clovelly. So move to London sometime after 1853.

Combe Martin

Slee, James   HM   45   leather dresser   3 Parkers Terrace

wife Elizabeth, 46, dressmaker, b Marwood, and son, John, leatherdresser, b Pilton [?] in c 1850 so move to London from Pilton some time after 1850. Pilton had a tannery and a glove factory.

Coldridge

Born, John   HM   40   tanner   78 West Street

wife Loveday, 38, born Coldridge. Had two month old son b Bermondsey. No other offspring present although possibly earlier children died young. So moved to London possibly in 1868 or 1869. No tannery known at Coldridge: nearest known tanneries at Winkleigh, Chulmleigh, or North Tawton, or Bow.

Phillips, Alexander   HM   30   tanner   11 West Street, Neckinger

wife Mary, 26, b Bow. Two daughters. Eldest Lily, 3, b Bermondsey. Suggests moved to London c 1866 or so.

Phillips, James   HM   38   tanner   28 Spa Road

wife Dinah, 38, born Coldridge, too. Dau Maria, 6, born Devon. son James, 5, born Bermondsey. So we can date London move to about 1866, unless Dinah returned to Devon to have her first child.

Colebrook

Lidscott, William   HM   45   tanner   15 Little George Street

wife Elizabeth, 36, born Dalton. [London parish?] Two daughters and two sons all born Bermondsey Eldest Emily J, 8. So move to London sometime before 1862.

Middlewick, Samuel   HM   36   tanner   18 Long Lane

wife Eliza, 38, born Bow. Son William Wilson, aged 9, born Crediton. Suggests move to London after 1861.

Norris, Robert   HM   40   tanner   10 West Street, Neckinger

wife Jane, 37, born Bow. Eldest dau, Louisa J, 9, born Bermondsey. Indicates moved to London by 1861. The nearest tannery to Colebrook would be Bow.

Tucker, George   HM   41   tanner   15 Steven Street

wife Ann, 40, from the same parish. Four offspring all born Bermondsey. Eldest George, 11. Means family were in London from 1860 or probably a little earlier.

Crediton

Badcock, James   lodger 26   currier   153 Church Grove
> unmarried

Bishop, James   HM   55   leatherdresser   4 Willow Street
> wife Elizabeth 53, born Plymouth. Son James, 20, a blacker of leather, born Bermondsey. Move to London made by 1850.

Brook, William   HM   74   tanner   16 Alice Street
> wife Rebecca, 74, born Woodbury [probably Woodbury, near Exeter]. How long had they been living in Bermondsey?

Greenslade, Frank   lodger 20   currier   153 Church Grove
> unmarried. Aged 20, suggests that his move to Bermondsey was quite recent, say 1869-1870.

Hawkins, John   HM   33   tanner   10 Black Swan Yard
> wife Elizabeth, 27, born Crediton, too. Two offspring listed. Daughter Susan, 7, born Bermondsey. So the Hawkins family had moved to London by circa 1863.

Haydon, William   HM   24   tanner   14 Brook Street
> wife Mary Ann, 26, born Barnstaple. Son William, six months, born Bermondsey. Suggest moved to London in period 1867-1870.

Cullompton

Allen, Robert   HM   64   leather dresser   6 Cross Street
> wife Elizabeth, 57, also from Cullompton. Three sons, eldest John, 24, warehouseman, born Bermondsey. Move to London therefore before the year 1847. Second son Robert, 22, a leatherdresser and third son, Charles, 16, a groom.

Potter, Henry   HM   30   tanner   45 Alscot Road
> Charlotte, wife, 28, b Godalming [Surrey]. Daughter Charlotte Elizabeth, 8, born Bermondsey. Daughter Amy, 6, born Godalming. Moved to London by 1862-1864.

Dodbrooke [next to Kingsbridge]

Williams, William   HM   53   leather dresser   19 Brandon Street
> wife Mary Ann, 51, born Modbury. Two offspring: eldest Edward, 16, born Bermondsey. Move to London therefore before 1855.

Exeter

Berry, John   unm   23   tanner   55 Linsey Street
> a lodger or 'boarder'.

Evans, John   HM   61   leather dresser   34 Church Street
> wife Catherine, 58, born 'Wrexford' – probably Wexford, Ireland. Dau Catherine, 17, b Middlesex dau Alice May, 14, b Bermondsey. Moved to London area circa 1853.

French, William   HM   58   leather grounder   3 Swan Mead
> wife Sarah Ann, 50, born Bow Lane, London. Eldest son George, 15, working with father, born Bermondsey. Therefore in London by 1856.

Friend, William   HM   34   tanner   34 Ernest Street
> wife Eliza, 33, also from Exeter. Daughter Sarah Jane, aged 10, born Exeter. Son William Henry, 2, born Bermondsey. Move to London in period 1862-1869.

Hall, William   HM   31   currier   81 Spa Road
> Georgina, wife, 32, b Exeter. Five offspring all born London. Eldest dau Georgina, 12. So in London by say 1858-9. William's father and mother, 65 and 66, also living in the household, also b Exeter.

Tucker, William   HM   61   tanner   3 Brandon Street
> wife Ann, 60, born Devon. No offspring living in household. William's parish: St Mary Major, Exeter.

Westaway, John   HM   40   leather dresser   3 Oaks Cottages
> wife Margaret, 37, born Bristol. Son James, 10, born Bermondsey. Move to London, via Bristol [?], before 1861.

Hennock

Blandford, Samuel   HM   50   tanner   8 Mary's Old Court
> wife Mary, 50, b Chagford, as were all their three offspring recorded on census night, the youngest being Ellen, 9. Move to Bermondsey by 1863 or later. Samuel's birthplace recorded by enumerator as Hinniock. Hennock's quite near Chagford, on Dartmoor. There was an 18th century tannery at Hennock, location unknown. Alternatively the reference is to Hemyock.

North Tawton

Bolt, William   HM   52   tanner   22 Spa Road
> wife Susan, 61, also born North Tawton. Offspring, if any, no doubt living elsewhere.

Bradford, George   HM   24   tanner   35 New Street
> wife Susan, 22, born Bow. Son George born Bermondsey. We can surmise the move to London was in about 1869-70. Brother Henry Bradford, 17, tanner, also resident. Possibly born Daventry.

Merchant, William   HM   39   tanner   55 Little George Street
> wife Mary, also from North Tawton. Six offspring, three born North Tawton, three born Bermondsey. Move occurred between 1861 and 1864.

Skinner, [?] Henry [?]   lodger 20   tanner   41 Albert Street
> in household belonging to Mary Ellis, a housekeeper, 48, born North Tawton. Suggests a recent move to London by Skinner: in the period 1868-1871.

Skinner, James   HM   43   tanner   59 Little George Street
> wife Mary, 43, also from N Tawton. Two sons William, 18, and John, 16, tanners, born N Tawton. Emily, dau, 10, born Bristol. Alfred, 8, and two other younger sons born Bermondsey. Move from N Tawton to Bristol in period 1856-61. Move to Bermondsey probably in 1862. Henry Skinner, above, maybe the eldest son of James and Mary?

Sandford

Hunt, Danial [?sic]   HM   34   tanner   3 Little Tailia Street
> wife Jane, 32, born Bow. Offspring include Daniel, 7, born Bermondsey. Moved to London before 1863.

Hunt, William   HM   52   tanner   78 Lucey Street
> wife not present on census night and no offspring either.

Turner, Robert   HM   43   tanner   18 Maltby Street
> wife Mary, 45, born Woolfardisworthy. Two sons; eldest Charles, 15, born Bermondsey, a telegraph boy. So they were in London before 1855. John Turner, brother of the above, b Sandford, a tanner, also living in the household.

Stockleigh Pomeroy

Westcott, John   HM   40   tanner   11 Georges Place
> wife Hannah, 38, born in Stockleigh also. No tannery there, but there were three in nearby Crediton. Three offspring; Mary, eldest, aged 8, born Bermondsey. Suggests they moved to London by 1862.

Swimbridge

Pile, George   HM   45   tanner   29 Gedling Street
> wife Louise, 44, from Chilter, Sussex. 7 offspring: eldest son George, 20, tanner, born Bermondsey indicates family moved to London c 1850.

Tiverton

Broadmead, Thomas   HW   66   tanner   26 Steven Street
> The widower lived with his son John, 40, tanner, born Tiverton. So move to London was after 1851. The household included James Newbury, lodger, 36, tanner, born Shute, Devon, and his wife, Mary Ann, 38, from Melbury, Devon [Possibly Melbury, Dorset?].

Carpenter, Henry   HM   31   tanner   5 Riley Street
> wife Jane, 31, born Eastbourne [Sussex]. Shared household with a carpenter born Plymouth and his wife, born Bermondsey.

Ellis, Thomas   HM   68   tanner   21 Alfred Street
> wife Ann, 67, born Essex. Offspring, if any, living elsewhere by this time. An Essex wife might suggest the move to London was as early as the 1830s? The Tiverton tanneries didn't last into the late 19th century.

Ford, Albert G   HM   21   journeyman tanner 12 Brandon Street
> wife Jane born Bermondsey. Son John, 3, born Bermondsey. Moved to London circa 1867.

Uffculme

Tucker, George   HM   38   tanner   8 Williams Terrace
> wife Hannah, 33, born Taunton, Somerset, and working as a glover. No offspring listed
> James Stut, 23, unm, tanner, b Taunton, lodging [possibly Hannah's brother?].

Upton Hellions

Hutchings, James   HM   50   currier   1 Elizabeth Terrace
> wife Naomi, 44, from Chittlehampton. No offspring recorded: year of move unknown.

Winkleigh

Tucker, John   HM   31   tanner   35 Alscot Road
> wife Ann, 24, born Herefordshire. No offspring, so date of move to London undetermined.
> [Presumably Winkleigh. Enumerator has recorded Winkley, and Clements has questioned it.]

Witheridge

Hepper, Robert   lodger, widower
>   51   tanner   10 Albert Street
> staying with widow Harriett Binham, 47, born Witheridge.

Devon – parish not specified or unclear

Allen, John   visitor 66   tanner   53 Little George Street
> no other details.

Boutt, William   HM   49   tanner   3 Parkers Buildings
> wife Mary, 47, born Winkleigh. William b Britistown. No such place. Could be High Bickington or
> Bridestowe or perhaps Bishop's Tawton. No offspring. Offspring were employed as two domestic
> servants, 14 and 12, both born Bristol. So move was via Bristol, quite a centre for leather manufacture
> in its own right. Move to London after say 1860.

Choron ? James   lodger 32   tanner   15 Steven Street
> wife Ann, 33, born Poughill, Devon. James' surname possibly Chown. No offspring.

Clark, J Bun   HM   44   journeyman tanner 15 Cross Street
> wife Catherine, 46, born Devon, as were 3 sons, aged 23-17; fourth son R Bun, 12, born Bermondsey
> so move to London took place in period 1854-1858. Elder sons all bricklayers labourers, possibly
> building new houses for Devon tanners to live in!

Crook, William   HW   68   leather dresser   9 Guildford Place
> no family with him.

Field, Edward   HM   49   tanner   20 George Street
> Hanna, wife, 45, born Berkshire. Daughter Mary, 20, unmarried, born Bermondsey. So move
> to London by about 1850.

Glenfield, William   HM   27   tanner   10 Georges Place
> wife Agatha, 26, born Bermondsey and son James, 2, b Bermondsey. So William probably had
> moved to London by 1868, but not much earlier as he was only 27.

Haywood, John   HM   31   journeyman tanner 22 Brandon Street
> wife Fanny, 32, also from Devon. Two sons: eldest Charles, 6, born Bermondsey.
> Moved to London probably by 1864

Heard, William   HM   52   tanner   6 Alice Street
> wife Susannah, 49, born Devon. Daughter Emily, 12, born Bermondsey. Move to London took
> place sometime before 1858. (They also had a grand-daughter Annie Heard, 2, born Bermondsey,
> staying).

Hosgood, James   HM   27   tanner   4 Steven Street
> wife Elizabeth, 31, born Crediton. Three children, eldest Hannah E, 2, born Bermondsey.
> So move to London sometime before 1868, but probably after 1863.

Martin, James   HM   43   tanner   14 William Street
> wife Mary A, 47, born Devon West, like her husband. This presumably means Tavistock or Bideford
> way. Four children. Eldest Rhoda, 13, nursemaid, born Bermondsey. So in London by circa 1857.

Shallice, John   HM   44   tanner   34 Spa Road
> wife Susan, 32, b Devon, as also son John, 12. Suggests moved to London circa 1860 or later.

Sutton, George   HM   38   tanner   26 Spa Road
> wife Emma, 38, b Devon. Eldest dau Alice b Bermondsey, aged 12. So moved to London by 1858.

Sutton, John   HM   56   tanner   6 George Street
> wife Elizabeth, 50, also from Devon. No offspring but 3 visitors staying in the household:
> George Pillar, a fellmonger, born in Devon, James Morrits [?], a widower, 37, born Colebrook,
> and George Churchward, unmarried, 16, tanner, born Devon.

Tucker, William   HM   62   tanner   21 George Street
> wife Sarah, 58, born London.

Turner, William   HM   34   tanner   6 Swan Mead
> wife Susannah, 31, born Bermondsey. Elder daughter Florence, 6, born Bermondsey
> so William came to London by about 1864.

Index

A

Aberystwyth
  Catharine and Ellen,
    schooner 8
Alphington
  tanners
    Berry family 19
    Berry, William 19
    Dingle, Samuel 19
    Sanders, John 19
    Wippell and Rew 13
    Wippell, James 19
    Wright, Richard 19
  tannery 19
Ashburton
  Ashburton Brewery 21
  tanneries
    East of the church 21
    Lawrence Street 21
    Old Mill 21
  tanners
    Evans, Lavington
      21, 22, 51
    Furneaux, Mr 22
    Higgins, John 21
    Mann, John Vere 21
    Mann, William 21
    Parham, Benjamin 22
    Rendell, John 22
Atherington
  landowner
    Mayne, Robert 148
  tanner
    Snell, Anthony 148
Axminster
  carpet maker
    Whitty, Thomas , jnr
      24
  tanneries
    Lyme Street 24
    Westwater 24
  tanners
    Colmer, Francis 24
    Haycraft, Richard 24
    Liddon, John Bunter
      24
    Stocker, James 24
    Wyat, William 24
  woolstapler
    Haycraft, Richard 24
Axminster Carpets 44
Axmouth
  harbour 25
  tanners
    Newbury, Lydia 25
    Newbury, Thomas 25
  tannery
    Borough House 25

B

Bampton
  fellmonger
    Oxenham, William 26

lime merchant
  Periam, John Trowey
    27
tanneries
  Frog Street 26
tanners
  Farrant, Samuel George
    27
  Farrant, Thomas 26
  Norman, Henry 26
  Oxenham, John 26
  Periam, William
    26, 27
  Rowe, George 26, 27
  Williams, Charles 27
Bark mills
  Edge runner stones 8
    Hartland 76
    Honiton 80
    South Molton 6
Bark mills, early 13
  Cumbria 13
  Paris, near 13
Barne, George 32
Barnstaple
  cholera, outbreak of 31
  tanneries 28
    Bear Street 28
    Boutport Street 29, 31
    Joy Street 28
    Lichadon Street 28
    Pilton Bridge 29
    Rackfield or Pilton
      Bridge 29, 106
    Vicarage Street 28
  tanners
    Adams, George 29
    Adams, S & G, & Co
      29
    Adams, Samuel 28
    Adams, Samuel
      Norrish 29
    Baker, John 28
    Ballment, A 31
    Bembridge, Samuel 29
    Davis, John Leworthy
      31
    Rice, James 30
    Rice, Samuel 29
    Sanders, John 29, 31
    Sanders, Samuel 30
    Sanders, William
      29, 31
    Smyth family 29
Bermondsey 152-158
Bickleigh
  tanneries
    Higher Brithayes
      32, 134, 135
    Millhayes 32
  tanners
    Barne, George 32
    Braddick, William 32
    Jarman, Richard 32
Bideford
  tanners
    Lee, George 34
    Long, George 34

    Narraway, John Whit-
      lock 34
    Prouse, James 34
    White, Elizabeth 34
    White, Joseph 34
    White, William 34
  tannery
    Westcombe 34
Bidgood, John 148
Board of Trade 37
Bow
  tanneries
    Halse 35
  tanners
    Packer, George 35
    Price, Samuel 36
    Sanders, James Lee
      35, 83
    Stanlake, John 36
    Wreford, Samuel 35
Bradford
  Sanderson Murray and
    Elder 95
  woollen spinner
    Brooks, Edward 43
Bradninch
  Devon Valley Mill 37
  paper makers
    Dewdney, Thomas 37
    Matthews, William 37
  tanners
    Bowden, Joseph 37
    Catour, Adam 37
    Drew, Robert 37
    Elliot, Abraham 37
    Martyn, William 37
    Segar, William 37
    Sharland, Thomas 37
    Tannere, Reginald 37
  tannery
    Bindles 37
Branscombe, William 148
Braunton
  tanner
    Darracott, James 148
Bridestowe
  tanners
    Bevan, John 38
    Edgecumbe, Arthur 38
    Palmer, James 38
    Sloley, William 38
    Woodrow, Alexander
      38
  tannery
    Tanyard Court 38
Broadclyst
  tanners
    Beare Tanning Co 39
    Boutcher, Emanuel 39
    Boutcher, William 39
    Cock, William 39
    Gould, William
    Boucher 39
    Wish, William Trump
      39, 143
  tannery
    Beare 39
Broadhembury
  Dulford Mill 40

tanners
  Hussey, William 40
  Payne, Andrew 40
  Sharland, Edward
    15, 40
  Shiles, Elizabeth 40
  Shiles, Henry 40
tannery
  Dulford 15, 40
Broadhempston
  tailor
    Waycott, John 41
  tanners
    Francis, William 41
    Mann, William 41
    Thuell, John 41
    Wilcocks, William 41
  tannery
    Forder Green 41
Buckerell
  tanners
    Cockram, William 42
    Hawker, Henry 42
  tannery
    Hamlet 42
Buckfast
  Higher Mill 42
Buckfastleigh
  Chapel Street
    Park View House 42
  Fullaford House 43
  Harewood House 43
  Higher Town
    Jordan Street 42
  Market Street
    Maiden House 43
  serge manufacturer
    Hamlyn, John 42
  tanners
    Furneaux, Thomas 42
    Hamlyn Brothers 42
    Hamlyn, Joseph 42
    Hamlyn, Joseph junior
      43
    Hamlyn, William 42
  tannery
    Chapel Street 42
  tannery staff
    Edmonds, James 42
  Town Mill 42
  West Mill 41
  woollen manufacturers
    Berry, John, & Sons 44
    Hamlyn Bros 44
  woolstapler
    Furneaux, John 42
Buckland Monachorum
  landowner
    Toll, John 45
  Lower Didhams 45
  tanners
    Brown, T 45
    Dawe, Joseph 45
    Dawe, Sampson 45
    Dunning, John 45
    Martyn, John 45
  tannery
    Coombe 45

Butterleigh
  Combe farm 134
  rector
    Barne, John 135

C

Cardiff
  St Fagans
    National History
    Museum 9, 12, 50
Carn Brea
  ironfounder
    Bartle 92
Chagford
  woollen mills
    Higher Factory 98
    Lower Factory 98
Chalmers, Sir Charles 135
Chard
  ironfounder
    Hawker, Joseph 52
Chardstock
  tannery 24
Cheriton Fitzpaine
  tanneries
    Lower Waterhouse
    15, 46
    West Upham 15, 46
  tanners
    Drake, Thomas 47
    Sharland family 8
    Sharland, Henry 47
    Sharland, Thomas M C
    15, 16, 47, 147
    Sharland, William
    47, 135
Cholwill, Thomas 76
Chrome tanning 150
Chudleigh
  tanners
    Berry, John 48
    Berry, Prudence 48
    Burd, Mr 48
    Caseley, William 48
    Westwood, John 48
  tannery
    Exeter Street 48
Chulmleigh
  currier
    Wreford, John 49
  Fore Street 49
  South Molton Street 49
  tanners
    Tanner, John 49
    Wreford, Grace 49
    Wreford, Samuel
    49, 135
  tanner's apprentice
    Violet, Elizabeth 49
  tannery
    Ford 49
Churchward 148
Co-operative Wholesale
  Society 44
Coleridge, Samuel Taylor 9
Colyton
  solicitor
    Snook, John 50

surgeon
  Snook, John S 50
tanneries
  Chantry Bridge, below
  50
  Hamlyn's or Baker's
  50
  Purlebridge 50
tanners
  Baker, J & J F
  8, 50, 51
  Baker, John 51
  Baker, W 51
  Evans, Robert
  Buncombe 50
  Evans, William
  Nathaniel 50
  Hoare, Nicholas 50
  Parr, Andrew 52
  Reed, Aaron 50
  Reede, John 50
  Roade, Thomas 50
  Roper, Mr 50
  Wishlade, Aaron 50
Cordoba 8
  Shoe leather 8
Crediton
  Bere Mills 54
  boot and shoe factories 8
  Fordton Mills 54
  Four Mills 54
  shoemakers
    Elston, George 53, 99
    Elston, John 98
    Gimblett, Samuel
    Squire 53, 56, 98
  tanneries
    East Town 55
    High Street 54
    Parliament Street 54
  tanners
    Adams, B P 56
    Adams, Bruce 56
    Adams, Edward
    28, 55, 56, 75, 103
    Adams, John 56
    Adams, Richard 56
    Adams, William Her-
    bert 56
    Francis and Son 55
    Francis, John 55
    Haycraft, Mrs 55
    Keagles and Pring 54
    Melhuish, George 54
    Moggeridge, Philip 55
    Roberts, Samuel 55
    Shute, Stephen 53
    Snell, John 55
    Snell, William 55
  woolstapler
    Shute, Stephen 53
Cullompton
  fellmonger
    Ewens, C B 62
  fire of 1839 58, 136
  mob rioting 59
  Pound Square 59
  tanneries 58

  Court 63
  Crow Green 59
  Lower King's Mill 60
  tanners
    Ewens, Biddlecombe
    62
    Ewens, C B, & Son 62
    Mortimore, Richard
    59, 61, 136
    Sellwood and Sons 59
    Sellwood, Binford 59
    Sellwood, Daniel 58
    Sellwood family
    8, 136
    Sellwood, John 58
    Whitby, James 13, 58
Culmstock
  sergemaker
    Fry, Robert 148
  tanners
    Baker, Charles 148
    Fry, Robert 148

D

Dalwood
  tanneries 63
    Hutchins Barton 62
    Newton's 62
  tanners
    Gould, John 63
    Gould, William 63
    Hodges, Samuel 63
    Hodges, Thomas 63
    Lugg, Richard 63
    Tookes, Barnard 63
Darke, John 76
Dartmouth
  landowner
    Seale, Sir John 64
  tanner
    Sutcliffe, Henry 64
Davy, Sir Humphry 7, 9
Devonport
  chandler
    Poole, Mr 132
  Chapel Street 64
  King Street 64
  Morice Square Baptist
    Chapel 109
  tanners
    Blight & Son 64
    Blight, Charles Henry
    64
    Blight, Jane 64
    Blight, John 64

E

East Budleigh
  tanner
    Carpenter, Mr 64
  tannery 64
Exbourne
  Tatershall family 83, 100
Exeter
  builder
    Phillips, David 40
  cattle market 68

  City of 13
  curriers
    Rew, James 70
    Tanner, Frederick 109
  Duryard, oaks from 13
  Exeter Archaeology 65
  fellmonger
    Aplin, Robert 66, 70
  glovemakers
    Tanner, James Jones
    71, 109
    Tanner, William 109
  grocer, tea dealer
    Wippell, Joseph 15
  hides from 52, 100
  ironfounders
    Bodley Brothers
    61, 139
    Bodley, George
    13, 58, 82, 101
    Bodley's Old Quay
    Foundry 13, 16, 36,
    68, 83, 95, 126
    Huxhams & Brown 13
    Northam 103, 116
  leather dressers
    Tanner, James Jones
    71
    Tanner, William 71
  London Inn 49, 135
  mayor
    Crugge, William 71
  merchant
    Bozoun, Richard 65
  paper manufacturer
    Tremlett, William 71
  Royal Albert Memorial
    Museum & Art Gallery
    56
  sheriff
    Tanner, James Jones
    71
  shoemaker
    Mortimer, Richard 68
  South Street 65
  tanneries
    Commercial Road 71
    Haven Banks 65
    Heavitree 65, 66, 70
    Lion's Holt 65, 71
    Marsh Barton 72
    Shilhay 71
    St Thomas 65
    Westgate 65
  tanners
    Ball, James 70
    Crook, George 68
    Crugge, William 71
    Dymond, Harriet 70
    Dymond, Joseph
    Sparkes 70
    Francis, James 68
    Francis, William
    68, 69
    Hitchcock, John
    66, 70
    King, James 68
    Rew, James 70, 135

Rew, William 70
Sanders, James Lee 68, 145
Searle, Mr 13
Searle, Richard 68
Searle, Tom Hayden 69
Sweet, Charles 68
Tanner, Frederick 71
Tremlett Brothers Ltd 71
Tremlett, Charles Henry 71
Tremlett, H R 60
Underhay, William 66, 70, 135
Wilson, Alfred 71
Wilson and Tremlett 71
Wilson, James 71
Waterbeer Street 145

F

Fareham
  tannery, near
    Wallington 15
Fire at tanneries
  Barnstaple
    Bear Street 28
  Bradninch
    Bindles 37
  Buckfastleigh
    Chapel Street 43
  Chudleigh
    Exeter Street 48
  Crediton
    East Town 55
  Cullompton
    Crow Green 58, 59, 60
  Exeter
    Heavitree 66, 70
    Westgate 71
  Holsworthy
    East Stanburys 79
  Moretonhampstead
    Ford Street 91
  Newton Abbot
    Branscombe's 94
  Newton St Cyres
    Coldharbour 148
  Ottery St Mary
    Mill Street 102
  Plymouth
    Stonehouse Lane 108
    Tavistock Street 110
  Totnes
    Lake Garden 139
floods affecting tanneries
  Newton Abbot
    Bradley Lane 95
Forest of Dean
  collieries in 71
Furse, George 122

G

Gittisham
  tanner
    Branscombe, William 148
Glove making
  Great Torrington 8
  Yeovil 8
Good, William
  shipbuilder 7
Great Torrington
  Cordwainers, Company of 73
  curriers
    Adams, John 73, 75
    Rude, James 73
  fellmonger
    Sheppard, Benjamin 73
  glovemaking 73
  glover
    Stoneman, C W 74
  Leather Hall 73
  mayor
    Greek, George 73
  tanneries
    Caddywell 74
    High Street 74
    Mill Street 73
    New Street 73
  tanners
    Adams, Charles 103
    Adams, George Doe 75
    Adams, John 28, 103
    Adams, Richard 74, 75, 103
    Kingdon, John 73
    Kingdon, John Bound 73
    Rude, James 74
    Rude, John 74
    Stoneman, George 73, 103
Gunnislake
  cordwainer
    Baker, Edward 54

H

Hartland
  tanners
    Cholwill, Thomas 76
    Galsworthy, William 76
    Juell, Richard 76
    Prust, Joseph 76
    Prust, Thomas 76
    Prust, William 76
    Wilcock, John 76
  tannery 76
Hatherleigh
  tanners
    Darke, John 76
    Facy, Leonard 76
  tannery 76
Hemyock
  clergyman
    Lightfoot, Nicholas 77

landowners
  Lightfoot, Rev Nicholas 77
  Rowcliffe, William 77
tanneries
  Prings & Scaddings 77
  Tanhouse 77
tanners
  Clode, Thomas 77
  Marks, John 77
  Waldron, Clement 77
Hides
  Argentina, from 126, 146
  Buenos Ayres 66, 70, 107
  Exeter, from 52
  export to Rouen 65
  Rio Grande 7
  Uruguay, from 126
Holcombe Rogus
  tanners
    Garnsey, Richard 78
    Jarman, Elias 78
  tannery
    Ford Place 78
  wood turner
    Scott, James 78
Holsworthy
  Bude Canal 79
  butcher
    Bennett, Mr 79
  carpenter
    Sleeman, Mr 79
  Cole's Mill 79
  surgeon
    Pearse, Mr 79
  tanneries
    East Stanburys 79
    South Chasty 79
  tanners
    Bennett, William 79
    Cole, William S 79
    Fary, Leonard 79
    Hoskin, John 79
    Hoskin, Richard 79
    Kingford, John 79
Honeychurch
  St Mary's 144
Honiton
  tanneries
    High Street/Silver Street 80
    King Street 80
  tanners
    Adams, Robert 80
    Ashley, Edward 80, 89
    Ashley, John 80
    Ashley, Martin 80
    Beed and Darke 80
    Colesworthy, John 80
    Harrison & Pearce 80
    Harrison, Richard J I 80
    Harrison, Richard Patch 80
    Levermore, Philipp 80
    Wheaton, William George 80

Tracey Mill 80
Horrabridge
  Horrabridge Mills 44
  woollen mill 43
Horse power in tanneries 21, 22, 28, 49, 102, 104, 117, 122, 145

I

Ilsington
  tanner
    Motton, John 81
  tannery
    Knighton 81
Ipplepen
  landowners
    Harris, John 82
    Studdy, T B 82
  tanners
    Philpe, W 82
    Savery, William 82
  tannery
    Combe Fishacre 82
Ivybridge
  tanners
    Head & Sons 83
    Head, Samuel 83
    Sanders, John 83
    Tattershall, George 83
    Tattershall, John 83
    Wellington, William 85
    Westlake, Richard 83
  tannery
    Fore Street 83
  Union Corn Mills 83

J

Jarman, John 33
Jersey
  Attorney General
    Lempiere, Philip 147

K

Kingsbridge and Dodbrooke
  banker
    Balkwill, Benjamin 84
  King of Prussia inn 84
  Quay House 84
  tanneries
    Church Street, Dodbrooke 84
    Market Place 84
    Wallingford, Dodbrooke 85
  tanners
    Barry, James 84
    Beer & Balkwill 84
    Beer, Samuel 84
    Beer, William 84
    Beer, William R 84
    Bligh, Nicholas 84
    Branscombe & Cridland 84
    Branscombe, William 84
    Brown, Henry 84

Cowling, Pritchard & Gay 84
Gillard, J 84
Grant, Henry 84
Grant, Robert 84
Hele, William 84
Knight, John 84
Lock, Hercules 84
Miller, John 84
Pinhay, Robert 84
Pritchard, James, & Co 84
Wellington, James 85
Wyatt, Cowling & Pritchard 84
Wyatt, Joseph 84
Kingskerswell
tanner
Hole, William Mengery 86, 145
Kingston
landowner
Froude, Joan 86
tannery
Kingston Town 86

L

Lamb, Charles 9
Lane, Robert 148
Leather mills 13
Bradninch 13
Cullompton 13
Exeter 13
Pilton 13, 106
South Brent 13
Tavistock 130
Torrington, Great 13
Upton Pyne 13, 109
Leather tax 135
Leats
Plymouth
Drake's Leat 8, 107, 108, 111, 112
Stonehouse Leat 108
Tavistock
Lower Leat 131
Town Leat 131
Tiverton
Town Leat 136
Uffculme 141
Whimple 142
London
British Museum 138
Covent Garden opera 138
Cumberland Terrace 109
Drury Lane theatre 138
Dulwich, gallery at 138
Great Exhibition, 1851 13
Hanover Square 138
National Gallery 138
Queen Street
Well Court 71, 110
Regent's Park 138
St Mary Lothbury 49
Thames Tunnel 138
Tooley Street 138

transport to
Russell's flying waggons 120
Loxbeare
Leigh Barton 87
tanners
Ashford, John 16, 87
Ashford, John Henry 16
Besley, Henry 87
Moon, Thomas 87
Sharland, Peter 87
tannery
Chopland 16, 87

M

Martyn, John 32
Mayne, Robert 148
Millbrook
tanners
Blight and Sons 64
Blight, John Thomas 64
Milton Abbot
farmers
Courtice, Mary 88
Courtice, Richard 88
Courtice, Thomas 88
landowner
Carpenter, Rev. J P 88
tanners
Courtice, Mary 88
Courtice, Mrs 9
Courtice, Richard 88
Courtice, Thomas 88
Marshall, Charles 88
Mason, Isaac 88
Node, Thomas 88
Symons, Charles 88
tanner's apprentice
Blake, George 88
tannery
Park, Chillaton 88
Modbury
currier
Ashley, Martin 89
fellmonger
Choake, Henry 89
tanneries
Brownston Street 88
New Road/Poundwell Street 89
tanners
Ashley, Charles 89
Ashley, Richard 89
Choake, Henry 89
Cridland, Francis 89
Horsewell, R 89
Lightfoot, John 89
woolstapler
Cridland, Francis 89
Monmouth Rebellion 50
Moretonhampstead
curriers
Aggett, James 91
Neck, James 91
Pasmore, Samuel 91

dressmaker
Cole, Miss 91
Forder House 91
ironmonger
Loveys, Mr 91
landowner
Snow, William 92
Moreton House 91
Pitt House 91
tanneries
Ford Street 91
Leign, Doccombe 92
Steward 92
tanners
Bragg, George 91
Germon, John 92
Germon, Richard Medland 92
Nosworthy, John 92
White, Thomas 91
tawer
White, Thomas 91
Musbury
landowner and farmer
Gillett, Francis 93
Maidenhayne 93
Malvern House 93
tanners
Collins, Samuel 93
Gillett, Compton 93
Gillett, Elizabeth 9
tannery
Fore Street 93

N

National History Museum, St Fagans 9, 12, 50
Navy, Royal
blue serge 98
Nether Stowey
tanner
Poole, Thomas 9
Newton Abbot
accountants
Channon & Co 95
fellmonger
Branscombe, Samuel, senior 94
ironfounders
Beare 94
Polyblank 94
Webber 94
magistrates
Vicary, Robert 95
Vicary, William 95
tanneries
Branscombe's 95
Vicary's 95
Vicary's bark mill 95
tanners
Branscombe, Samuel 94
Goodenough 94
Vicary, Charles G 95
Vicary, J, and Brothers 95
Vicary, John 94, 95
Vicary, Moses 94, 98

Vicary, Robert 94
Vicary, William 94
woolstaplers
Vicary, John 95
Vicary, William 95
Newton St Cyres
clothiers
Northcote family 53
tanners
Bidgood, John 148
Lane, Robert 148
Ponsford, George 148
Nile, Battle of the 135
North Tawton
Burton Hall 98
landowner
Fellowes, Hon Newton 98
magistrate
Vicary, John Fulford 98
Manor Mills 98
Nichols Nymett House 98
Park House 98
sergemakers
Fulford family 98
Sweet, Charles 98
tanners
Sweet, Charles 98
Vicary, William 98
tannery
Fore Street 99
Taw floods 98
Waterloo Cottages 98
woollen manufacturers
Fulford, John 98
Fulford, Robert 98
Shaws of Halifax 98
Vicary, Gilbert Doke 94, 98
woollen mill worker
Wilson, Joshua, of Rochdale 98
Northampton 53

O

Oak bark
bark harvest 56
Cumbria, from 52
Exeter, from 120
export 7, 135
Forest of Dean, from 52
Fulford Estate, from 69
Okehampton Park
bark house 100
scarcity 7
Wales, from 52
Offwell
Offwell Woods
bark mill 101
Okehampton
currier
Ashley, William 100
tanners
Braddick, William 100
Breghe, Henry 100
Breghe, John 100
Burd, Thomas 100

Landick, Frank 100
Landick, Laura 9, 100
Landick, Samuel 100
Newcombe, John 100
Newcombe, Thomas
100
Nosworthy, John 100
Perin, John 100
Pike, William 100
Sampson, Henry 100
Sampson, John 100
Stanbury, John 100
Stondon, John 100
Webber, John 100
tannery
Westbridge 101
Ottery St Mary
shoemaker
Huxtable, Mr 102
tanners
Palmer, Bartholomew
101
Salter, Richard 101
Taylor, George 101
Taylor, Richard 102
tannery
Mill Street 101

P

Paignton
tanner
Codner, John 148
Parrock, John 148
Payhembury
tanners
Parrock, John 148
Venn, Henry 148
Peninsular War 107
Petrockstowe
Berry Farm 103
tanners
Adams, George 103
Adams, Richard 103
Lucas, William
103, 104
Moase, George 103
Powlesland, William
103
Pyke, Alexander 103
Stoneman, George 103
tannery
Quarry Hills 103
Pilton
Hope Mills 105
Ladywell 106
landowners
Rennels, William 105
Rolle, Sir Henry 105
leather dresser
Bemridge, Samuel 106
leather mill
Rawleigh 106
tanners
Cawsey, Lewis 105
King, John 105
King, Thomas 106
Mortimer, Mr 106
Oldfield, Joseph 106

Sanders, John 106
tannery
Bradiford 104
toy manufacturer
Lee, John 106
Plymouth
banker
Strode, Simon Radford
109
Cambridge Street 112
fellmongers
Tanner, Bodkin, Ivory
& Co 109
Frankfort Street 112
Gibbons Lane 110
landowners
Yonge family 108
leather merchants
Prance, William 109
Tanner, James
Newman 109
Mill Street 112
mills
Canvas Factory 111
Cement Mill 111
Drakes Place 111
Lower Grist Mill 111
Providence Mill 111
Portland Square
109, 110
Sherwell House 109
Sherwill Chapel 110
tanneries
Coxside, Sutton Road
113
Devonport 64
Exeter Street 112
Frankfort Street/
Cambridge Street 111
Mill Street 112
Old Town Gate 108
Portland Place/
Stonehouse Lane 108
Tavistock Road 109,
112
tanners
Ashford, Peter
16, 112
Branscombe, William,
jnr 111
Cridland, Henry 108
Dove, W H 112
Greet, Henry 108
Head, J, & Son 108
Head, John 108
Hender, Thomas 112
Hern, Aaron 108
Lewis, John 108
Martin, Richard 112
Steer, William 108
Sweet, William 111
Tanner, Charles Sheen
109
Tanner, James
Newman 71, 109
Waddon, John 108
Ward Bros & Co
112, 113

Ward, William
Osmond 113
woolstapler
Greet, Henry 108
Plymouth and Portsmouth
Steam Packet Company
16
Plympton
Fore Street 115
tanners
Adams, Thomas 114
Brown, Thomas
45, 115
Burnell, Emanuel 114
Burnell, Joseph 114
Drew, George 115
Eales, William 115
Maddock, John 114
Port, William 114
Watts, Roger 114
Weekes, Joseph 114
tannery
Tan Street 114
Porlock 123
tannery 123
Portsmouth 138

R

Railway
atmospheric 8
Bristol and Exeter 116
Great Western
138, 139, 148
South Devon 94
Taunton - Barnstaple 128
Reform Act 138
Rewe
landowners
Egremont, Earl of 116
Ilchester, Lord 116
tanner
Cleeve, Thomas 116
tannery
Chowns 117
Russell's flying waggons
120

S

Sampford Courtenay
tanners
Snell, John 117
Westaway, John 117
tannery
Halford Manor 117
Sampford Peverell
mercer and shopkeeper
Row, Thomas 15
tanners
Combe, John 118
Jones, John 118
Morrell, Thomas 118
Webber, James 118
Sandford
landowners
Hamlyn, Mr 119
Lake, William 119
tanners
Kelland, Richard 119

Snell, Andrew 119
tanner's apprentice
Arthur, John 119
tannery
Doggetsbeer 118
Send, Surrey
tannery 15
Shobrooke
tanneries
Sanctuary 8, 121
Week or Tanner's
Wyke 121
tanners
Frost, Mathew 120
Frost, Matthew 13
Reynolds, Richard
13, 19, 120, 135
Shoe factories
Crediton 8
Kendal 8
Northampton 8
Street 8
Shumac or sumac 151
Singer, Charles
sewing machine designer
53
Snell, Anthony 148
South Devon Railway 94
South Molton
currier
Dunn, Richard 126
mayor
Hole, Lewis 120
surgeon
Furse, Robert 122
tanners
Barons, Richard 122
Berry, William 122
Brooks, Jonathan 122
Furse, George 122
Gay, George 122
Gay, John 122
Pearce, Charles 123
Pearce, Robert 122
Pearce, Thomas 123
Smyth, Thomas 122
Smyth, Walter 123
Smyth, William Gould
122
Trix, Mr F 122
Upton, John 122
tannery
East Street 122, 124
tannery manager
Southcomb, George
123
widow
Smyth, Grace 123
Southey, Robert 9
Sowton
Venn Farm 145
Steam engines
in tanneries
13, 19, 35, 39, 60,
62, 63, 66, 67, 68, 69
70, 71, 74, 80, 111,
113, 120, 121, 122, 124,
126, 128, 137, 139

Stoke Gabriel
  tanner
    Churchward, Mr 148
Sutcliffe, Henry 64
Swimbridge
  brewery
    Swimbridge Bitter 128
  tanners
    Fulford, A A 127
    Fulford, H 127
    Liverton, Bert 127
    Morrish, John 129
    Smyth, John
      13, 123, 126
    Smyth, William 126
    Upham, Mr 126
  tannery 126, 128
  Tannery House 126

T

Tanneries
  Alphington 8, 19-20
  Ashburton 8, 21-23
  Atherington 148
  Axminster 24
  Axmouth 25
  Bampton 26-27
  Barnstaple 8, 28-31
  Bedminster, Bristol 145
  Beverley 60, 72
  Bickleigh, Tiverton 8, 32
  Bideford 34
  Bow 7, 35
  Bradninch 37
  Braunton 148
  Bridestowe 38
  Bristol 13
  Broadclyst 8, 14, 39
  Broadhembury 15, 40
  Broadhempston 41
  Buckerell 42
  Buckfastleigh 42
  Buckland Monachorum
    45, 115
  capacity and output
    14, 39, 68, 82, 83,
    84, 92, 117, 119, 142
  Cheriton Fitzpaine
    7, 14, 15, 16, 46-47
  Chichester 13, 17, 147
  Chudleigh 48
  Chulmleigh 49
  Colyton 8, 9, 50-52
  Crediton 7, 8, 53-57
  Crewkerne 123
  Cullompton 7, 8, 58-
    62, 72
  Culmstock 148
  Dalwood 63
  Dartmouth 64
  Devonport 64
  Dodbrooke 84
  East Budleigh 64
  Exeter 65-72
    Haven Banks 8
    Heavitree
      8, 65, 66, 70
    Lions Holt 8, 65, 71
    St Thomas 8

Westgate 8, 71
Fareham 13, 147
Gittisham 148
Great Torrington 73-75
  Caddywell 74
  High Street 74
  Mill Street 73
  New Street 73
Hartland 76
Havant 13
Holcombe Rogus 78
Holsworthy 79
Honiton 80-81
Ilsington 81
Ipplepen 82
Ivybridge 83
Kingsbridge 8, 84-85
Kingskerswell 86
Kingston 86
Launceston 112
Loxbeare 7, 16, 87
Mieux Abbey 7
Millbrook, Cornwall 64
Milton Abbot 88
Modbury 89-90
Moretonhampstead
  8, 91-92
Musbury 93
Newnham, Gloucester-
  shire 145
Newton Abbot 8, 94-97
Newton Ferrers 148
Newton St Cyres 148
North Tawton 98-99
Okehampton 100
Ottery St Mary 13,
  101-102
Paignton 148
Payhembury 148
Petrockstowe
  73, 75, 103-104
Pilton 105
Plymouth 16, 107-113
  Frankfort Street 14
Plympton 114
Plymtree 148
Pompeii 7
Porlock 123
Rewe 116
Rhaeader 9, 12
Sampford Courtenay 117
Sampford Peverell
  14, 118
Sandford 119
Send, Surrey 15
Shobrooke 8, 120-121
South Molton 7, 8,
  122-125
steam power 13
Stoke Canon 148
Stoke Gabriel 148
Swimbridge 7, 8,
  126-129
Tavistock 130-133
Tiverton 8, 134-136
  Townsend 7
Torrington 8
Totnes 8, 137
Uffculme 7, 141

Upottery 142
Wallington, Hampshire
  15
Whimple 11, 142-143
Willand 148
Winkleigh 7, 144
Woodbury 8, 15,
  145-147
Yatton, Somerset 126
Tanning
  Chrome tanning 8
Tasmania 32
Tavistock
  Canal 130
  Gill, Rundle and Bridg-
    man 43
  landowner
    Bedford, Duke of 130
  tanneries
    Bannawell Street 130
    Brook Street 130
    Taviton 130
  tanners
    Abbott, Richard 132
    Carter, John 132
    Carter, Samuel 132
    Carter, William 132
    Martin, Richard 132
  Tavistock Abbey 130
  Vigo Bridge 132
  West Indies, export to
    130
Tawing 151
Tax
  leather 135, 148
  thangavell 137
Teignmouth
  harbour 95
Thames Tunnel 138
Tiverton
  Angel inn 135
  banks and bankers
    Barne, John 32, 136
    Dickinson, Lewis and
      Besly 135
    Dunsford & Co 32
    Dunsfords' and Barne
      32
    Tiverton and Devon-
      shire Bank 135
  Brunswick House 136
  Cottey House Farm 136
  fellmongers
    Aplin family 136
  Fore Street 136
  Gold Street 136
  historian
    Dunsford, Martin 134
  landowners
    Kings College, Cam-
      bridge 134
    Newte, Richard 134
  Leat, Town 136
  mercer
    Dunsford, Henry 135
  St Peter's church 136
  tanneries
    Fairby 134
    Manley 134

New Place 32, 134
Town's End 136
tanners
  Aplin, J B 136
  Barne, George 37,
    49, 66, 70, 120, 134
  Newton, John 134
  Ware, John 136
tanner's apprentice
  Carter, Robert 136
Tiverton Corporation
  32, 135
Torre, abbot of 137
Totnes
  Fore Street 137
  Kingsbridge Inn 140
  Leechwell Street
    137, 139
  magistrate
    Chaster, John W 139
  Orchard Terrace 137
  quay 140
  saddler
    Chaster, Walter Preston
      138
  Snail Mill 137
  tanneries
    Bridgetown 137
    Lake Garden 137
  tanners
    Chaster, John Webber
      138
    Hayward, George 137
    Langman, Andrew 137
    Langman, John 137
    Mitchell, Samuel 139
    Nayle, Robert 137
    Rouswill, John 137
    Searle, Thomas 137
    Searle, Thomas J 137
    Setter, Samuel 140
    Skinner, Richard 139
    Windeatt, Mr 137
Trade, Board of 49, 148
Trix, F 122

U

Uffculme
  tanneries
    Bodmiscombe 141
    village, in 141
  tanners
    Broom, Francis
      141, 142
    Hussey, Richard 141
Upton Pyne
  leather mills 109

V

Valonia
  7, 13, 52, 59, 95, 151

W

Ward, William Osmond 133
Water power in taneries
13, 21, 22, 24, 26,
29, 32, 38, 39, 40,
42, 45, 46, 49, 50,
51, 59, 64, 78, 82,
83, 87, 88, 93, 95,
99, 100, 101, 102,
104, 105, 108,
112, 115, 119, 121,
130, 132, 137, 141,
142, 144
Whimple
cider manufacturer
Whiteway, Henry
142, 143
tanners
Broom, Edward 143
Broom, Edward
Richard 143
Richards, Edward
141, 142

Salter, Nathaniel 142
Sanders, John 143
Trump, John 143
tannery
Lower Fordton 142
Widgery, William 56
Willand
Burnrew Lodge 58
tanner
Osmond, Thomas 148
Windsor Castle 138
Winkleigh
tanners
Bowden, Anthony 144
Dunning family 8, 83
Dunning, John 144
Dunning, Richard 144
tannery
Woodterrill 144
Wiveliscombe
tanner
Webber, William 118

Woodbury
agricultural implement
makers
Berry, Edwin 147
Berry family 15
Izel Cottage 147
landowners
Rolle Estate 145
Vicars Choral 145
New House 147
tanneries
Copplestones,
Broadway 145
Gilbrook 145
Green, The
15, 145, 146
tanners
Collings, William 145
Copplestone, Anthony
145
Copplestone, John 145
Gibbings, Thomas
17, 147
Hole, Thomas 145

Hole, William 145
Sanders, William 145
Sharland, Peter
101, 147
Ware & Sons 145
Ware, Edward 145
Ware, Harold 146
Ware, Henry 145
Ware, Thomas
145, 147
Ware, William Walter
145
Weeks, Thomas 145
Wippell, Henry 147
Thorn Farm 147
Wordsworth, William 9

Y

Yatton
tannery
Court de Wyck 126
Yeovil
glovemaking 8